FIGHTING VEHICLES OF THE WORLD

FIGHTING VEHICLES OF THE WORLD

OVER 600 TANKS AND AFVS OF THE WORLD

PHILIP TREWHITT & CHRIS McNAB

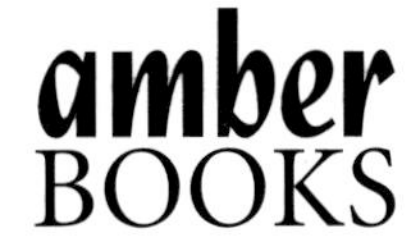

First published in 2004 by
Amber Books Ltd
Bradley's Close
74–77 White Lion Street
London N1 9PF
www.amberbooks.co.uk

ISBN 1-904687-03-2

Printed in Singapore

Picture credits
Pages 7 and 8 courtesy of TRH Pictures Ltd.
All artworks courtesy of Art-Tech Ltd.

Contents

Introduction

Although all the combatant armies relied heavily on horses at the beginning of World War I, the benefits of using armoured vehicles to provide mobility, firepower and protection were evident from the first days of the conflict. The British Admiralty was soon pressing commercial motor cars such as the Lanchester and Rolls-Royce into service as armoured cars. Their well-made suspension needed little reinforcing, and with a machine gun mounted on the top and some additional armour these vehicles proved versatile and useful for reconnaissance.

But even armoured cars could not operate effectively against entrenched and well-defended positions, and the stalemate of the Western Front gave impetus to the development of armoured fighting vehicles. It was realised that a new form of mobile strike force was needed. The 'tank', as it was codenamed for reasons of security, was to break the deadlock. Well armoured and bristling with weapons, the idea was to cross trenches using the long tracks of the early vehicles and destroy enemy resistance with impunity.

The idea was sound enough, and when they first appeared at the Battle of the Somme in 1916 they proved effective in frightening German conscripts, if not in

The Bradley armoured personnel carrier (APC) – seen here on exercise – is designed to carry a squad of men into battle alongside American Abrams tanks.

The M1 Abrams tank is widely regarded as the best tank in the world thanks to its speed and armour protection which served in well in Iraq in 2003.

fulfilling their intended role. Early models were highly unreliable and the tactics employed – using tanks individually to support infantry attacks – were ineffective. However, by the time of Cambrai in 1917, improvements had been made. German efforts to catch up with the Allies proved unsuccessful, and by the end of the war tanks were being produced and used in considerable quantities by the Allies only.

If Germany lagged behind the Allies in armoured warfare at the end of World War I, during the interwar period they developed a tank arm which was to have a huge impact on warfare. It was not the quality of the armoured vehicles but the way in which they were used that proved the value of the armoured fighting vehicle. Whereas the French, and the British to some extent, used their armour in small units in an infantry support role, the German Army believed in the value of massed armoured formations. The early panzers proved too much for the Allies. However, the German panzer divisions suffered heavy casualties in the early campaigns, and all sides realised that the future of armoured warfare lay in bigger, better-armed and better-armoured vehicles.

With the development of the superb Panzer V Panther, developed in response to the Russian T-34, and then the Tiger and King Tiger tanks, the Germans maintained a slight armoured advantage throughout the war. However, no matter how powerful and how invulnerable a vehicle was, if it was not mechanically reliable and not available in numbers, then its value was limited.

Increasing use of tanks led to development of specialist tank destroyers, and the concept of mobile firepower continued with self-propelled artillery, with any useful artillery weapon being mounted on a mobile tracked chassis. Like the tank destroyer, the self-propelled gun was not designed for the all-purpose fighting vehicle role; its job was to move to a spot, fire and then move again when required. Both were inferior to tanks in terms of mobility and armour protection.

One of the more startling aspects of the development in armoured vehicles is the number of variants of the vehicles produced. Most main battle tanks since World War II have been adapted for a number of different roles, such as flamethrower and combat engineer tank. Most have also been equipped with an amphibious capability. For transporting personnel or equipment across difficult terrain, the halftrack, first used by the German Army in World War II, has proved an excellent and lasting innovation. The American M3 and the German SdKfz 251 were the forefathers of modern tracked personnel carriers such as the Bradley M2 Infantry Fighting Vehicle. Modern developments in wheeled vehicles have cut the mobility deficit between the tracked and wheeled vehicle over rough terrain, and the greater speed and lower maintenance of the latter vehicle may soon supplant tracked personnel carriers.

MODERN TANKS

With the complexities of modern tanks, such as the Leclerc, the M1 Abrams and the Challenger, crews must be ever more expert and ever more specialist. The dangers of throwing inadequately trained crews in inferior equipment into battle against such specialists in the best vehicles available was fully illustrated in the 1991 Gulf War. The Iraqi armoured divisions were decimated by the Coalition forces who suffered practically no casualties themselves, a scenario largely repeated during the 2003 invasion of Iraq.

The vehicles included in this book are the most influential and important fighting machines in land warfare since World War I. Trucks have been included because they have played an essential role. Though most are not tracked and do not carry a main gun, they are the lifeblood of mechanised armies. Similarly, light vehicles are also included because they too are essential to the success of mechanised armies. In addition, many of these light vehicles take part in hit-and-run operations. The modern American M998 'Hummer', for example, can be armed with numerous weapons ranging from machine guns to anti-tank missiles. In this way it becomes a fighting vehicle, one that can knock out many tanks currently in service around the world.

Little Willie

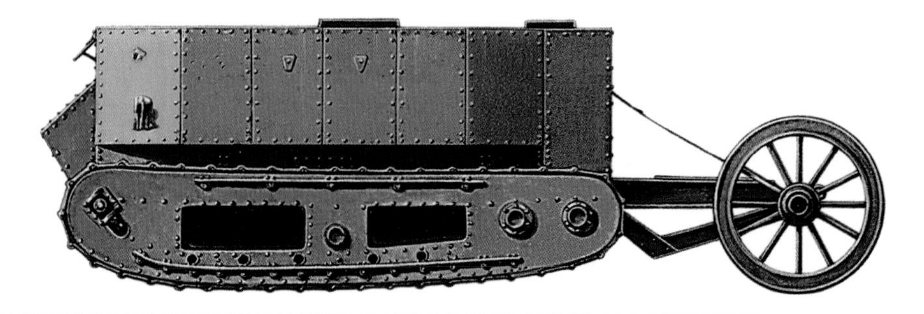

Little Willie can lay claim to being the progenitor of all armoured fighting vehicles. In 1915, two British Army officers, Colonel Ernest Swinton and Colonel Maurice Hankey, convinced Winston Churchill, then First Lord of the Admiralty, that petrol-driven tractors armoured with steel plates could cross enemy trenches while remaining impervious to small-arms fire. They were called tanks to keep their real purpose obscure, as they resembled water tanks. Little Willie appeared in prototype form in September 1915, but its performance was disappointing. Its Daimler six-cylinder engine could only power the 17.7-ton vehicle at 3.2km/h (2mph) on rough ground. It was also unable to traverse significant trenches, but nonetheless, Little Willie began the race for armoured development.

Country of origin:	United Kingdom
Crew:	3
Weight:	18,300kg (40,400lb)
Dimensions:	Length: 8.07m (26.48ft); width: 3.47m (11.38ft); height: 3.2m (11ft)
Range:	Not available
Armour:	(Mild steel) 6mm (0.23in)
Armament:	None
Powerplant:	1 x Daimler 6-cylinder petrol, developing 105hp (78.29kW) at 100rpm
Performance:	Maximum road speed: 3.2km/h (2mph)

Char d'Assaut St Chamond

The St Chamond was the French Army's own development. The first prototype appeared in 1916 and the vehicle entered service a year later. Like the Schneider, the St Chamond was based on the Holt tractor. An unusual petrol engine-driven electric transmission added an extra 5.1 tonnes (five tons) to the design weight. The hull extended both forward and rear of the track which, when combined with the weight, caused the St Chamond to become stuck on rough ground or over trenches. Its poor cross-country performance restricted its use in action, its last major action being a counterattack near Reims in July 1918. Many were converted into Char de Ravitaillement supply carriers. By the end of the war, only 72 out of 400 produced were still in service.

Country of origin:	France
Crew:	9
Weight:	23,400kg (51,480lb)
Dimensions:	length with gun 8.83m (28ft 11.75in); length of hull 7.91m (25ft 11.5in); width 2.67m (8ft 9in); height 2.34m (7ft 5.66in)
Range:	59km (36.7 miles)
Armour:	17mm (0.67in)
Armament:	one Modèle 1897 75mm gun; up to four machine guns
Powerplant:	one 90hp (67kW) Panhard four-cylinder petrol engine powering a Crochat-Collardeau electric transmission
Performance:	maximum road speed 8.5km/h (5.3mph)

Char d'Assaut Schneider

The Char d'Assaut Schneider was developed as an armoured tractor for towing armoured troop sledges across to the German trenches on the Western Front. Based on the American Holt agricultural tractor, the first were available in the middle of 1917. The petrol tanks were very vulnerable to enemy fire and burned easily. Used mainly for infantry support rather than as personnel carriers, they were restricted by poor cross-country mobility, mainly due to their short tracks and long body which hindered the vehicle when crossing obstacles. The gun version ceased production in May 1917, to be replaced by the Char de Ravitaillement variant, used for carrying stores. Attrition and poor reliability led to less than 100 being in service at the end of the war.

Country of origin:	France
Crew:	7
Weight:	14,800kg (32,560lb)
Dimensions:	length 6.0m (19ft 8in); width 2.0m (6ft 6.66in); height 2.39m (7ft 10in)
Range:	48km (30 miles)
Armour:	11.5mm (0.45in)
Armament:	one 75mm gun, two additional machine guns
Powerplant:	one 55hp (41kW) Schneider four-cylinder petrol engine
Performance:	maximum road speed 6km/h (3.7mph)

Renault FT 17

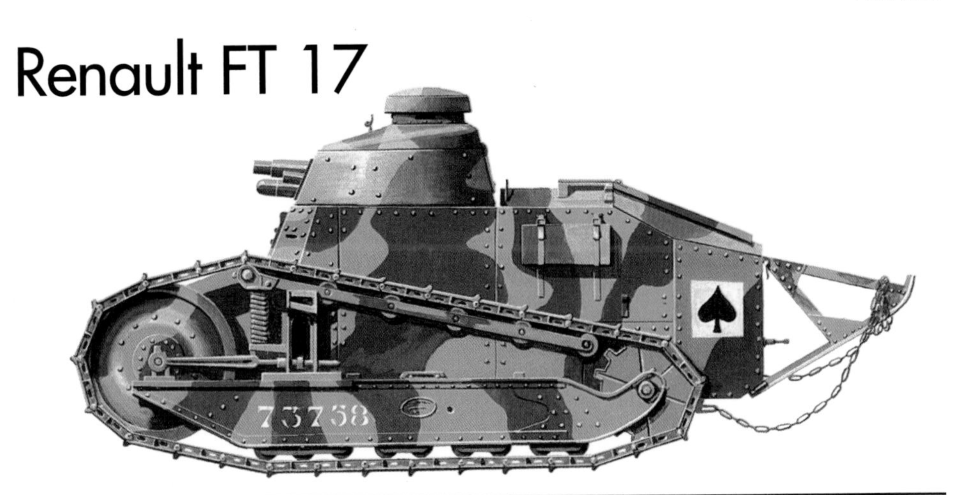

The FT 17 was one of the most successful of all World War I tanks. It was the first of the classic tank design with features mounted directly onto the hull and a turret with a 360-degree traverse. They were ordered in large numbers (over 3000 during World War I) and needed to be, for they had been designed with little thought for maintenance and repair and as a result were often out of action. A self-propelled gun version and a radio-equipped version were among variants produced. In action, they were used en masse. For example, 480 were used in a counterattack near Soissons in July 1918 alone. They remained in service right up until 1944, when the Germans used captured FT 17s for street-fighting in Paris. By this time, of course, they were hopelessly out of date.

Country of origin:	France
Crew:	2
Weight:	6600kg (14,520lb)
Dimensions:	length with tail 5.0m (16ft 5in); width 1.71m (5ft 7.33in); height 2.133m (7ft in)
Range:	35.4km (22 miles)
Armour:	16mm (0.63in)
Armament:	one 37mm gun or one machine gun
Powerplant:	one 35hp (26kW) Renault four-cylinder petrol engine
Performance:	maximum road speed 7.7km/h (4.8mph)

Medium Tank Mk A

The World War I Medium Tank Mk A light tank was designed not so much for crossing obstacles as for exploiting breakthroughs brought about by heavier tanks. The emphasis was thus on speed and mobility. Designed by William Tritton, the Mk A was soon nicknamed 'Whippet'. The prototype was powered by London bus engines and was ready in February 1917, but it was not until late 1917 that the first production models appeared. The Whippet first saw combat in March 1918, being used initially to plug gaps in the line. Its worth was proved in counterattacks, making deep forays behind the lines and creating havoc in the German rear areas. After the war, the Mk A saw service in Ireland and a number were exported to Japan in the 1920s.

Country of origin:	United Kingdom
Crew:	3 or 4
Weight:	14,300kg (31,460lb)
Dimensions:	length 6.10m (20ft); width 2.62m (8ft 7in); height 2.74m (9ft)
Range:	257km (160 miles)
Armour:	5-14mm (0.2-0.55in)
Armament:	two Hotchkiss machine guns
Powerplant:	two 45hp (33.6kW) Tylor four-cylinder petrol engines
Performance:	maximum road speed 13.4km/h (8.3mph)

Sturmpanzerwagen A7V

The Sturmpanzerwagen A7V was an enormous vehicle, hurriedly designed following the appearance of British tanks in 1916. Ground clearance was only 40mm (1.57in) and the length of track on the ground was too short for a vehicle of its size. The result was an unstable vehicle with poor cross-country performance. 100 A7Vs were ordered in December 1917, but the German war machine was already stretched and only about 20 were ever produced. Their shortcomings over rough ground were manifested in March 1918 when they first saw action, and they often lagged behind the infantry they were designed to support. Variants included the Uberlandwagen, an open-topped, unarmoured supply version, and the A7V/U with 'all-round' tracks. Post-war, they were used by the Polish Army for some years.

Country of origin:	Germany
Crew:	18
Weight:	33,500kg (73,700lb)
Dimensions:	length 8.0m (26ft 3in); width 3.06m (10ft 0.5in); height 3.30m (10ft 10in)
Range:	40km (25 miles)
Armour:	10-30mm (0.39-1.18in)
Armament:	one 57mm gun; six machine guns
Powerplant:	two 100hp (74.6kW) Daimler petrol engines
Performance:	maximum road speed 12.9km/h (8mph)

Tank Mk V

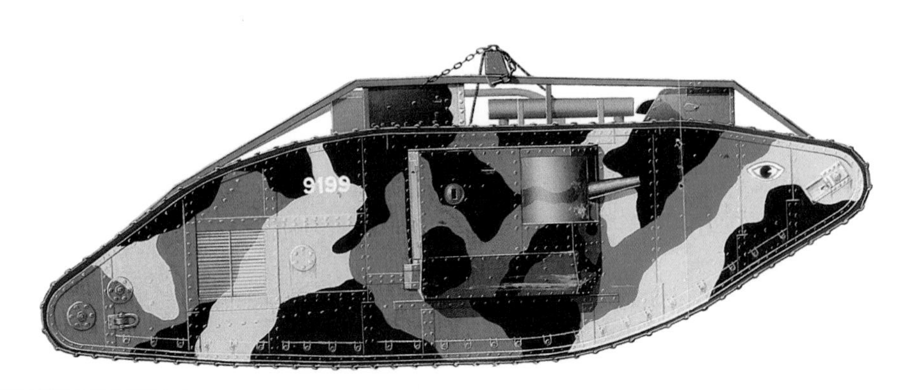

The Tank Mk V was the last of the lozenge-shaped tanks to see service in any number. It was designed to take part in the massive armoured thrusts envisaged for 1919. Improvements on earlier models included a Wilson epicyclic gearbox which allowed the tank to be driven by one man as opposed to two in earlier models. There was a cupola for the commander. Semaphore arms were mounted to give effective communication for the first time. The Tank Mk V* variant had a new 1.83m (6ft) section introduced into the hull to improve trench-crossing capability and provide extra internal space. From mid-1918, the tank saw action with the British and Americans. Post-war variants included bridge-laying and mine-clearing versions, and it remained in service with the Canadians until the early 1930s.

Country of origin:	United Kingdom
Crew:	8
Weight:	29,600kg (65,120lb)
Dimensions:	length 8.05m (26ft 5in); width over sponsons 4.11m (13ft 6in); height 2.64m (8ft 8in)
Range:	72km (45 miles)
Armour:	6-14mm (0.24-0.55in)
Armament:	two 6-pounder guns, four Hotchkiss machine guns
Powerplant:	one 150hp (112kW) Ricardo petrol engine
Performance:	maximum road speed 7.4km/h (4.6mph)

Panzer I

The Panzer I was the first German tank to go into mass production, with nearly 600 having being ordered by July 1934. Three separate companies were engaged to build the tank (deliberately to spread experience of tank manufacture as widely as possible) and over 800 had been produced by June 1936, when production ceased. To avoid being seen to break the Treaty of Versailles, which prohibited the Germans from building tanks, the design was disguised as an 'agricultural tractor'. The Panzer I Ausf A was found in varying numbers in all panzer units and served extensively during the early campaigns of World War II. However, its limitations in armour and armament were soon evident, and it had been withdrawn from frontline service by 1941.

Country of origin:	Germany
Crew:	2
Weight:	5500kg (12,100lb)
Dimensions:	length 4.02m (13.2ft); width 2.06m (6ft 7in);
	height 1.72m (5ft 7in)
Range:	145km (81 miles)
Armour:	6-13mm (0.2-0.5in)
Armament:	two 7.92mm MG13 machine guns
Powerplant:	one Krupp M305 petrol engine developing 60hp (45kW)
Performance:	maximum road speed 37 km/h (21mph); fording 0.85m (2ft 10in); vertical obstacle 0.42m (1ft 5in); trench 1.75m (5ft 9in)

Panzer II Light Tank

The first production model PzKpfw II Ausf A appeared in 1935, having been designated as a tractor since German rearmament was hindered by the restrictions of the Treaty of Versailles. The initial tanks were a collaboration between the firms of MAN and Daimler-Benz. The Ausf B, C, D, E, and F versions were built during the years up to 1941, the main improvements being in the thickness of the armour. The tank formed the backbone of the invasions of Poland and France, with around 1000 seeing service. By the time of the invasion of the USSR in 1941, the tank was obsolete but was used as the basis for the Luchs reconnaissance tank. Other variants included an amphibious version designed for the invasion of Britain and the Flammpanzer II flame-throwing tank.

Country of origin:	Germany
Crew:	3
Weight:	10,000 kg (22,046lb)
Dimensions:	length 4.64m (15ft 3in); width 2.30m (7ft 6.5in); height 2.02m (6ft 7.5in)
Range:	200km (125miles)
Armour:	(Ausf F version) 20-35mm (0.8-1.38in)
Armament:	one 20mm cannon; one 7.92mm machine gun
Powerplant:	one Maybach six-cylinder petrol engine developing 140hp (104kW)
Performance:	maximum road speed 55km/h (34mph); fording 0.85m (2ft 10in); vertical obstacle 0.42m (1ft 5in); trench 1.75m (5ft 9in)

SOMUA S-35 Medium Tank

The SOMUA S-35 was one of the first tanks used to mechanise the French cavalry in the mid-1930s. It was a very advanced vehicle for its time and many of its features were to become standard for future tank designs, such as cast, rather than rivetted, armour. A radio was fitted as standard and the tank was supplied with a sufficiently powerful main armament to be still in service in German hands on D-Day in June 1944. Production was slow and there were only around 250 in frontline service by the time the Germans invaded in 1940. The major drawback was that the commander was required to operate the gun and the radio as well as his normal duties. Despite this reduced effectiveness, the S-35 was still the best Allied tank available in service in 1940.

Country of origin:	France
Crew:	3
Weight:	19,500kg (42,900lb)
Dimensions:	length 5.38m (17ft 7.8in); width 2.12m (6ft 11.5in); height 2.62m (8ft 7in)
Range:	230km (143 miles)
Armour:	20-55mm (0.8-2.2in)
Armament:	one 47mm gun; one coaxial 7.5mm machine gun
Powerplant:	one SOMUA V-8 petrol engine developing 190hp (141.7kW)
Performance:	maximum road speed 40km/h (24.85mph); fording 1.0m (3ft 3in); vertical obstacle 0.76m (2ft 6in); trench 2.13m (7ft)

Type 95 Light Tank

The Type 95, known as the KE-GO, was developed in the early 1930s to meet the requirements of the Japanese Army at that time. When production ceased in 1943, over 1100 had been built. The major drawback of the vehicle was that the commander had to operate the gun in addition to his normal duties, which impeded combat effectiveness. While this was acceptable when faced with infantry in Manchuria, it proved disastrous when up against American armour in the later years of the war. Despite later upgunning, the tank's poor armour and lack of firepower ensured that it was wholly inadequate. The Type 95 also served as the basis for the Type 2 KA-MI amphibious tank which was widely used in the early Pacific campaigns of World War II.

Country of origin:	Japan
Crew:	4
Weight:	7400kg (16,280lb)
Dimensions:	length 4.38m (14ft 4in); width 2.057m (6ft 9in); height 2.184m (7ft 2in)
Range:	250km (156miles)
Armour:	6-14mm (0.25-0.6in)
Armament:	one 37mm gun; two 7.7mm machine guns
Powerplant:	one Mitsubishi NVD 6120 six-cylinder air-cooled diesel engine developing 120hp (89kW)
Performance:	maximum road speed 45km/h (28mph); fording 1.0m (3ft 3in); vertical obstacle 0.812m (2ft 8in); trench 2.0m (6ft 7in)

T-28 Medium Tank

Inspired by British and German tank designs, the T-28 medium tank had a centrally mounted main turret and two auxiliary machine-gun turrets in front. The vehicle's suspension was directly copied from the British Vickers vehicle, and though the prototype was armed with a 45mm main gun, production models were equipped with the more powerful 76.2mm low-velocity gun. There were a number of different models and variants, some of which were produced as a result of combat experience. The T-28C, for example, was given additional armour on the hull front and turret as a result of the Red Army's unhappy time in the Russo-Finnish War. An interesting variant was the T-28(V), a commander's tank fitted with a radio which had a frame aerial round the turret.

Country of origin:	USSR
Crew:	6
Weight:	28,509kg (62,720lb)
Dimensions:	length 7.44m (24ft 4.8in); width 2.81m (9ft 2.75in); height 2.82m (9ft 3in)
Range:	220km (136.7 miles)
Armour:	10-80mm (0.39-3.15in)
Armament:	one 76.2mm gun; three 7.62mm machine guns
Powerplant:	one M-17 V-12 petrol engine developing 500hp (373kW)
Performance:	maximum road speed 37km/h (23mph); fording not known; vertical obstacle 1.04m (3ft 5in); trench 2.90m (9ft 6in)

Renault R-35 Light Tank

The Renault R-35 was designed in the mid-1930s to replace the ageing World War I-vintage Renault FT 17. By 1940, some 1600 had been built and it was the most numerous French tank in service, even though it never managed to fulfil its role as the FT 17's replacement. An adequate vehicle, it was no match for German panzers, particularly as it was deployed piecemeal against their massed formations. The gun was unable to penetrate even light German armour and many were abandoned during the French retreat in May 1940. The Germans used the R-35 as a garrison and training tank and adapted many for use as artillery tractors, ammunition carriers and self-propelled artillery carriages. For the latter, the turrets were removed and used for coastal defences.

Country of origin:	France
Crew:	2
Weight:	10,000kg (22,046lb)
Dimensions:	length 4.20m (13ft 9.25in); width 1.85m (6ft 0.75in); height 2.37m (7ft 9.25in)
Range:	140km (87 miles)
Armour:	40mm (1.57in)
Armament:	one 37mm gun; one coaxial 7.5mm machine gun
Powerplant:	one Renault four-cylinder petrol engine developing 82hp (61kW)
Performance:	maximum road speed 20km/h (12.4mph); fording 0.80m (2ft 7in); vertical obstacle 0.50m (1ft 7.7in); trench 1.60m (5ft 3in)

Char B1 Heavy Tank

The first B1s appeared in 1937. Despite its appearance, which was reminiscent of World War I tanks, the Char B1 was a powerful tank for the time and carried a range of advanced design features such as self-sealing fuel tanks. The crew were seated some way from each other, however, which made internal communication difficult. These crews needed to be highly trained to operate the B1 to full advantage, and such crews were rare in 1940. In addition, the tank's complexities made maintenance difficult and many broke down in combat. Those that entered the fray were really too cumbersome for their powerful armament to have much effect. The Germans later employed captured Char B1s as training tanks or self-propelled artillery carriages.

Country of origin:	France
Crew:	4
Weight:	31,500kg (69,300lb)
Dimensions:	length 6.37m (20ft 10.8in); width 2.50m (8ft 2.4in); height 2.79m (9ft 1.8in)
Range:	180km (112 miles)
Armour:	14-65mm (0.6-2.6in)
Armament:	one 75mm gun; one 45mm gun
Powerplant:	one Renault six-cylinder petrol engine developing 307hp (229kW)
Performance:	maximum road speed 28km/h (17.4mph); fording not known; vertical obstacle 0.93m (3ft 1in); trench 2.74m (9ft)

PzKpfw 38(t)

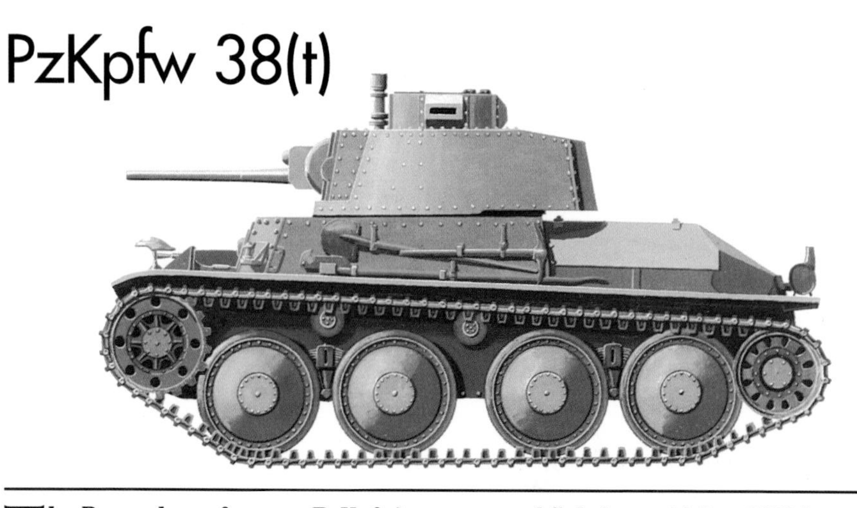

The Panzerkampfwagen (PzKpfw) – armoured fighting vehicle – 38(t) began life as the Czech-designed LT vz 38, although none had entered service with the Czech Army prior to the German occupation of Czechoslovakia in 1938. More than 1400 were built for the Axis forces between 1939–42. When it became outclassed as a light tank, the type was used widely as a reconnaissance vehicle and the chassis was used as the basis for a large number of vehicles, including the Marder tank destroyer, several self-propelled anti-aircraft guns, a weapons carrier and the Hetzer tank destroyer, which continued in service with the Swiss Army until the late 1960s. During its combat career its armour thickness was steadily increase. For example, the Ausf E version onwards had armour 50mm (2in) thick.

Country of origin:	Germany
Crew:	4
Weight:	9700kg (21,340lb)
Dimensions:	length 4.546m (14ft 11in); width 2.133m (7ft); height 2.311m (7ft 7in)
Range:	200km (125miles)
Armour:	10-25mm (0.4-1in); later increased from Ausf E version onwards to 50mm (2in)
Armament:	one 37.2mm Skoda A7 gun; two 7.92mm machine-guns
Powerplant:	one Praga EPA six-cylinder water-cooled inline petrol engine developing 150hp (112kW)
Performance:	maximum road speed 42km/h (26mph); fording 0.9m (3ft); vertical obstacle 0.787m (2ft 7in); trench 1.879m (6ft 2in)

Infantry Tank Matilda

The Mk I Matilda was developed in response to a 1934 requirement for an infantry tank. Well armoured for its day, it was a small, simple tank. However, despite being sturdy enough to withstand hits from most German tank guns in the early stages of World War II, it was too poorly armed to be of much use as the war progressed. The Mk II had improved armament and this helped the Matilda to fare reasonably well in combat, particularly in North Africa where it was widely used in the run-up to El Alamein in 1942. Following its replacement in frontline service, the Matilda was used for a variety of specialised roles, such as mine-clearing (the Baron); as a flame-thrower tank (the Frog); and as the basis of a Canal Defence Light for illuminating night operations.

Country of origin:	United Kingdom
Crew:	4
Weight:	26,926kg (59,237lb)
Dimensions:	length 5.613m (18ft 5in); width 2.59m (8ft 6in); height 2.51m (8ft 3in)
Range:	257km (160 miles)
Armour:	20mm - 78mm (0.8in - 3.1in)
Armament:	one 2-pounder gun; one 7.92mm Besa machine gun
Powerplant:	two Leyland 6-cylinder petrol engines each developing 95hp (71kW) or two AEC diesels each developing 87hp (65kW)
Performance:	maximum speed 24km/h (15mph); maximum cross-country speed 12.9km/h (8mph); fording 0.914m (3ft 0in); vertical obstacle 0.609m (2ft); trench 2.133 (7ft)

Panzer III Medium Tank

Following a 1935 German Army requirement for a light medium tank design, Daimler-Benz began mass production of the Pzkpfw III in September 1939. The early Ausf A, B and C models saw action in Poland, and in 1940 the Ausf F entered production, with heavier armour and an uprated engine. By the time the final version, the Ausf N, ceased production in August 1943, when the army was fighting in Russia, the tank carried twice as big a gun and weighed twice as much as the original prototype. Variants included an amphibious version, a command vehicle, an armoured recovery vehicle, an observation vehicle and one adapted for desert warfare. In addition, the chassis was used for a number of self-propelled guns right to the end of World War II in 1945.

Country of origin:	Germany
Crew:	5
Weight:	22,300kg (49,060lb)
Dimensions:	length 6.41m (21ft); width 2.95m (9ft 8in); height 2.50m (8ft 2.5in)
Range:	175km (110 miles)
Armour:	30mm (1.18in)
Armament:	(Ausf M version) one 75mm L/24 gun; one 7.92mm machine gun
Powerplant:	one Maybach HL 120 TRM 12-cylinder petrol engine developing 300hp (224kW)
Performance:	maximum road speed 40km/h (25mph); fording 0.8m (2ft 8in); vertical obstacle 0.6m (2ft); trench 2.59m (8ft 6in)

Panzer IV Medium Tank

The PzKpfw IV was built under a 1934 requirement from the German Army Weapons Department and was later to become the backbone of the Wehrmacht's panzer arm. The tank was in production right throughout the war, with the final version, the Ausf J, appearing in March 1944. In total, nearly 9000 vehicles were built by Krupp, with the basic chassis remaining the same in all models, but with heavier armour and armament being added as requirements changed. Despite the extra weight, the PzKpfw IV retained a good power-to-weight ratio throughout its production life and thus had good mobility. Like the Panzer III, the chassis was used as the basis for various self-propelled guns as well as armoured recovery vehicles and bridge-layers and the Jagdpanzer IV tank destroyer.

Country of origin:	Germany
Crew:	5
Weight:	25,000kg (55,000lb)
Dimensions:	length 7.02m (23ft); width 3.29m (10ft 9.5in); height 2.68m (8ft 9.5in)
Range:	200km (125miles)
Armour:	50-60mm (1.97-2.4in)
Armament:	(Ausf H version) one 75mm gun; two 7.92mm MG 34 machine guns
Powerplant:	one Maybach HL 120 TRM 12-cylinder petrol engine developing 300hp (224kW)
Performance:	maximum road speed 38km/h (24mph); fording 1.0m (3ft 3in); vertical obstacle 0.6m (2ft); trench 2.20m (7ft 3in)

Fiat L6/40 Light Tank

The Fiat L6/40 arose from a 1930s design based on the British Carden-Loyd Mark VI tankette. Intended primarily for export, the first production models arrived in 1939 and a total of 283 were built. At the time of its introduction, the L6/40 was roughly equivalent to the German PzKpfw II, but was never really suitable for frontline service. However, it saw service with reconnaissance and cavalry units in Italy, North Africa and Russia. Variants included a flame-thrower version and a command tank, the latter having extra communications equipment and an open-topped turret. In addition, a number of L6/40s were converted into Semovente L40 self-propelled anti-tank guns. Like most Italian tanks in World War II, it was hopelessly outclassed when it came up against Allied armour.

Country of origin:	Italy
Crew:	2
Weight:	6800kg (14,960lb)
Dimensions:	length 3.78m (12ft 5in); width 1.92m (6ft 4in); height 2.03m (6ft 8in)
Range:	200km (124miles)
Armour:	6-40mm (0.23-1.57in)
Armament:	one Breda Model 35 20mm cannon; one coaxial Breda Model 38 8mm machinegun
Powerplant:	one SPA 18D four-cylinder petrol engine developing 70hp (52kW)
Performance:	maximum road speed 42km/h (26mph); fording 0.8m (2ft 8in); vertical obstacle 0.7m (2ft 4in); trench 1.7m (5ft 7in)

Fiat M 13/40 Medium Tank

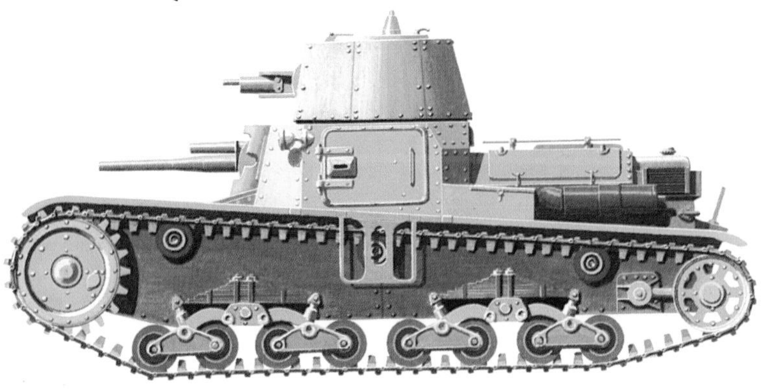

The M 13/40 was based on an earlier design, the M 11/39, which was not produced in numbers as it was considered already obsolete by the time of its introduction. The M 13/40 used the same chassis but had a redesigned hull with better armour. Nearly 800 were produced in total and the tank was widely used in North Africa during Italian attempts to drive British and Commonwealth forces out of the region. In combat the M 13/40's shortcomings became very apparent: it was cramped, unreliable and caught fire easily when hit by anti-tank rounds. Many abandoned and captured M 13/40s were pressed into service by the British and Australian forces and used to fill a serious shortage of Allied tanks in early 1941. They did not remain in Allied service for long.

Country of origin:	Italy
Crew:	4
Weight:	14,000kg (30,800lb)
Dimensions:	length 4.92m (16ft 2in); width 2.2m (7ft 3in); height 2.38m (7ft 10in)
Range:	200km (125miles)
Armour:	6-42mm (0.24-1.65in)
Armament:	one 47mm gun; two Modello 38 8mm machine guns (one coaxial, one anti-aircraft)
Powerplant:	one SPA TM40 eight-cylinder diesel engine developing 125hp (93kW)
Performance:	maximum road speed 32km/h (20mph); fording 1.0m (3ft 3in); vertical obstacle 0.8m (2ft 8in); trench 2.1m (6ft 11in)

Hotchkiss H-39 light Tank

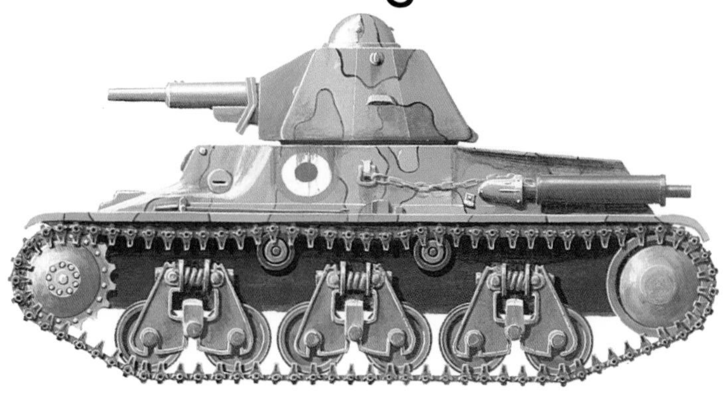

The Hotchkiss H-39 first appeared in 1939, intended for use by French cavalry formations. Despite production problems common to all French tanks in the period before World War II, about 1000 were built. The tank gave a good account of itself in combat during the German invasion of France in 1940, but had too little firepower to compete with enemy armour. In addition, French tactics at the time envisaged tanks being used as infantry support rather than in mass formations, diminishing its effectiveness. After the surrender, the Germans employed the H-39 for occupation duties. Some saw action with the Free French and Vichy French forces in the Middle East, where they were later used by the Israelis, remaining in service until 1956.

Country of origin:	France
Crew:	2
Weight:	12,100kg (26,620lb)
Dimensions:	length 4.22m (13ft 10in); width 1.95m (6ft 4.8in); height 2.15m (7ft 0.6in)
Range:	120km (74.5 miles)
Armour:	40mm (1.57in)
Armament:	one 37mm gun; one coaxial 7.5mm machine gun
Powerplant:	one Hotchkiss six-cylinder petrol engine developing 120hp (89.5kW)
Performance:	maximum road speed 36km/h (22.3mph); fording 0.85m (2ft 10in); vertical obstacle 0.50m (1ft 8in); trench 1.80m (5ft 11in)

Infantry Tank Mk III Valentine

In 1938 Vickers was asked to produce an infantry tank based upon their A10 Cruiser tank. There were initial doubts about the new Valentine's two-man turret, which would limit the possibility of increased armament at a later date, but as war was imminent necessity overcame this caution. Mass production began in 1940 and the Valentine soon proved to be a sturdy, reliable vehicle, if a little slow. Armament was gradually improved as the war progressed, and the Valentine saw service in all theatres. Variants included a mobile bridge, a flame-thrower tank, a mine-clearing tank and a self-propelled gun. Over 8000 Valentines were built before production ceased in 1944, thus making the Valentine one of the most important British tanks in numbers if nothing else.

Country of origin:	United Kingdom
Crew:	3
Weight:	17,690kg (38,918lb)
Dimensions:	length 5.41m (17ft 9in); width 2.629m (8ft 7.5in); height 2.273m (7ft 5.5in)
Range:	145km (90 miles)
Armour:	8-65mm (0.3-2.6in)
Armament:	one 2-pounder gun; one 7.62mm machine gun
Powerplant:	one AEC diesel developing 131hp (98kW) in Mk III or GMC diesel developing 138hp (103kW) in Mk IV
Performance:	maximum speed 24km/h (15mph); fording 0.914m (3ft); vertical obstacle 0.838m (2ft 9in); trench 2.286 (7ft 6in)

KV-1 Heavy Tank

Design on the KV-1 began in 1938, with the intention that it should be the successor to the T-35 heavy tank. The first models were field-tested during the Red Army's disastrous 1940 campaign in Finland. Nevertheless, the KV-1 set the standard for Soviet tank design for several years to come and proved to be a formidable vehicle, being used as an assault tank or to spearhead breakthroughs. However, the tank was not particularly mobile and suffered from automotive problems. In addition, it was uparmoured progressively without any increase in power being allotted, which resulted in poor power-to-weight ratio and performance. The importance of the KV-1 is that it paved the way for later generations of Russian heavy tanks, such as the Josef Stalin.

Country of origin:	USSR
Crew:	5
Weight:	43,000kg (94,600lb)
Dimensions:	length 6.68m (21ft 11in); width 3.32m (10ft 10.7in); height 2.71m (8ft 10.7in)
Range:	150km (93.2 miles)
Armour:	100mm (3.94in)
Armament:	one 76.2mm gun; four 7.62mm machine guns
Powerplant:	one V-2K V-12 diesel engine developing 600hp (448kW)
Performance:	maximum (rarely achieved) road speed 35km/h (21.75mph); fording not known; vertical obstacle 1.20m (3ft 8in); trench 2.59m (8ft 6in)

T-34/76A Medium Tank

The T-34 was an advanced tank for its era, produced in vast numbers to an excellent design, a design borne from two decades of Soviet experimentation and a readiness to embrace the best of foreign ideas. Mass production began in 1940 and its powerful gun and thick armour came as a nasty surprise to the Germans in 1941-42. Finesse was sacrificed for speed of production, but their rough and ready appearance belied their effectiveness. The T-34 was used in every role from recovery vehicle to personnel carrier and reconnaissance, and distinguished itself at every turn forcing the Germans back on the defensive. It is no exaggeration to say that the T-34 was the most decisive tank of World War II. The upgunned T-34/85 tank introduced in 1944 is still in use with some Third World armies today.

Country of origin:	USSR
Crew:	4
Weight:	26,000kg (57,200lb)
Dimensions:	length 5.92m (19ft 5.1in); width 3.0m (9ft 10in); height 2.44m (8ft)
Range:	186km (115 miles)
Armour:	18-60mm (0.71-2.36in)
Armament:	one 76.2mm gun; two 7.62mm machine guns
Powerplant:	one V-2-34 V-12 diesel engine developing 500hp (373kW)
Performance:	maximum road speed 55km/h (34mph); fording 1.37m (4ft 6in); vertical obstacle 0.71m (2ft 4in); trench 2.95m (9ft 8in)

Cruiser Tank Mk VI Crusader

The Crusader's attractive design belied the fact that by the time it first appeared in 1941 it was already outdated. Fast and mobile (their suspension was so tough that theoretical maximum speed was often exceeded), they were thinly armoured and lacked firepower, being no match for their German counterparts. Reliability was also a problem. Even with gradual improvements, the Crusader failed to prove itself in the North African campaigns and was replaced as quickly as possible by the M4 Sherman. Once withdrawn from frontline combat duties, the Crusader was adapted for a variety of roles, such as anti-aircraft tank, recovery vehicle and combat engineer tank with a dozer blade. Many saw service in the last years of the war as artillery tractors, pulling the 17-pounder gun.

Country of origin:	United Kingdom
Crew:	3
Weight:	20,067kg (44,147lb)
Dimensions:	length 5.994m (19ft 8in); width 2.64m (8ft 8in); height 2.235m (7ft 4in)
Range:	204km (127 miles)
Armour:	40mm (1.57in)
Armament:	one 2-pounder gun; one coaxial 7.62mm machine gun
Powerplant:	one Nuffield Liberty Mk III petrol engine developing 340hp (254kW)
Performance:	maximum road speed 43.4km/h (27mph); maximum cross-country speed 24km/h (15mph); fording 0.99m (3ft 3in); vertical obstacle 0.686m (2ft 3in); trench 2.59 (8ft 6in)

Medium Tank M3

The M3 was developed by the Americans following the realisation, based on observation of the armoured battles in France in 1940, that a more powerful armament would be required than that mounted on the M2 in development at the time. The M3 was shipped to British forces with minor modifications and was known as the General Grant. The Grant proved highly effective against the Afrika Korps in North Africa in its first actions in May 1942, and was popular with the tank crews of hard-pressed British forces. The original version retained by US forces was known as the General Lee. Reliable and hard-wearing, its only drawback was the limited traverse of the hull-mounted main gun. The M3 saw action on all fronts and was widely exported after the war.

Country of origin:	United States
Crew:	6
Weight:	27,240kg (59,928lb)
Dimensions:	length 5.64m (18ft 6in); width 2.72m (8ft 11in); height 3.12m (10ft 3in)
Range:	193km (120 miles)
Armour:	12-38mm (0.47-1.5in)
Armament:	one 75mm hull-mounted gun; one 35mm gun on turret; four 7.62mm machine guns
Powerplant:	one Continental R-975-EC2 radial petrol engine developing 340hp (253.5kW)
Performance:	maximum road speed 42km/h (26mph); fording 1.02m (3ft 4in); vertical obstacle 0.61m (2ft); trench 1.91m (6ft 3in)

Cruiser Tank Ram Mk I

At the start of World War II, Canada had no tank units. With no possibility of obtaining tanks from a desperate Britain, the Canadians were forced to build their own. The decision was taken to use the basic components of the American M3, but swap the sponson-mounted main gun for a turret mounting the readily available 40mm gun, with the option of upgunning later. Production began at the end of 1941, but the tank never saw action as by the time it arrived in Europe, the M4 Sherman was being produced in numbers and it was decided to adopt this as the standard for Canadian units. Many Rams had their turrets removed and were used as armoured personnel carriers. The Ram's greatest contribution to the Allied victory was as the basis for the Sexton self-propelled gun.

Country of origin:	Canada
Crew:	5
Weight:	29,484kg (64,864lb)
Dimensions:	length 5.79m (19ft); width 2.895m (9ft 6in); height 2.667m (8ft 9in)
Range:	232km (144 miles)
Armour:	25-89mm (1-3.5in)
Armament:	one 2-pounder gun; two coaxial 7.62mm machine guns
Powerplant:	one Continental R-975 radial petrol engine developing 400hp (298kW)
Performance:	maximum road speed 40.2km/h (25mph); vertical obstacle 0.61m (2ft); trench 2.26m (7ft 5in)

Medium Tank M4A2

The M4 Sherman used the same basic hull and suspension as the M3, but mounted the main armament on the gun turret rather than the hull. Easy to build and an excellent fighting platform, it proved to be a war-winner for the Allies. By the time production ceased in 1945, over 40,000 had been built. There were many variants, including engineer tanks, assault tanks, rocket launchers, recovery vehicles and mine-clearers. The British employed the Sherman extensively, notably at El Alamein in 1942. Though outgunned by German tanks and with insufficient armour to compete in the later stages of the war, the sheer numbers produced overwhelmed enemy armoured forces. Its hardiness kept it in service with some South American countries until very recently.

Country of origin:	United States
Crew:	5
Weight:	31,360kg (69,000lb)
Dimensions:	length 5.9m (19ft 4in); width 2.6m (8ft 7in); height 2.74m (9ft)
Range:	161km (100 miles)
Armour:	15-76mm (0.59-2.99in)
Armament:	one 75mm gun; one coaxial 7.62mm machine gun; 12.7mm anti-aircraft gun on turret
Powerplant:	twin General Motors 6-71 diesel engines developing 500hp (373kW)
Performance:	maximum road speed 46.4km/h (29mph); fording 0.9m (3ft); vertical obstacle 0.61m (2ft); trench 2.26m (7ft 5in)

Infantry Tank Mk IV Churchill

The Churchill began life as a 1939 requirement which envisaged a return to trench-warfare, and was thus slow and heavily armoured. The final prototype, however, was a much lighter vehicle than had first been thought of, not unlike a World War I tank in appearance. Rushed into production at a time when invasion seemed imminent, it suffered early reliability problems and was not fully introduced until 1943. Early combat experience during the Dieppe raid in 1942 was disappointing, but the Cromwell proved mobile over rough terrain in North Africa. The tank excelled in its specialised variants, such as the AVRE, the Crocodile flame-thrower tank, the bridgelayer and many more. The tank gave excellent service and the final Churchill was not retired until the 1960s.

Country of origin:	United Kingdom
Crew:	5
Weight:	40,642kg (89,412lb)
Dimensions:	length 7.442m (24ft 5in); width 2.438m (8ft); height 3.454m (11ft 4in)
Range:	144.8km (90 miles)
Armour:	16-102mm (0.6-4in)
Armament:	one 6-pounder gun; one coaxial 7.62mm machine gun
Powerplant:	one Bedford twin-six petrol engine developing 350hp (261kW)
Performance:	maximum speed 20km/h (12.5mph); maximum cross-country speed about 12.8km/h (8mph); fording 1.016m (3ft 4in); vertical obstacle 0.76m (2ft 6in); trench 3.048m (10ft)

Medium Tank M4A3

The M4A3 was one of the most developed of all the Sherman variants used during World War II. It differed from the M4A2 mainly in the design of its turret and suspension (using a more effective horizontal volute spring system) and in its armament, employing the larger and more powerful 76mm gun as well as having thicker armour. This particular model was the production type most favoured by the US Army. Ford built 1690 A3s between June 1942 and September 1943, before ceasing tank production. Manufacture was then taken over by Grand Blanc from February 1944. Improved features included a vision cupola for the commander, a loader's hatch and so-called 'wet stowage' for the ammunition. In addition, its petrol engine was specifically developed for the vehicle.

Country of origin:	United States
Crew:	5
Weight:	32,284kg (71,024lb)
Dimensions:	length, with gun 7.52m (24ft 8in), and over hull 6.27m (20ft 7in); width 2.68m (8ft 9.5in); height 3.43m (11ft 2.875in)
Range:	161km (100 miles)
Armour:	15-100mm (0.59-3.94in)
Armament:	one 76mm gun; one 7.62mm coaxial machine gun
Powerplant:	one Ford GAA V-8 petrol engine developing 400 or 500hp (335.6 or 373kW)
Performance:	maximum road speed 47km/h (29mph); fording 0.91m (3ft); vertical obstacle 0.61m (2ft); trench 2.26m (7ft 5in)

Cruiser Tank Mk VIII Cromwell

The Cromwell was produced in response to a requirement for a more heavily armed and armoured tank to replace the Crusader. The first Cromwells appeared in 1943 armed with a 6-pounder gun. However, it was realised that this would be inadequate and the tanks were soon being equipped with heavier weaponry, which gave some parity with contemporary German tanks. That said, most units were equipped with the M4 Sherman, but the Cromwell gave valuable service as a training tank in the run-up to D-Day and was used for many other roles, such as mobile observation posts and armoured recovery vehicles. Although not quite equal to German tanks, the Cromwell was at least better than previous British efforts and fared reasonably well in combat.

Country of origin:	United Kingdom
Crew:	5
Weight:	27,942kg (61,472lb)
Dimensions:	length 6.42m (21ft 0.75in); width 3.048m (10ft); height 2.51m (8ft 3in)
Range:	278km (173 miles)
Armour:	8-76mm (0.3-3in)
Armament:	one 75mm gun; one coaxial 7.62mm machine gun
Powerplant:	one Rolls-Royce Meteor V-12 petrol engine developing 570hp (425kW)
Performance:	maximum speed 61km/h (38mph); fording 1.219m (4ft); vertical obstacle 0.914m (3ft); trench 2.286 (7ft 6in)

Panzer V Panther

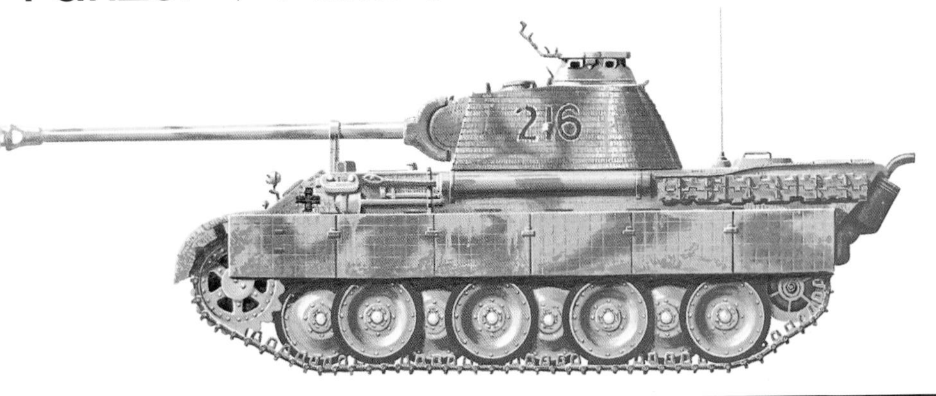

The Panther is widely considered to be one of the best tanks of World War II. Designed to combat the Soviet T-34 tanks which were outclassing the PzKpfw IV on the Eastern Front in early 1942, the Panther fulfilled the requirement for a tank with a powerful gun, good mobility and good protection. MAN completed the first production models in September 1942. The early versions suffered from mechanical problems, particularly at the Battle of Kursk in July 1943, borne from a lack of proper testing. However, once the problems were ironed out, the Panther saw action in all theatres and proved to be very effective. Over 4500 were built up to early 1945, and they continued to see service with the French Army in the immediate post-war period.

Country of origin:	Germany
Crew:	4
Weight:	45,500kg (100,100lb)
Dimensions:	length 8.86m (29ft 0.75in); width 3.43m (11ft 3in);
	height 3.10m (10ft 2in)
Range:	177km (110miles)
Armour:	30-110mm (1.2-4.3in)
Armament:	one 75mm gun; three 7.92mm MG34 machine guns (one coaxial, one anti-aircraft, one on hull front)
Powerplant:	one Maybach HL 230 12-cylinder diesel developing 700hp (522kW)
Performance:	maximum road speed 46km/h (29mph); fording 1.70m (5ft 7in); vertical obstacle 0.91m (3ft 0in); trench 1.91m (6ft 3in)

Panzer VI Tiger

The Tiger heavy tank was produced by Henschel based on a 1941 design and entered production in August 1942. A total of 1350 were built before production ceased in August 1944 and the type was replaced by the King Tiger. There were three main variants: a command tank, a recovery vehicle fitted with a winch and the Sturmtiger, which was fitted with a rocket launcher. The Tiger was an excellent tank, but complicated and therefore difficult to produce in large numbers and maintain. The overlapping wheel suspension had a tendency to clog with mud and stones which, if it froze in cold conditions such as during the Russian winter, could immobilise the vehicle. It first saw action against the British in Tunisia in 1942 and thereafter appeared on all fronts.

Country of origin:	Germany
Crew:	5
Weight:	55,000kg (121,000lb)
Dimensions:	length 8.24m (27ft); width 3.73m (12ft 3in); height 2.86m(9ft 3.25in)
Range:	100km (62miles)
Armour:	25-100mm (1-3.94in)
Armament:	one 88mm KwK 36 gun; one 7.92 coaxial MG 34 machine gun
Powerplant:	one Maybach HL 230 P45 12-cylinder petrol engine developing 700hp (522kW)
Performance:	maximum road speed 38km/h (24mph); fording 1.20m (3ft 11in); vertical obstacle 0.79m (2ft 7in); trench 1.8m (5ft 11in)

Panzer VI Tiger II

The Henschel design for the Tiger II (King Tiger) was completed in October 1943. Early production models carried a turret designed by Porsche, but after the first 50 models had been built, the tanks were wholly produced by Henschel. The tank was similar to the Panther and used the same engine, although its heavier armour, impenetrable to most Allied weapons, resulted in a lower power-to-weight ratio and consequent loss of speed and mobility. The main problem with the Tiger II was unreliability. Many were abandoned by their crews when they broke down or ran out of fuel, as their bulk made them difficult to move or conceal. The Tiger II first saw combat on the Eastern Front in May 1944 and in the battles in Normandy in the autumn of that year.

Country of origin:	Germany
Crew:	5
Weight:	69,700kg (153,340lb)
Dimensions:	length 10.26m (33ft 8in); width 3.75m (12ft 3.5in); height 3.09m (10ft 1.5in)
Range:	110km (68miles)
Armour:	100-150mm (3.94-5.9in)
Armament:	one 88mm KwK 43 gun; two 7.92 MG34 machine guns (one coaxial, one on hull front)
Powerplant:	one Maybach HL 230 P30 12-cylinder petrol engine developing 700hp (522kW)
Performance:	maximum road speed 38km/h (24mph); fording 1.60m (5ft 3in); vertical obstacle 0.85m (2ft 10in); trench 2.5m (8ft 2in)

IS-2 Heavy Tank

The IS-2 (Josef Stalin) was a development of the earlier KV series of Russian tanks. It was a lighter tank than the KVs with improved transmission and suspension and a redesigned hull and turret. The first examples appeared in 1944, helping to exploit the strategic initiative which the Red Army had achieved by that stage of World War II on the Eastern Front. A massive vehicle, the tank was well-armed and armoured, the only drawback of the early versions was a slow rate of fire using separate charges and shells. This was remedied by the time the IS-3 entered production. Symbolically, Josef Stalin tanks were at the head of the advance to Berlin in 1945 and remained in production after the war being the world's most powerful tank for well over a decade.

Country of origin:	USSR
Crew:	4
Weight:	46,000kg (101,200lb)
Dimensions:	length 9.9m (32ft 5.8in); width 3.09m (10ft 1.6in); height 2.73m (8ft 11.5in)
Range:	240km (149 miles)
Armour:	132mm (5.2in)
Armament:	one 122mm gun; one 12.7mm machine gun; one 7.62mm machine gun
Powerplant:	one V-2-IS (V-2K) V-12 diesel developing 600hp (447kW)
Performance:	maximum road speed 37km/h (23mph); fording not known; vertical obstacle 1.0m (3ft 3in); trench 2.49m (8ft 2in)

Centurion

The Centurion Main Battle Tank had its origins in World War II, when it was developed as a cruiser tank. The first prototype appeared in 1945 and the tank entered production shortly after. The Centurion saw action in Korea, Vietnam, Pakistan and the Middle East. Nearly 4500 were built before production ceased in 1962 and it was replaced by the Chieftain. However, its excellent capacity for upgrading ensured that it has remained in service beyond the 1960s with foreign armies. Among the many variants are an armoured recovery vehicle (as well as an amphibious recovery vehicle which was used in the Falklands conflict in 1982), a bridge-layer and an AVRE. It is considered one of the most successful tank designs in the history of warfare.

Country of origin:	United Kingdom
Crew:	4
Weight:	51,723kg (113,792lb)
Dimensions:	length 9.854m (32ft 4in); width 3.39m (11ft 1.5in); height 3.009m (9ft 10.5in)
Range:	205km (127 miles)
Armour:	51-152mm (2-6in)
Armament:	one 105mm gun; two 7.62mm machine guns; one 12.7mm machine gun
Powerplant:	Rolls-Royce Meteor Mk IVB V-12 petrol, developing 650hp (485kW)
Performance:	maximum road speed 43km/h (27mph); fording 1.45m (4ft 9in); vertical obstacle 0.91m (3ft); trench 3.352m (11ft)

T-54

The prototype of the T-54 was completed in 1946 and production began some years later. The T-54 and its variants were produced in larger numbers than any other Soviet tank after World War II (around 50,000), also being produced in Czechoslovakia, Poland and China. The T-54 was continually updated prior to the arrival of the T-55, with gun-stabilisers and an infrared capability being added. Variants included flame-throwers, dozers, bridge-layers, mine-clearers, recovery vehicles and a combat engineer vehicle. The tank saw extensive combat in Angola, North Africa, the Far East and in particular the Middle East, where it suffered by comparison to Israeli Centurion and M48 tanks during the Arab-Israeli wars. The T-54 was archetypal Soviet tank: it was simple and produced in mass numbers.

Country of origin:	USSR
Crew:	4
Weight:	35,909kg (79,000lb)
Dimensions:	length 9m (29ft 6.3in); width 3.27m (10ft 8.75in); height 2.4m (7ft 10.5in)
Range:	400km (249 miles)
Armour:	20-250mm (0.79-9.84in)
Armament:	one 100mm gun; two 7.62mm machine guns (one coaxial, one in bow); one 12.7mm anti-aircraft machine gun
Powerplant:	one V-12 diesel engine developing 520hp (388kW)
Performance:	maximum road speed 48km/h (30mph); fording 1.4m (4ft 7in); vertical obstacle 0.8m (2ft 7.5in); trench 2.7m (8ft 10.25in)

T-10 Heavy Tank

The T-10 was developed in the USSR after the end of World War II to fulfil the perceived need for a heavy tank, shared by both the USA and UK. At least 2500 were built up to the late 1950s. It was kept purely for the domestic market and was designed to provide long-range fire-support for the T-54/55s, and act as a spearhead for thrusts through heavily defended areas. Its cramped confines required the use of separate-loading ammunition as there was insufficient room for complete shells. After leaving frontline service it was, like all Soviet tanks, kept in reserve for many years. The decrease in speed compared to the earlier T-34 was surprising given the Red Army's emphasis on speed and mass during and after World War II. The Soviets certainly possessed mass, but vehicles such as the T-10 reduced overall speed.

Country of origin:	USSR
Crew:	4
Weight:	49,890kg (109,760lb)
Dimensions:	length (including gun) 9.875m (32ft 4.75in); length (hull) 7.04m (23ft 1in); width 3.566m (11ft 8.5in); height 2.25m (7ft 4.5in)
Range:	250km (155 miles)
Armour:	20-250mm (0.79-9.84in)
Armament:	one 122mm gun; two 12.7mm machine guns (one coaxial, one anti-aircraft)
Powerplant:	one V-12 diesel engine developing 700hp (522kW)
Performance:	maximum road speed 42km/h (26mph); vertical obstacle 0.9m (35.5in); trench 3.0m (9ft 10in)

M48 A3

When the Korean War began, the US military had no medium tanks in production. The M47 appeared as an interim measure but work immediately began on the M48. The first 'Pattons' were completed in July 1952. The speed of development resulted in numerous teething troubles for the early Pattons, including poor reliability and a short operating range. The A3 was a highly modified version designed to rectify these failings, and the M48 served successfully in Vietnam, India and with the Israelis in the Middle East. The M48 has been used as the basis for flame-thrower tanks, recovery vehicles and an AVLB. The A5 was an upgraded version produced in the mid-1970s which extended the M48's shelf-life considerably, and it is still being used in some countries today.

Country of origin:	United States
Crew:	4
Weight:	47,040kg (103,488lb)
Dimensions:	length 8.6m (28ft 6in); width 3.6m (11ft 11in); height 3.2m (10ft 3in)
Range:	463km (288 miles)
Armour:	12.7-120mm (0.5-4.72in)
Armament:	one 90mm gun; one 7.62mm coaxial machine gun; one 12.7mm machine gun in commander's cupola
Powerplant:	one Continental AVDS-1790-2A 12-cylinder diesel engine developing 750hp (560kW)
Performance:	maximum road speed 48.2km/h (30mph); fording 1.219m (4ft); vertical obstacle 0.915m (3ft); trench 2.59m (8ft 6in)

Conqueror Heavy Tank

The FV214 Conqueror was the result of a requirement for a post-war heavy tank for the British Army for the expected massed armoured clash with the tanks of the Warsaw Pact on the central European plain. The British were determined that the experience of 1940, when their tanks had been out-gunned by the German panzers, would not happen again. Based on the Centurion, nearly 200 Conquerors were built between 1955 and 1958, mostly deployed in support of Centurion squadrons in the British Army of the Rhine. Unfortunately the Conqueror proved too cumbersome and difficult to maintain. Its advantage over the Centurion was limited to a longer-range gun, and when the Centurion was upgunned there was no longer a role for the Conqueror. The type was phased out during the 1960s.

Country of origin:	United Kingdom
Crew:	4
Weight:	64,858kg (142,688lb)
Dimensions:	length (gun forwards) 11.58m (38ft 0in); length (hull) 7.72m (25ft 4in); width 3.99m (13ft 1in); height 3.35m (11ft 0in)
Range:	155km (95 miles)
Armour:	17-178mm (0.66-7in)
Armament:	one 120mm rifled gun; one 7.62mm coaxial machine gun
Powerplant:	one 12-cylinder petrol engine developing 810hp (604kW)
Performance:	maximum road speed 34km/h (21.3mph); vertical obstacle 0.91m (3ft); trench 3.35m (11ft 0in)

M103 Heavy Tank

The advent of the Cold War saw the Americans begin work on a new tank designed for direct assault and long-range anti-tank support for medium tanks against Soviet armour. Early prototypes of what was to become the M103 showed deficiencies in both the turret and gun control equipment. Despite modifications, the 200 built by Chrysler for deployment in Europe were found to be difficult to employ because of their size (which made concealment difficult), weight and small range, as well as poor reliability. They were phased out during the 1960s. Their bulk required a specialised recovery vehicle, built on the M103's chassis and named the M51. Nevertheless, the M103 was part of a trend for bigger and more heavily armed tanks on NATO's frontline.

Country of origin:	United States
Crew:	5
Weight:	56,610kg (124,544lb)
Dimensions:	length 11.3m (37ft 1.5in); width 3.8m (12ft 4in); height 2.9m (9ft 5.3in)
Range:	130km (80 miles)
Armour:	12.7-178mm (0.5-7in)
Armament:	one 120mm rifled gun; one 7.62mm coaxial machine gun; one 12.7mm anti-aircraft machine gun
Powerplant:	one Continental AV-1790-5B or 7C V-12 petrol engine developing 810hp (604kW)
Performance:	maximum road speed 34km/h (21mph); vertical obstacle 0.91m (3ft); trench 2.29m (7ft 6in)

Type 59

The Type 59 was a Chinese version of the T-54 which had been supplied in numbers by the USSR in the early 1950s. Early models were very basic, with no gun stabilisation or infrared night vision equipment, though the latter was supplied to later models by the British company MEL. A laser rangefinder was also added later, but unusually this was mounted on the front of the turret, where it was vulnerable to shell splinters and small-arms fire. The tank can generate its own smoke screen by injecting diesel fuel into the exhaust pipe, and extra fuel can be mounted in drums on the rear hull. The Type 59 was exported in some quantity to Albania, the Congo, North Korea, Pakistan, Sudan and Vietnam, the latter proving an unwise choice given the subsequent war between China and Vietnam in 1979.

Country of origin:	China
Crew:	4
Weight:	36,000kg (79,200lb)
Dimensions:	length 9m (27ft 6in); width 3.27m (10ft); height 2.59m (7ft 8in)
Range:	600km (375 miles)
Armour:	39-203mm (1.5-8in)
Armament:	one 100mm gun; two 7.62mm machine guns; one 12.7mm machine gun
Powerplant:	one Model 12150L V-12 diesel engine developing 520hp (388kW)
Performance:	maximum road speed: 50km/h (31.3mph); fording 1.4m (4ft 7in); vertical obstacle 0.79m (2ft 7in); trench 2.7m (8ft 10in)

M60A3

The development of the American M60 series of tanks began in 1956 following a decision to create an improved version of the M48. Built by General Dynamics, the M60 entered service in 1960, but was quickly superseded by the A1 to A3 versions. The A3 is notable for its laser fire-control system and thermal sights amongst various other modifications. The two main variants are an AVLB and a Combat Engineer Vehicle, armed with a demolition charge and dozer blade. The M60A3 has been widely exported to Austria, Italy (where it was built under licence), North Africa and many Middle East countries. It is still in service in Africa and the Middle East, particularly in Turkey and Israel, while in the United States its bridgelayer version remains in National Guard use.

Country of origin:	United States
Crew:	4
Weight:	48,872kg (107,520lb)
Dimensions:	length 9.436m (30ft 11.5in); width 3.631m (11ft 11in); height 3.27m (10ft 8.25in)
Range:	500km (310 miles)
Armour:	25-127mm (0.98-5in)
Armament:	one 105mm gun; one 12.7mm machine gun; one 7.62mm coaxial machine gun
Powerplant:	one Continental 12-cylinder diesel engine developing 750hp (560kW)
Performance:	maximum road speed 48.28km/h (30mph); fording 1.219m (4ft); vertical obstacle 0.914m (3ft); trench 2.59m (8ft 6in)

T-62

The Russian T-62 was a development of the T-54/55 series of tanks, but due to the cost of each tank never managed to replace its predecessor which in fact outlived it in production. Produced from 1961 until the early 1970s, the T-62 had an unusual integral shell case ejection system. The recoil of the gun ejected the case out of a trapdoor in the turret, thus saving space but reducing the overall rate of fire. Capable of deep-fording by means of a snorkel over the loader's hatch, the tank was fitted with infrared night-vision equipment, turret-ventilation system, nuclear, biological and chemical (NBC) protection and the ability to create an instant smoke screen by injecting diesel into the exhaust. The tank was first used operationally in the Middle East during the Arab-Israeli wars.

Country of origin:	USSR
Crew:	4
Weight:	39,912kg (87,808lb)
Dimensions:	length 9.34m (28ft 6in); width 3.3m (10ft 1in); height: 2.4m (7ft 5in)
Range:	650km (406 miles)
Armour:	15-242mm (0.59-9.52in)
Armament:	one 115mm U-5TS gun; one 7.62mm coaxial machine gun
Powerplant:	one V-55-5 V-12 liquid-cooled diesel, developing 580hp (432kW)
Performance:	maximum road speed: 60km/h (37.5mph); fording 1.4m (4ft 7in); vertical obstacle 0.8m (2ft 7.5in); trench 2.7m (8ft 10.25in)

Chieftain Mk 5

The Chieftain was designed in the late 1950s as a successor to the Centurion, with production beginning in 1963. Over 900 entered service with the British Army, with considerable numbers being sold to Kuwait and Iran (they saw service in the Iran-Iraq War). Until the Leopard 2 entered German service in 1980, the Chieftain was the best armed and armoured main battle tank in the world, and remained the mainstay of British armoured forces on NATO's frontline in Germany, with frequent technological additions such as laser-rangefinders and thermal-imaging devices until being slowly replaced by the Challenger in the late 1980s. It included a bridge-layer, engineer tank and recovery vehicle amongst its variants. The Chieftains in British Army service are now in reserve.

Country of origin:	United Kingdom
Crew:	4
Weight:	54,880kg (120,736lb)
Dimensions:	length (with gun forward) 10.795m (35ft 5in); length (hull) 7.518m (24ft 8in); width 3.657m (11ft 8.5in); height (overall) 2.895m (9ft 6in)
Range:	500km (310 miles)
Armour:	classified
Armament:	one 120mm rifled gun; one 7.62mm coaxial machine gun;
	six smoke dischargers
Powerplant:	one Leyland six-cylinder multi-fuel engine developing 750hp (560kW)
Performance:	maximum road speed 48km/h (30mph); fording 1.066m (3ft 6in); vertical obstacle 0.914m (3ft); trench 3.149m (10ft 4in)

Leopard 1

Germany's design for the intended 1960s Franco–German joint venture was the Leopard 1 and it was this vehicle that the Germans eventually adopted independently of the French. Built by Krauss-Maffei, the first production vehicles appeared in 1965 and production continued until 1979, a total of 2237 being built for the German Army and many more for export. There were four basic versions, differing in armour, turret-type and fire-control systems. The tank formed the basis of a complete family of vehicles designed to support the vehicle on the battlefield. Optional equipment for the tank included a snorkel for deep-wading and a hydraulic blade to be attached to the front. The Leopard 1 was undoubtedly one of the best tanks designs to have come out of Europe, but is now outdated.

Country of origin:	West Germany
Crew:	4
Weight:	39,912kg (87,808lb)
Dimensions:	length (with gun forward) 9.543m (31ft 4in); length (hull) 7.09m (23ft 3in); width 3.25m (10ft 8in); height (overall) 2.613m (8ft 7in)
Range:	600km (373 miles)
Armour:	classified
Armament:	one 105mm gun; one coaxial 7.62mm machine gun; 7.62mm anti-aircraft machine gun; four smoke dischargers
Powerplant:	one MTU 10-cylinder diesel engine developing 830hp (619kW)
Performance:	maximum road speed 65km/h (40.4mph); fording 2.25m (7ft 4in); vertical obstacle 1.15m (3ft 9.25in); trench 3m (9ft 10in)

AMX-30

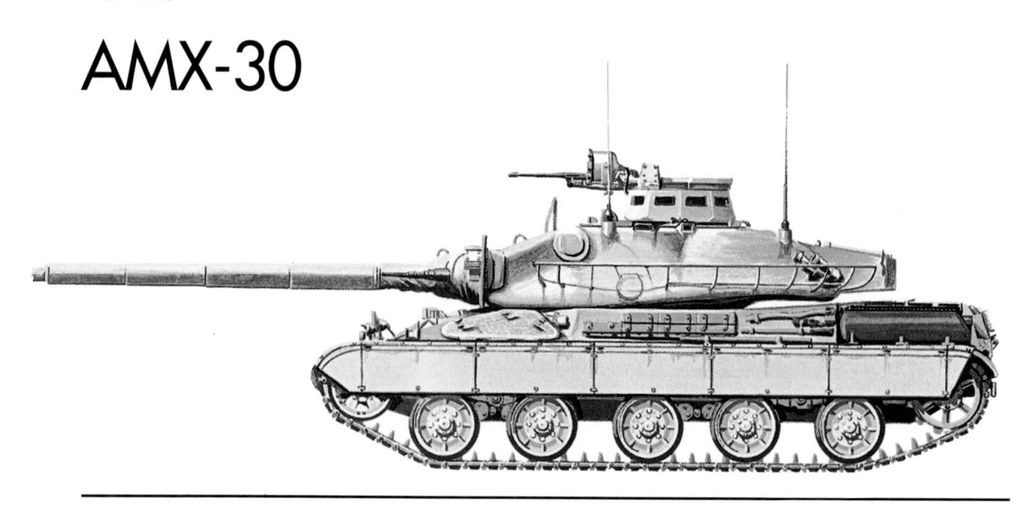

Until the mid-1950s, both France and Germany relied on American M47s for their armour, though France also had a number of the excellent German Panther tanks. A requirement was drawn up for a new main battle tank, lighter and more powerfully armed than the M47, to supply both countries. However, typically, each adopted their own design. The French produced the AMX-30, the first production tanks appearing in 1966, half of which were destined for export. The AMX-30 chassis has been used for a number of other vehicles including the Pluton tactical nuclear missile launcher, as well as a self-propelled anti-aircraft gun, a recovery vehicle, bridge-layer and engineer vehicles. The tank has seen service with the Iraqi, Saudi Arabian and Spanish Armies in addition to the French.

Country of origin:	France
Crew:	4
Weight:	35,941kg (79,072lb)s
Dimensions:	length (with gun forward) 9.48m (31ft 1in); length (hull) 6.59m (21ft 7in); width 3.1m (10ft 2in); height (overall) 2.86m (9ft 4in)
Range:	600km (373 miles)
Armour:	15-80mm (0.6-3.1in)
Armament:	one 105mm gun; one coaxial 20mm cannon; one 7.62mm machine gun
Powerplant:	one Hispano-Suiza 12-cylinder diesel, developing 720hp (537kW)
Performance:	maximum road speed 65km/h (40mph); vertical obstacle 0.93m (3ft 0.6in); trench 2.9m (9ft 6in)

Stridsvagn 103 (S-tank)

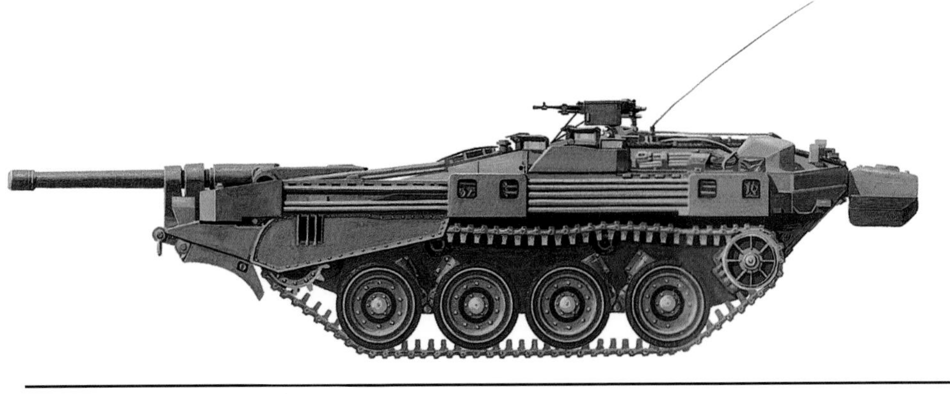

Immediately after World War II, Sweden's armoured forces consisted mainly of light tanks. To fill this gap, work began on an indigenous heavy tank with the gun fixed to the chassis rather than a turret, with aiming being achieved by turning the vehicle and raising or lowering the suspension – an entirely new concept in tank design. Its only real drawback was that it was unable to fire on the move, but as Sweden was only likely to be engaged in defensive actions, this was not too problematic. Bofors began production in 1966, and 300 were completed by the time they ceased in 1971. The tank included a dozer blade and a flotation screen for amphibious capability. The radical Swedish S-tank generated considerable foreign interest, but few export orders.

Country of origin:	Sweden
Crew:	3
Weight:	38,894kg (85,568lb)
Dimensions:	length (with gun) 8.99m (29ft 6in); length (hull) 7.04m (23ft 1in); width 3.26m (10ft 8.3in); height (overall) 2.5m (8ft 2.5in)
Range:	390km (242 miles)
Armour:	90-100mm (3.54-3.94in)
Armament:	one 105mm gun; three 7.62mm machine guns
Powerplant:	one diesel engine developing 240hp (119kW) and a Boeing 553 gas turbine, developing 490hp (366kW)
Performance:	maximum road speed 50km/h (31mph); fording 1.5m (4ft 11in); vertical obstacle 0.9m (2ft 11.5in); trench 2.3m (7ft 6.5in)

T-72

The T-72 came into production in 1971. Smaller and faster than such tanks as the Chieftain, the T-72 was poorly armoured with less versatility and effective firepower than its competitors. This became brutally clear in 1982 when Syrian T-72s proved no match for Israeli Merkava tanks and were knocked out in droves. The T-72 was designed for a conscript army and thus is easy to operate and maintain. This accounts for its export success, being transferred to 14 other countries. It is quite versatile, though, and can be equipped for deep-fording, unlike most other tanks, within a matter of minutes, as well as being fully nuclear, biological and chemical (NBC) protected. Variants include a command vehicle, an anti-tank Cobra missile launcher and an armoured recovery vehicle.

Country of origin:	USSR
Crew:	3
Weight:	38,894kg (85,568lb)
Dimensions:	length 9.24m (30ft 4in); width 4.75m (15ft 7in); height 2.37m (7ft 9in)
Range:	550km (434 miles)
Armour:	classified
Armament:	one 125mm gun; one 12.7mm anti-aircraft machine gun; one 7.62mm coaxial machine gun
Powerplant:	one V-46 V-12 diesel engine developing 840hp (626kW)
Performance:	maximum road speed 80km/h (50mph); fording 1.4m (4ft 7in); vertical obstacle 0.85m (2ft 9in); trench 2.8m (9ft 2in)

Type 74

The Type 74 main battle tank, a successor to the Type 61, entered production on a small scale in the late 1975, with the production rate never increasing above around 50 vehicles per year which meant a very high unit cost. The tank carries a laser rangefinder, computerised fire-control and nuclear, biological and chemical (NBC) defence system as standard. However, the Type 74 has an unusual cross-linked hydro-pneumatic suspension system, which allows it to raise or lower different parts of the chassis in order to cross difficult terrain or to engage targets outside of the gun's normal elevation/depression range. Internal layout is conventional, with a centre turret and rear powerplant. The Type 74 forms the basis of the Type 87 35mm self-propelled anti-aircraft gun tank.

Country of origin:	Japan
Crew:	3
Weight:	38,000kg (83,600lb)
Dimensions:	length 9.42m (28ft 8in); width 3.2m (9ft 10in); height 2.48m (7ft 7in)
Range:	300km (188 miles)
Armour:	classified
Armament:	one 105mm gun; one 7.62mm coaxial machine gun; one 12.7mm anti-aircraft machine gun; two smoke dischargers
Powerplant:	one 10ZF V-10 liquid-cooled diesel, developing 720hp (536kW)
Performance:	maximum road speed: 55km/h (34.4mph); fording; 1m (3ft 4in); vertical obstacle 1m (3ft 4in); trench 2.7m (8ft 10in)

T-80

The T-80 entered service with the Soviet Red Army in the mid-1980s. A development of the T-72 main battle tank. Like the T-72, the tank had an automatic loader for the main gun, thus allowing the crew to be kept to a minimum of three. The main gun was a standard fully stabilised 125mm weapon as fitted in the T-72, but was capable of firing a much greater range of ammunition, including depleted uranium rounds for extra armour-piercing capability. A laser rangefinder led to an improved fire-control system. Like all Soviet tanks, the T-80 was capable of making its own smoke screen and carried four dischargers on the hull for launching chaff or decoys to distract enemy missiles. Adjustable ground clearance provided extra cross-country mobility.

Country of origin:	USSR
Crew:	3
Weight:	48,363kg (106,400lb)
Dimensions:	length 9.9m (32ft 6in); width 3.4m (11ft 2in); height 2.2m (7ft 3in)
Range:	450km (281 miles)
Armour:	classified
Armament:	one 125mm gun; one coaxial 7.62mm machine gun; one 12.7mm anti-aircraft machine gun
Powerplant:	one multi-fuel gas turbine, developing 1000hp (745kW)
Performance:	maximum road speed 70km/h (43.75mph); fording 5m (16ft 5in); vertical obstacle 1m (3ft 4in); trench 2.85m (9ft 4in)

TAM

For many years the Argentinian Army relied on World War II Sherman tanks to form the basis of its armoured forces. By the early 1970s, these were becoming difficult to maintain. Most foreign tanks of the period were too heavy for domestic conditions and thus a new tank was ordered from Thyssen Henschel of West Germany. Once developed, production moved to Buenos Aires and production began towards the end of the 1970s. The hull of the TAM was based on that of the MICV in use with the West German Army. The armour is comparatively poor against that of other main battle tanks, such as the Leopard 1 and the AMX-30, but is well-sloped to give as much protection as possible. The tank was not produced in time to have any impact on the 1982 Falklands conflict.

Country of origin:	Argentina
Crew:	4
Weight:	30,500kg (67,100lb)
Dimensions:	length, gun forward 8.23m (25ft 2in); width 3.12m (9ft 6in); height 2.42m (7ft 5in)
Range:	900km (560 miles)
Armour:	classified
Armament:	one 105mm gun; one coaxial 7.62mm machine gun; one 7.62mm anti-aircraft machine gun
Powerplant:	one V-6 turbo-charged diesel engine developing 720hp (537kW)
Performance:	maximum road speed: 75km/h (46.9mph); fording 1.5m (4ft 11in); vertical obstacle 1m (3ft 3in); trench 2.5m (8ft 2in)

Type 69

The Type 69 was the replacement for the Type 59. First seen in public in 1982, during a parade in Beijing, the tank was very similar in appearance to the Type 59, but was fitted with a new 105/106mm gun, probably based on that of the Soviet T-62, examples of which were captured by the Chinese during border clashes with the USSR. There are a number of variants, including a self-propelled anti-aircraft gun, armoured bridgelayer and armoured recovery vehicle. The latter has a Type 69 chassis but the turret removed and replaced by a superstructure; there is also a dozer blade at the front and crane at the rear. Large quantities of the Type 69 were exported to Iraq in the early 1980s, with Saudi Arabia acting as intermediary, to make up for losses experienced during the war with Iran.

Country of origin:	China
Crew:	4
Weight:	36,500kg (80,300lb)
Dimensions:	length 8.68m (26ft 6in); width 3.3m (10ft 1in); height 2.87m (8ft 10in)
Range:	375km (250 miles)
Armour:	100mm (3.94in)
Armament:	one 100mm gun; one 12.7mm machine gun; two 7.62mm machine guns; two smoke rocket dischargers
Powerplant:	one V-12 liquid-cooled diesel engine developing 580hp (432kW)
Performance:	maximum road speed: 50km/h (31.3mph); fording 1.4m (4ft 7in); vertical obstacle 0.8m (2ft 7in); trench 2.7m (8ft 10in)

M1 Abrams

The M1 Abrams was the next stage in American tank development after the M60. Chrysler completed the prototypes in 1978 and the first production vehicles appeared in 1980 with 30 tanks a month being built in following years. Its advanced Chobham armour makes the M1 the best-protected US main battle tank yet. Its gas turbine engine is smaller and easier to service than a diesel engine, but the extra fuel requirement negates the space saved, which is perhaps why the idea was rejected for the Leopard 2. Thermal sights, laser rangefinder and gun stabilisation system give the M1 excellent firepower on the move, be it day or night. In the 1991 Gulf War, the Abrams knocked out Iraqi T-72s with impunity – no Abrams were destroyed by enemy fire. In the 2003 Iraq war, only a handful were lost.

Country of origin:	United States
Crew:	4
Weight:	54,269kg (119,392lb)
Dimensions:	length 9.766m (32ft 0.5in); width 3.655m (12ft); height 2.895m (9ft 6in)
Range:	450km (280 miles)
Armour:	classified
Armament:	one 105mm gun; two 7.62mm machine guns (one coaxial, one on loader's hatch); one 12.7mm machine gun
Powerplant:	Avco Lycoming AGT-1500 gas turbine, developing 1,500hp (1119kW)
Performance:	maximum road speed 72.5km/h (45mph); fording 1.219m (4ft); vertical obstacle 1.244m (4ft 1in); trench 2.743m (9ft)

Leopard 2

The Leopard 2 was an offshoot of a cancelled joint development between the USA and West Germany in the late 1960s, the project being the MBT-70. The West Germans continued the project, however, first production vehicles were delivered in 1977 and exports were soon equipping the Dutch Army. The Leopard 2 is equipped with laser-rangefinder, thermal-imaging, a nuclear, biological and chemical (NBC) defence system and amphibious capability. Its fire-system is unusual in that the cartridge cases are combustible. When the shell is fired, all that remains is the base of the cartridge, which frees up extra space. It has a 30 percent better power-to-weight ratio than the Leopard 1, which results in increased cross-country mobility and thus survivability. The latest Leopard variant is the 2A6.

Country of origin:	West Germany
Crew:	4
Weight:	54,981kg (120,960lb)
Dimensions:	length (with gun forward) 9.668m (31ft 8.7in); length (hull) 7.772m (25ft 6in); width 3.7m (12ft 1.7in); height (overall) 2.79m (9ft 1.75in)
Range:	550km (342 miles)
Armour:	classified
Armament:	one 120mm gun; one coaxial 7.62mm machine gun; one 7.62mm anti-aircraft machine gun; eight smoke dischargers
Powerplant:	one MTU 12-cylinder multi-fuel, developing 1,500hp (1119kW)
Performance:	maximum road speed 72km/h (45mph); fording 1m (3ft 3in); vertical obstacle 1.1m (3ft 7.25in); trench 3m (9ft 10in)

Merkava

Prior to the Six-Day War in 1967, Israel had relied on Sherman and Centurion tanks for its armoured forces. However, doubts as to future supplies and also concerns that these tanks did not fully meet Israeli requirements prompted development of an indigenous tank. The first production Merkavas appeared in 1980 and saw action for the first time against Syrian forces in Lebanon in 1982. Compared to other modern main battle tanks, the Merkava is slow and has a poor power-to-weight ratio. However, it is designed for specific tactical requirements, which differ from those of most other tank producers. The emphasis is on crew survivability, which explains the Merkava's small cross-section which makes it less of a target, and well-sloped armour for greatest protection.

Country of origin:	Israel
Crew:	4
Weight:	55,898kg (122,976lb)
Dimensions:	length 8.36m (27ft 5.25in); width 3.72m (12ft 2.5in); height 2.64m (8ft 8in)
Range:	500 miles (310 miles)
Armour:	classified
Armament:	one 105mm rifled gun; one 7.62mm machine gun
Powerplant:	one Teledyne Continental AVDS-1790-6A V-12 diesel engine developing 900hp (671kW)
Performance:	maximum road speed 46km/h (28.6mph); vertical obstacle 1m (3ft 3.3in); trench 3m (9ft 10in)

Olifant Mk 1A

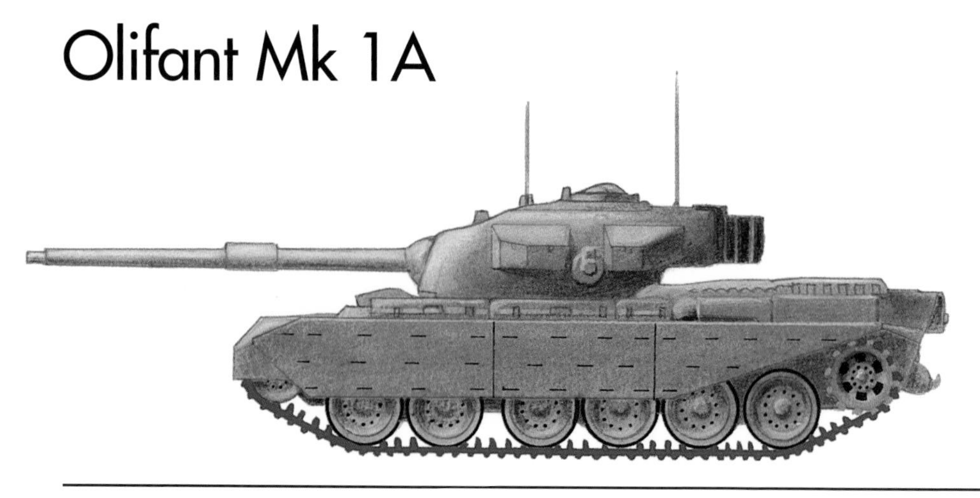

Like the Israelis with their Sho't programme, the South Africans took a basic Centurion tank and upgraded it to produce an indigenous main battle tank specifically suited to their needs, with improved firepower and mobility. The fire control system of the Olifant ('Elephant') remained that of the original Centurion, but the tank was fitted with a hand-held laser rangefinder for the commander and image-intensifier for the gunner. The Mk 1B version of the Olifant is much different, with a lengthened hull, new engine and transmission, and updated armour, as well as enhanced fire control systems. Variants include an armoured recovery vehicle and repair vehicle. The Olifant is undoubtedly the best indigenous tank design on the African continent.

Country of origin:	South Africa
Crew:	4
Weight:	56,000kg (123,200lb)
Dimensions:	length 9.83m (30ft); width: 3.38m (10ft 4in); height: 2.94m (8ft 11in)
Range:	500km (313 miles)
Armour:	17-118mm (0.66-4.6in)
Armament:	one 105mm gun; one 7.62mm coaxial machine gun; one 7.62mm anti-aircraft machine gun; 2 x 4 smoke dischargers
Powerplant:	one V-12 air-cooled turbocharged diesel, developing 750hp (559kW)
Performance:	maximum road speed: 45km/h (28.1mph); fording 1.45m (4ft 9in); vertical obstacle 0.9m (2ft 11in); trench 3.352m (11ft)

Challenger 1

The Challenger 1 was introduced in 1982 as a replacement for the Chieftain. It reflected British thinking on tank design, being heavily armed and armoured. It was slower than contemporary Warsaw Pact vehicles, but made up for it with its composite Chobham armour, which was virtually impenetrable to enemy rounds, and the greater accuracy of its armament. In any case, NATO thinking regarding the war in central Europe with the forces of the Soviet Union and her allies, always placed the emphasis on defence and holding enemy forces until reinforcements arrived. Its armour and nimbleness, despite its lack of speed, allow for good survivability. As tanks become more complex, this is important as they are often easier to replace than their crews. The Challenger 1 is no longer in UK service.

Country of origin:	United Kingdom
Crew:	4
Weight:	62,000kg (136,400lb)
Dimensions:	length, gun forward: 11.56m (35ft 4in); width 3.52m (10ft 8in); height 2.5m (7ft 5in)
Range:	400km (250 miles)
Armour:	classified
Armament:	one 120mm gun; two 7.62mm machine guns; two smoke dischargers
Powerplant:	one liquid-cooled diesel engine developing 1200hp (895kW)
Performance:	maximum road speed: 55km/h (35mph); fording 1m (3ft 4in); vertical obstacle 0.9m (2ft 10in); trench 2.8m (9ft 2in)

Type 80

The Chinese Type 80 main battle tank was a development of the T-69 series. It differs in design by having a brand new hull, as well as a larger main armament and a more modern computerised fire-control system, which includes a laser rangefinder, mounted either over the gunner's sights, or over the 105mm gun itself, depending on the version. The vehicle carries a snorkel which can be fitted to allow for deep fording. It has an in-built fire-detection/ suppression system and the capability of being easily uparmoured (by the addition of composite armour plates) to give increased battlefield survivability. Crew configuration is as follows: the driver sits at the front left with some of the ammunition, while the loader, commander and gunner sit in the turret.

Country of origin:	China
Crew:	4
Weight:	38,000kg (83,600lb)
Dimensions:	length 9.33m (28ft 6in); width 3.37m (10ft 4in); height 2.3m (7ft)
Range:	570km (356 miles)
Armour:	classified
Armament:	one 105mm gun; one 7.62mm coaxial machine gun; one 12.7mm coaxial machine gun
Powerplant:	one V-12 diesel engine developing 730hp (544kW); manual transmission
Performance:	maximum road speed: 60km/h (37.5mph); fording 1.4m (4ft 7in); vertical obstacle 0.8m (2ft 7in); trench 2.7m (8ft 10in)

AMX-40

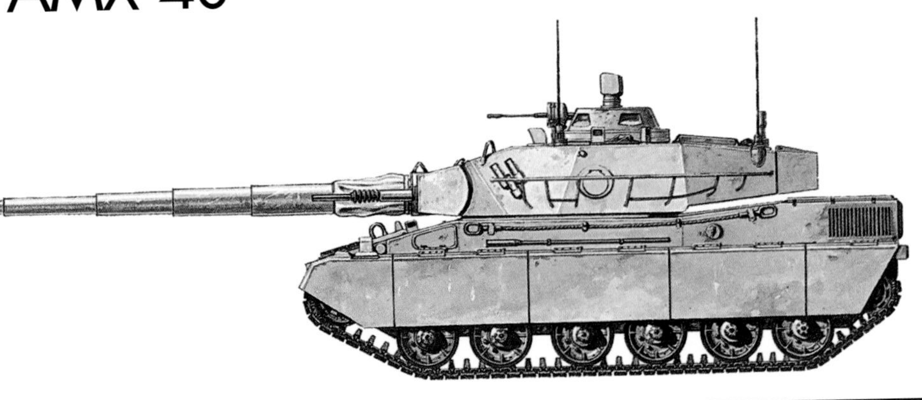

Designed in the early 1980s, primarily for export, the GIAT-built AMX-40 was a significant improvement on its predecessor, the AMX-30, in the key areas of armour, mobility and firepower. The tank has a laser rangefinder, gun stabilisation equipment and a low-light television for night-fighting. One interesting feature is the ammunition stowage. Carried in the turret and surrounded by bulkheads, the ammunition compartment is designed so that if it is hit, the ammunition will explode upwards, away from the crew below. As it was intended for export, the French Army was forced to rely on the AMX-30 until the advent of the Leclerc. The AMX-40 carries the traditional number of crew for a main battle tank: four (commander, gunner, radio operator and driver).

Country of origin:	France
Crew:	4
Weight:	43,000kg (94,600lb)
Dimensions:	length 10.04m (32ft 11.3in); width 3.36m (11ft 0.3in); height 3.08m (10ft 1.3in)
Range:	600km (373 miles)
Armour:	classified
Armament:	one 120mm gun; one 20mm cannon in cupola; one 7.62mm machine gun
Powerplant:	one Poyaud 12-cylinder diesel engine developing 1100hp (820kW)
Performance:	maximum road speed 70km/h (44mph); fording 1.30m (4ft 3in); vertical obstacle 1.0m (6ft 7in); trench 3.20m (10ft 6in)

ENGESA EE-T1 Osorio

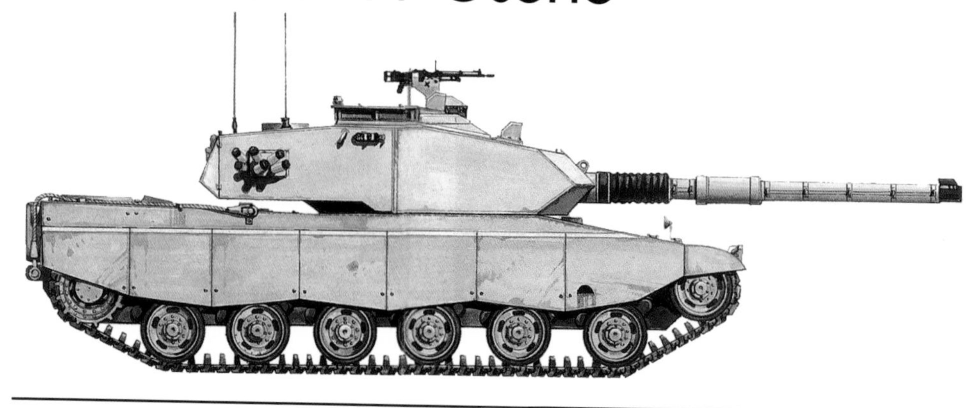

Designed to meet both home and export markets, the first prototype Osorio was completed in 1985. The layout is conventional with laser rangefinder, stabilisers to allow firing whilst on the move and thermal-imaging cameras, as well as a full nuclear, biological and chemical (NBC) defence system. The tank can be fitted with two different sizes of main gun. Variants include a bridgelayer, armoured recovery vehicle and an anti-aircraft gun vehicle. There is little innovation in the design of the Osorio compared to the latest designs being produced in Europe and the United States. However, it is attractive for smaller countries which lack the capacity to manufacture their own main battle tank, and for whom the European and American tanks are too expensive and complicated.

Country of origin:	Brazil
Crew:	4
Weight:	39,000kg (85,800lb)
Dimensions:	length 9.995m (32ft 9.5in); width 3.26m (10ft 8.3in); height 2.371m (7ft 9.3in)
Range:	550km (342 miles)
Armour:	classified
Armament:	one British 105mm/French 120mm gun; one 7.62mm machine gun
Powerplant:	one 12-cylinder diesel engine developing 1000hp (745kW)
Performance:	maximum road speed 70km/h (43.5mph); fording 1.20m (3ft 11in); vertical obstacle 1.15m (3ft 4in); trench 3.0m (9ft 10in)

Type 88

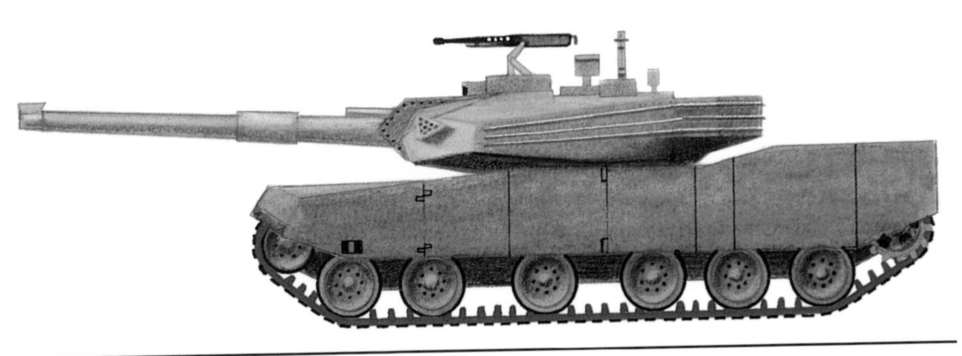

Also known as the K1, the Type 88 was developed by General Dynamics in the early 1980s in response to a South Korean requirement for a main battle tank which could be locally built. The main smoothbore armament has a thermal sleeve and fume extractor and uses a computerised fire-control system based on the M1 ballistic computer and an environmental sensor package. The vehicle has a nuclear, biological and chemical (NBC) system designed to give individual crew protection. Its successor, the K1A1, is now in service, armed with a larger 120mm smoothbore gun and improved fire control system. An AVLB variant, based on the K1 chassis, has been designed in the UK and 56 were ordered by the South Koreans. The tank has not been exported, despite competing for a Malaysian tank order.

Country of origin:	South Korea
Crew:	4
Weight:	52,000kg (114,400lb)
Dimensions:	length 9.67m (29ft 6in); width: 3.59m (10ft 11in); height: 2.25m (6ft 10in)
Range:	500km (313 miles)
Armour:	classified
Armament:	one 105mm gun; one 7.62mm coaxial machine gun; one 12.7mm anti-aircraft machine gun; 2 x 6 smoke dischargers
Powerplant:	one liquid-cooled turbocharged diesel, developing 1200hp (895kW)
Performance:	maximum road speed: 65km/h (40.6mph); fording 1.2m (3ft 11in); vertical obstacle 1m (3ft 4in)

C1 Ariete

The C1 Ariete main battle tank was developed in response to a 1982 specification of the Italian Army for a replacement for its obsolete M47 Pattons. It has the typical slab-sided appearance of modern main battle tanks due to its special composite armour. The Ariete is conventional in layout, with the driver at the front right, a power-operated turret in the centre, gunner on the right, loader on the left and the powerplant at the rear of the vehicle. The main smoothbore armament has a thermal sleeve and fume extractor and uses the latest Galileo computerised fire-control system, the thermal vision night sight and laser rangefinder giving high single-shot kill probability, whether moving or stationary. An armoured recovery vehicle and AVLB based on the C1 chassis are expected to follow.

Country of origin:	Italy
Crew:	4
Weight:	54,000kg (118,800lb)
Dimensions:	length 9.67m (29ft 6in); width 3.6m (11ft); height: 2.5m (7ft 7in
Range:	600km (375 miles)
Armour:	classified
Armament:	one 120mm gun; one 7.62mm coaxial machine gun; one 7.62mm anti-aircraft machine gun; 2 x 4 smoke dischargers
Powerplant:	one IVECO FIAT MTCA V-12 turbocharged diesel engine developing 1250hp (932kW)
Performance:	maximum road speed: 66km/h (41.3mph); fording 1.2m (3ft 11in); vertical obstacle 2.1m (6ft 11in); trench 3m (9ft 10in)

Type 85

The Type 85 main battle tank entered production on a small scale in the late 1980s. The tank was based on the chassis of the Type 80, but, in something of an innovation for Chinese tanks, it was given an all-welded turret instead of the usual cast steel type, armour being increased all round. It also carried improved communications equipment. The increased main armament (125mm as opposed to the 105mm of the Type 80) is fed by an automatic loader, which allows the crew to be reduced to a minimum. However, space inside is reduced by the ammunition being made up of separate projectile and charge. The Type 85 is still in production and has been exported to Pakistan, where it is known as the Type 85-IIM. It is still inferior to American and European tanks.

Country of origin:	China
Crew:	3
Weight:	41,000kg (90,200lb)
Dimensions:	length 10.28m (31ft 5in); width: 3.45m (10ft 6in); height: 2.3m (7ft)
Range:	500km (312 miles)
Armour:	classified
Armament:	one 125mm gun; one 7.62mm coaxial machine gun; one 12.7mm anti-aircraft machine gun; two smoke grenade launchers
Powerplant:	one V-12 supercharged diesel engine developing 730hp (544kW)
Performance:	maximum road speed: 57.25km/h (35.8mph); fording 1.4m (4ft 7in); vertical obstacle 0.8m (2ft 7in); trench 2.7m (8ft 10in)

Leclerc

The Leclerc was designed to replace the French Army's fleet of AMX-30 tanks. Development began in 1983, and the first production Leclercs appeared in 1991. The Leclerc is an excellent vehicle. An automatic loading system for the main armament and remote-control machine guns allow the crew to be cut down to three. The tank can be fitted with extra fuel tanks to increase operational range, and standard equipment includes a fire-detection/suppression system, thermal-imaging and laser rangefinder for the main gun, and a land navigation system. The on-board electronic systems are fully integrated to allow automatic reconfiguration in case of battlefield failure or damage. As well as those in French service, around 390 Leclercs have been exported to the United Arab Emirates.

Country of origin:	France
Crew:	3
Weight:	53,500kg (117,700lb)
Dimensions:	length 9.87m (30ft); width 3.71m (11ft 4in); height 2.46m (7ft 6in)
Range:	550km (345 miles)
Armour:	classified
Armament:	one 120mm gun, one 12.7mm machine gun, one 7.62mm machine gun, 3 x 9 smoke dischargers
Powerplant:	one SAEM UDU V8X 1500 T9 Hyperbar eight-cylinder diesel engine developing 1500hp; SESM ESM500 automatic transmission
Performance:	maximum road speed: 73km/h (45.6mph); fording 1m (3ft 3in); vertical obstacle 1.25m (4ft 1in); trench 3m (9ft 10in)

Type 90

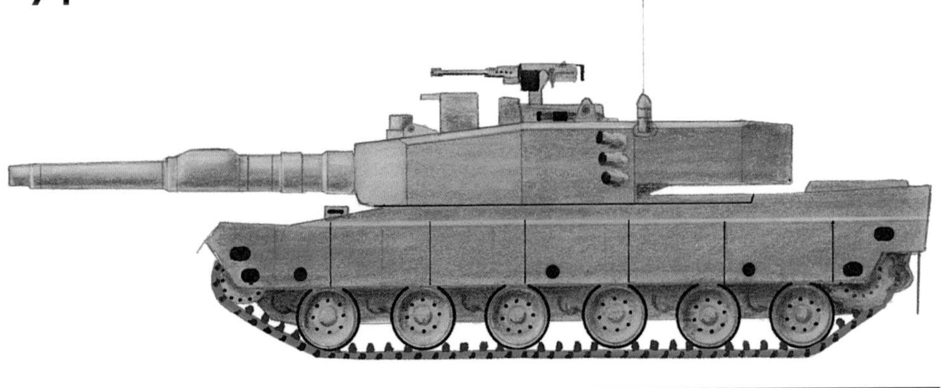

The Type 90 main battle tank was placed in development in the mid-1970s to meet the needs of the Japanese Ground Self-Defence Force. It entered production on a small scale in the 1992. Its slow production rate makes this the most expensive unit cost tank produced by any nation in the world. The vehicle carries a laser rangefinder, computerised fire control and NBC system as standard, as well as thermal imaging and night-driving capability. Like the Type 74, the vehicle has a cross-linked hydro-pneumatic suspension system, which allows it to raise or lower different parts of the chassis in order to cross difficult terrain or to engage targets outside of the gun's normal elevation/depression range. Variants include the Type 90 ARV with dozer blade and winch and the Type 91 AVLB bridgelayer.

Country of origin:	Japan
Crew:	3
Weight:	50,000kg (110,000lb)
Dimensions:	length 9.76m (29ft 10in); width: 3.4m (10ft 5in); height 2.34m (7ft 1in)
Range:	350km (219 miles)
Armour:	classified
Armament:	one 120mm gun; one 7.62mm coaxial machine gun; one 12.7mm anti-aircraft machine gun; two smoke dischargers
Powerplant:	one 10ZG V-10 fuel-injection diesel, developing 1500hp (1118kW)
Performance:	maximum road speed: 70km/h (43.8mph); fording 2m (6ft 6in); vertical obstacle 1m (3ft 4in); trench 2.7m (8ft 10in)

Challenger 2

The Challenger 2 is the current main battle tank of the British Army. The hull is similar to that of the Challenger 1, as is the powerpack, but the turret has been redesigned to fit updated armament, and the tank is in many ways a completely new tank. The first production versions appeared in mid-1994, boasting a carbon dioxide laser rangefinder, thermal-imaging and fully computerised fire-control systems, giving a high first-round hit probability. In addition, turret traverse is all electric and the gun is fully stabilised. It also has the capacity to be fitted with the Battlefield Information Control System in future years, to give even greater combat capability. A dozer can be fitted to the front of the hull. Nearly 400 were ordered by the British Army, with 18 being exported to Oman.

Country of origin:	United Kingdom
Crew:	4
Weight:	62,500kg (137,500lb)
Dimensions:	length 11.55m (35ft 4in); width 3.52m (10ft 8in); height 2.49m (7ft 5in)
Range:	400km (250 miles)
Armour:	classified
Armament:	one 120mm gun; two 7.62mm machine guns; two smoke rocket dischargers
Powerplant:	one liquid-cooled diesel engine developing 1200hp (895kW)
Performance:	maximum road speed: 57km/h (35.6mph); fording 1m (3ft 4in); vertical obstacle 0.9m (2ft 10in); trench 2.8m (9ft 2in)

Arjun Mk 1

The Arjun is India's first indigenous main battle tank design. The Indian Army's Combat Vehicle Research and Development Establishment encountered numerous problems with the project, resulting in significant delays which held up the in-service date until 1994. One of the main problems was the lack of an indigenous powerplant, which forced the Indians to use a German MTU diesel. The Arjun's main armament is a locally designed stabilised 120mm rifled gun capable of firing a variety of ammunition types, such as high explosive, high explosive anti-tank and high explosive squash head. The tank has an advanced fire-control system integrated with a combined day/night thermal imaging gunner's assembly with built-in laser rangefinder. In addition, there is a full weather sensor package.

Country of origin:	India
Crew:	4
Weight:	58,000kg (127,600lb)
Dimensions:	length 9.8m (32ft 2in); width 3.17m (10ft 5in); height 2.44m (8ft)
Range:	400km (250 miles)
Armour:	classified
Armament:	one 120mm gun; one 7.62mm machine gun
Powerplant:	one MTU MB 838 Ka 501 water-cooled diesel developing 1400hp (1044kW)
Performance:	maximum road speed 72km/h (45mph); fording 1m (3ft 3in); vertical gradient 1.1m (3ft 7in); trench 3m (9ft 10in)

L.40

The Italians were ahead of tactical thinking in one aspect of armoured vehicle production, when they developed one of the first tank destroyers in the late 1930s. This thinking proved useful when it was realised that their light tanks were of little combat value in North Africa in 1941. The chassis of the Semovente M 40 was fitted with a Böhler 47mm gun, one of the hardest hitting anti-tank weapons of its day. Around 280 of the tank destroyer vehicles were produced, and they fared adequately against Allied armour from 1942 onwards. Pressed into service by the Germans after the Italian surrender in 1943, the vehicle was unsuited for much of the Italian terrain and saw little action. Many had their armament removed and were converted into mobile command posts.

Country of origin:	Italy
Crew:	2
Weight:	6500kg (14,300lb)
Dimensions:	length 4.00m (13ft 1.5in); width 1.92m (6ft 3.6in); height 1.63m (5ft 4.2in)
Range:	200km (124 miles)
Armour:	6-42mm (0.23-1.65in)
Armament:	one Böhler 47mm gun or 8mm Breda modelo 38 machine gun
Powerplant:	one SPA 18D four-cylinder petrol engine developing 68hp (50.7kW)
Performance:	maximum road speed 42.3km/h (26.3mph); fording 0.8m (2ft 7in); vertical obstacle 0.8m (2ft 7in); trench 1.7m (5ft 7in);

M.41

The M 41 was the only heavy tank destroyer produced by Italy during World War II. Using the chassis of the M 14/41 tank, designers mounted a powerful anti-aircraft gun on the vehicle. Designed to operate at long range, the M 41 was not considered to require armour protection. The first production vehicles appeared in 1941, but only 48 were ever built, mainly because Italy's industrial plant was limited, but also because the gun was required for regular anti-aircraft duties. The M 41 proved effective in the open spaces of North Africa, but after being seized by the Germans after the Italian surrender proved to have little value in the mountainous terrain of Italy, where few tanks could operate. Most were therefore used as long-range artillery.

Country of origin:	Italy
Crew:	2 (on gun)
Weight:	17,000kg (37,400lb)
Dimensions:	length 5.205m (17ft 0.9in); width 2.20m (7ft 2.6in); height 2.15m (7ft 0.6in)
Range:	200km (124 miles)
Armour:	none
Armament:	one 90mm cannon
Powerplant:	one SPA 15-TM-41 eight-cylinder petrol engine developing 145hp (108.1kW)
Performance:	maximum road speed 35.5km/h (22mph); fording 1.0m (3ft 3in); vertical obstacle 0.9m (35.4in); trench 2.1m (6ft 10.7in)

Marder II

By 1941, the PzKpfw II was becoming obsolete. However, the production line was still in operation, so in order not to waste resources, the decision was taken to convert the chassis to a tank destroyer to tackle the large numbers of Soviet tanks on the Eastern Front. The standard Pak 40 anti-tank gun was mounted on the PzKpfw II's chassis. The combination of firepower and mobility worked well and the Marder II as it was known remained in production until 1944, with 1217 being made. The Marder II saw action in all theatres, particularly on the Eastern front, where some were later equipped with infrared systems for night-fighting. The Marder II proved an effective and versatile weapon and was the most widely used German self-propelled gun of World War II.

Country of origin:	Germany
Crew:	3 or 4
Weight:	11,000kg (24,200lb)
Dimensions:	length 6.36m (20ft 10.4in); width 2.28m (7ft 5.8in); height 2.20m (7ft 2.6in)
Range:	190km (118 miles)
Armour:	10mm (0.39in)
Armament:	one 7.5cm Pak 40/2 gun; one 7.92mm MG34 machine gun
Powerplant:	one Maybach HL 62 petrol engine developing 140hp (104.4kW)
Performance:	maximum road speed 40km/h (24.8mph); fording 0.9m (2ft 11in); vertical obstacle 0.42m (1ft 4in); trench 1.8m (5ft 11in)

M10

During the period immediately before its entry into World War II, the US Army developed a concept to defeat fast-moving armoured formations using powerfully armed tank destroyers deployed *en masse*. The M10 was a product of this concept. Based on the M4 Sherman tank chassis and using the M7 gun, developed from an anti-aircraft weapon, the M10 was lightly armed as it was not intended for close-quarter combat. Production ran from September to December 1942, with nearly 5000 being produced. The concept of separate tank destroyer battalions was soon proved ineffective, and thus most M10s were used more as assault forces. The M10 continued in service until the end of the war, but its large and bulky nature and the diminishing effect of its gun reduced its usefulness.

Country of origin:	United States
Crew:	5
Weight:	29,937kg (65,861lb)
Dimensions:	length 6.83m (22ft 5in); width 3.05m (10ft 0in); height 2.57m (8ft 5in)
Range:	322km (200 miles)
Armour:	12-37mm (0.47-1.46in)
Armament:	one 76.2mm M7 gun; one 12.7mm Browning machine gun
Powerplant:	two General Motors six-cylinder diesel engines each developing 375hp (276.6kW)
Performance:	maximum road speed 51km/h (32mph); fording 0.91m (3ft); vertical obstacle 0.46m (18in); trench 2.26m (7ft 5in)

Hetzer

Most tank destroyer conversions of existing tank chassis were rather cumbersome and lacked finesse in design. In contrast, the various Sturmgeschütz artillery vehicles had proved very effective tank killers, so it was decided to produce a light tank destroyer along the lines of a Sturmgeschütz. Based on the PzKpfw 38(t) chassis, the new Hetzer was put into production in 1943. Small, well-protected, with good mobility and able to knock out all but the heaviest tanks, the Hetzer was a tremendous success. By the time the factories were overrun in May 1944, 1577 had been built, including flame-thrower and recovery versions. The Czech Army took over production of the Hetzer after World War II and exports were still in service with the Swiss in the 1970s.

Country of origin:	Germany
Crew:	4
Weight:	14,500kg (31,900lb)
Dimensions:	length 6.20m (20ft 4.1in); width 2.50m (8ft 2.4in); height 2.10m (6ft 10.7in)
Range:	250km (155 miles)
Armour:	10-60mm (0.39-2.36in)
Armament:	one 7.5cm Pak 39 gun; one 7.92mm MG34 machine gun
Powerplant:	one Praga AC/2800 petrol engine developing 150-160hp (111.9-119.3kW)
Performance:	maximum road speed 39km/h (24.2mph); fording 0.9m (2ft 11in); vertical obstacle 0.65m (2ft 1in); trench 1.3m (4ft 3.2in)

Jagpanzer IV

Experience during 1942 suggested that the Sturmgeschütz vehicles would have to be upgunned if their role as tank destroyers was to continue. The armament of the Panther was selected, and while modifications were made to the Sturmgeschütz III to allow for this upgrade, the Panther gun was fitted to the chassis of the PzKpfw IV. Known as the Jagdpanzer IV, the first production models appeared in 1943. With a low silhouette and well-protected hull, the Jagdpanzer IV soon proved popular with crews, especially as the armament proved sufficient to knock out almost any enemy tank encountered. Under Hitler's instructions, some were later fitted with the more powerful L/70 gun, but the extra weight resulted in less mobility. A total of 1139 were produced between December 1943 and March 1945.

Country of origin:	Germany
Crew:	4
Weight:	25,800kg (56,933lb)
Dimensions:	length 8.58m (28ft 1.8in); width 2.93m (9ft 7.4in); height 1.96m (6ft 5.2in)
Range:	214km (133 miles)
Armour:	11-80mm (0.43-3.14in)
Armament:	one 7.5cm Pak 39 gun; two 7.92mm MG34 machine guns
Powerplant:	one Maybach HL 120 petrol engine developing 265hp (197.6kW)
Performance:	maximum road speed 35km/h (22mph); fording 1.2m (3ft 11in); vertical obstacle 0.6m (23.6in); trench 2.3m (7ft 6.6in);

Nashorn

In an effort to get sizeable numbers of tank destroyers into service on the Eastern Front, the Germans embarked on a series of hurried improvisations. A special weapon-carrier vehicle based on the PzKpfw IV chassis was adapted to take the 8.8cm Pak 43 gun. The first of these so-called Nashorns entered service in 1943. The Nashorn was a high vehicle which was difficult to conceal, a problem increased by poor armour with only the driver being fully protected. It was therefore used as a long-range weapon, in contrast to most other tank destroyers. Some 433 were built before production ceased in 1944. The powerful gun made the Nashorn a potent battlefield weapon, but it was too bulky for its prescribed role and only the lack of anything better kept it in production in Germany.

Country of origin:	Germany
Crew:	5
Weight:	24,400kg (53,680lb)
Dimensions:	length 8.44m (27ft 8.3in); width 2.86m (9ft 4.6in); height 2.65m (8ft 8.3in)
Range:	210km (130.5 miles)
Armour:	10-30mm (0.39-1.18in)
Armament:	one 8.8cm Pak 43 gun; one 7.92mm MG34 machine gun
Powerplant:	one Maybach HL 120 petrol engine developing 265hp (197.6kW)
Performance:	maximum road speed 40km/h (24.8mph); fording 0.8m (2ft 7.5in); vertical obstacle 0.6m (23.6in); trench 2.3m (7ft 6.6in)

Elefant

The Elefant stemmed from the Porsche design for the PzKpfw VI Tiger. Henschel was awarded the contract for the new tank, but it was decided to use the Porsche design as a tank destroyer. Hitler demanded that the new vehicle be ready for the 1943 offensive on the Russian Front, so development was rather hurried. As a result many broke down in their first action at the Battle of Kursk, and the lack of proper armour and ponderous mobility made them easy targets for Soviet gunners in the battle. In addition, the lack of machine guns meant that there was no defence against Soviet troops disabling them with explosive charges in close-quarter combat. The survivors were withdrawn to Italy, where unreliability and lack of spares ensured their continued ineffectiveness.

Country of origin:	Germany
Crew:	6
Weight:	65,000kg (143,000lb)
Dimensions:	length 8.128m (26ft 8in); width 3.378m (11ft 1in); height 2.997m (9ft 10in)
Range:	153km (95 miles)
Armour:	50-200mm (1.97-7.87in)
Armament:	one 8.8cm Pak 43/2 gun
Powerplant:	two Maybach HL 120 TRM V-12 petrol engines each developing 530hp (395.2kW)
Performance:	maximum road speed 20.1km/h (12.5mph); fording 1.0m (3ft 4in); vertical obstacle 0.8m (31.5in); trench 2.65m (8ft 8.3in)

M18

Whereas most tank destroyers of World War II were converted tanks, the M18 Hellcat was designed for the role from the outset. Development began in 1942 and the first production models appeared in 1943, over 2500 being produced before October 1944. The M18 proved to be one of the best US tank destroyers of the war. Much smaller than the M10, it carried a more powerful gun and was considerably faster, in fact being the fastest tracked vehicle of the war, a good power-to-weight ratio providing excellent agility and acceleration. More importantly, it was able to hold its own on the battlefield. Despite their success, the decline of enthusiasm for specialist tank destroyer units led to the M18 being used more as assault guns and artillery towards the end of the war.

Country of origin:	United States
Crew:	5
Weight:	17,036kg (37,557lb)
Dimensions:	length 6.65m (21ft 10in); width 2.87m (9ft 5in); height 2.58m (8ft 5.5in)
Range:	169km (105 miles)
Armour:	9-25mm (0.35-0.98in)
Armament:	one 76.2mm M1A1 gun; one 12.7mm machine gun
Powerplant:	one Continental R-975 C1 radial petrol engine developing 340hp (253.5kW)
Performance:	maximum road speed 88.5km/h (55mph); fording 1.22m (4ft); vertical obstacle 0.91m (3ft); trench 1.88m (6ft 2in)

Jagdpanther

The Jagdpanther was one of the first purpose-built tank destroyers, as opposed to a hasty tank-conversion. Using the Panther chassis, the prototype was demonstrated to Hitler in October 1943, who named it the Jagdpanther himself. The vehicle was superb. Fast, well-armoured and mounting a powerful gun, the Jagdpanther became one of the most famous of all World War II vehicles, able to knock out almost any tank it encountered. A machine gun and anti-magnetic mine paint helped with close-quarter defence. On all European fronts, the Jagdpanther became feared. Fortunately for the Allies, planned production levels were never reached, and by the time the factories were overrun in April 1945, only 382 had been completed, mainly due to the disruption caused by Allied bombing raids.

Country of origin:	Germany
Crew:	5
Weight:	46,000kg (101,200lb)
Dimensions:	length 9.90m (32ft 5.8in); width 3.27m (10ft 8.7in); height 2.715m (8ft 10.9in)
Range:	160km (99.4 miles)
Armour:	80-120mm (3.15-4.72in)
Armament:	one 8.8cm Pak 43/3 gun; one 7.92mm MG34 machine gun
Powerplant:	one Maybach HL 230 petrol engine developing 600-700hp (447.4-522kW)
Performance:	maximum road speed 55km/h (34.2mph); fording 1.7m (5ft 7in); vertical obstacle 0.9m (35in); trench 1.9m (6ft 3in)

Archer

The Archer stemmed from a British decision to increase anti-tank gun calibres from 57mm to 76.2mm. The new guns were too heavy for tanks then in existence. An interim solution was found by adapting the Valentine tank chassis for use as a tank destroyer. The first production Archer, as the new vehicle was known, appeared in March 1943, but it was October 1944 before the Archer saw any action. Initial worries about the rear-facing gun proved groundless. The low silhouette was ideal for ambushes, and the rear-facing gun meant that the vehicle could be driven away quickly without having to turn round, thus avoiding retaliation. In total 655 were produced by the end of World War II, and the Archer continued in service with the British until the mid-1950s.

Country of origin:	United Kingdom
Crew:	4
Weight:	16,257kg (35,765lb)
Dimensions:	length 6.68m (21ft 11in); width 2.76m (9ft 0.5in); height 2.25m (7ft 4.5in)
Range:	225km (140 miles)
Armour:	8-60mm (0.31-2.36in)
Armament:	one 17-pounder gun; one 0.303in Bren gun
Powerplant:	one General Motors 6-71 six-cylinder diesel engine developing 192hp (143.2kW)
Performance:	maximum road speed 32.2km/h (20mph); fording 0.91m (3ft); vertical obstacle 0.84m (2ft 9in); trench 2.36m (7ft 9in)

Hornet Malkara

The Hornet Malkara was developed in the 1950s to provide a long-range anti-tank capability. The vehicle was essentially a modified Humber one-tonne (0.98 tons) 4 x 4 truck chassis with a Malkara missile launcher mounted on the back. It was designed specifically to be dropped by parachute. The operator fired the missile from the cab and controlled it by means of a joystick attached to a wire unreeling from the missile sights, along which were sent electronic signals. The missile carried the largest warhead ever fitted to an anti-tank guided weapon even in modern times, and could destroy any tank in service at that time. It continued in service until being replaced by the Ferret Mk 5 in the 1970s. Although crude, it was an indicator of the way anti-tank weapons would develop towards the end of the century.

Country of origin:	United Kingdom
Crew:	3
Weight:	5700kg (12,540lb)
Dimensions:	length 5.05m (16ft 7in); width 2.22m (7ft 3.5in); height 2.34m (7ft 8in)
Range:	402km (250 miles)
Armour:	8-16mm (0.31-0.62in)
Armament:	two Malkara anti-tank missiles
Powerplant:	one Rolls-Royce B60 Mk 5A six-cylinder petrol engine developing 120hp (89kW)
Performance:	maximum road speed 64km/h (40mph); trench not applicable

M50 Ontos

The M50 Ontos was a tank destroyer designed mainly for use as an air-portable vehicle for the US Marine Corps. Its chassis was developed in the early 1950s by GMC, and its weaponry consisted of six RCL 106mm (4.17in) recoilless rifles, three mounted either side of a small central turret. Attached to the top four guns were 12.7mm (0.5in) spotting rifles. These would fire tracer rounds to assist targeting. Six 106mm (4.17in) rounds were pre-loaded and a further eight were kept inside the vehicle. A major disadvantage of the M50 was that the rifles could only be reloaded from the outside, thus exposing the crew to small arms fire. Production ceased in 1970 after the Ontos had seen service in Vietnam and the Dominican Republic; the vehicle was immediately withdrawn from service.

Country of origin:	United States
Crew:	3
Weight:	8640kg (19,051lb)
Dimensions:	Length: 3.82m (12.53ft); width: 2.6m (8.53ft); height: 2.13m (6.99ft)
Range:	240km (150 miles)
Armour:	13mm (0.51in) maximum
Armament:	6 x RCL 106mm (4.17in) recoilless rifles; 4 x 12.7mm (0.5in) M8C spotting rifles
Powerplant:	1 x General Motors 302 petrol, developing 145hp (108kW)
Performance:	Maximum road speed: 48km/h (30mph)

SPz lang HS30

The HS30 was destined to be blighted by technical problems throughout its active life. Consequently, only 2176 vehicles were built (out of a projected 4450) between 1958 and 1962. In the early 1970s, remaining HS30s were replaced with Marder mechanized infantry combat vehicles. The HS30 was a basic armoured personnel carrier which could carry five soldiers and a three-man crew inside an all-welded steel hull. It was not amphibious, neither did it have an NBC option, both serious deficits in the Cold War era. It was, however, well armed. A turret-mounted 20mm (0.78in) Hispano HS820 was the primary weapon, but ATGWs and M40A1 106mm (4.17in) recoilless rifles were further options, as shown above; however the back blast from a recoilless rifle would quickly give the vehicle's position away.

Country of origin:	West Germany
Crew:	3 + 5
Weight:	14,600kg (32,200lb)
Dimensions:	Length: 5.56m (18.24ft); width: 2.25m (7.38ft); height: 1.85m (6.07ft)
Range:	270km (170 miles)
Armour:	(Steel) 30mm (1.18in) maximum
Armament:	1 x 20mm (0.78in) Hispano HS820 cannon and other options
Powerplant:	1 x Rolls-Royce 8-cylinder petrol, developing 235hp (175kW) at 3800rpm
Performance:	Maximum road speed: 51km/h (32mph); fording: 0.7m (2.3ft); gradient: 60 percent; vertical obstacle: 0.6m (2ft); trench: 1.6m (5.3ft)

Raketenjadgpanzer 1

The Raketenjadgpanzer 1 was a ground-breaking anti-tank vehicle which entered service with the German Federal Armed Forces in 1961. It was a combination of a Hispano-Suiza HS-30 chassis used for the Schützenpanzer SPz 12-3 APC, and two French SS-11 ATGW launchers. When one missile was ready to fire, the other would be withdrawn inside the hull for rearming (this explains why only one launcher is visible in pictures). The SS-11 missile has a range of 3000m (9800ft). It is guided to its target using wire-command, which is controlled by a crew member using a periscope. Mobile ATGW launchers were a new concept in warfare at this time, and the Raketenjadgpanzer 1 had a large impact on military thinking.

Country of origin:	West Germany
Crew:	4
Weight:	13,000kg (28,665lb)
Dimensions:	Length: 5.56m (18.24ft); width: 2.25m (7.38ft); height: 1.7m (5.58ft)
Range:	270km (170 miles)
Armour:	(Steel) 30mm (1.18in)
Armament:	10 x SS-11 ATGWs
Powerplant:	1 x Rolls-Royce B81 Mk80F 8-cylinder petrol, developing 235hp (175kW) at 3800rpm
Performance:	Maximum road speed: 51km/h (32mph); fording: 0.7m (2.3ft); gradient: 60 percent; vertical obstacle: 0.6m (2ft); trench: 1.6m (5.2ft)

Type 60

Despite showing its age compared to modern ATGW launchers, the Komatsu Type 60 is still in service with the Japanese Ground Self Defence Force, though its future is uncertain. Its main tank-hunting armament comprises of two RCL 106mm (4.17in) recoilless rifles mounted on top of a low-tracked carrier. The guns are only able to traverse 10 degrees either side, so much targeting is reliant upon the driver aligning the vehicle with the target. The effective range of the RCL weapon is a little over 1000m (3280ft). Even with HEAT warheads, the Type 60 is really only suitable for engaging light armoured vehicles rather than modern MBTs, as the penetrative power of the 106mm (4.17in) gun is generally inadequate.

Country of origin:	Japan
Crew:	3
Weight:	8000kg (17,600lb)
Dimensions:	Length: 4.3m (14.1ft); width: 2.23m (7.32ft); height: 1.59m (5.22ft)
Range:	130km (80 miles)
Armour:	(Steel) 12mm (0.47in)
Armament:	2 x RCL 106mm (4.17in) recoilless rifles; 1 x 12.7mm (0.5in) MG
Powerplant:	1 x Komatsu 6T 120-2 6-cylinder diesel, developing 120hp (89kW) at 2400rpm
Performance:	Maximum road speed: 55km/h (34mph); fording: 0.7m (2.3ft) gradient: 60 percent; vertical obstacle: 0.6m (2ft); trench: 1.8m (5.9ft)

Raketenjadgpanzer 2

The Raketenjadgpanzer 2 (RJPZ 2) replaced its predecessor, the RJPZ 1, in 1967, using updated missile technology and boasting improved vehicle performance. The same SS-11 ATGW missile launchers were fitted, though the vehicle could carry 14 missiles as opposed to the 10 carried by the RJPZ 1. TOW and HOT ATGWs could also be fitted. Two SS-11 launchers at the front of the hull created a 180-degree arc of traverse to the front of the vehicle. A 7.62mm (0.3in) MG3 machine gun was mounted on the top right-hand side of the hull, and another in the bow. The hull itself was the same as that used for the Jadgpanzer Kanone 4-5 self-propelled anti-tank gun.

Country of origin:	West Germany
Crew:	4
Weight:	23,000kg (50,700lb)
Dimensions:	Length: 6.43m (21.09ft); width: 2.98m (9.78ft); height: 2.15m (7.05ft)
Range:	400km (250 miles)
Armour:	(Steel) 50mm (1.97in)
Armament:	14 x SS-11 ATGWs; 2 x 7.62mm (0.3in) MG3 MGs
Powerplant:	1 x Daimler-Benz MB 837A 8-cylinder diesel, developing 500hp (373kW) at 2000rpm
Performance:	Maximum road speed: 70km/h (43mph); fording: 1.4m (4.6ft); gradient: 60 percent; vertical obstacle: 0.75m (2.46ft); trench: 2m (6.6ft)

Jadgpanzer Jaguar 1 and 2

The Jadgpanzer Jaguar 1 self-propelled anti-tank vehicle was the result of the standardized upgrading of the Raketenjadgpanzer 2 to accommodate more advanced anti-tank missile technologies. Chassis structure remained the same – that of the Jadgpanzer Kanone 4-5 self-propelled anti-tank gun – though the glacis plate received extra armour to protect against modern MBT shells. The SS-11 missiles were exchanged for the new Euromissile K3S HOT ATGW. HOT is a command-to-line-of-sight system with an effective range of 4000m (13,100ft), and has penetrative capability even against modern explosive-reactive armour. The Jaguar 2 was simply the Jaguar 1 fitted with a TOW ATGW instead of the HOT.

Country of origin:	West Germany
Crew:	4
Weight:	25,500kg (56,200lb)
Dimensions:	Length: 6.61m (21.69ft); width: 3.12m (10.24ft); height: 2.55m (8.37ft)
Range:	400km (250 miles)
Armour:	(Steel) 50mm (1.97in) maximum
Armament:	1 x HOT ATGW system; 1 x 7.62mm (0.3in) MG3 MG
Powerplant:	1 x Daimler-Benz MB837A 8-cylinder diesel, developing 500hp (373kW) at 2000rpm
Performance:	Maximum road speed: 70km/h (43mph); fording: 1.4m (4.6ft); gradient: 60 percent; vertical obstacle: 0.75m (2.46ft); trench: 2m (6.6ft)

FV102 Striker

The FV102 Striker is actually a turretless Scorpion reconnaissance vehicle, its turret replaced by a hydraulically raised launcher box containing five BAC Swingfire anti-tank guided weapons. Five further missiles are stored internally. The Swingfire has an effective range of 4000m (13,100ft). The missile controller of the FV102 uses an Automatic Command Line of Site (ACLOS) system to target an enemy vehicle, at which point the launcher box is raised to a 35-degree angle before firing. Guidance during flight is by command wire. Eight periscopes provide good all-round visibility when the vehicle is in hatch-down position, and the missile controller has a x1 and x10 power monocular sight. The FV102 went into production in 1975.

Country of origin:	United Kingdom
Crew:	3
Weight:	8221kg (18,127lb)
Dimensions:	Length: 4.76m (15.62ft); width: 2.18m (7.15ft); height: 2.21m (7.25ft)
Range:	483km (300 miles)
Armour:	Classified
Armament:	5 + 5 x Swingfire anti-tank missiles; 1 x 7.62mm (0.3in) MG
Powerplant:	1 x Jaguar J60 No.1 Mk100B 6-cylinder petrol, developing 195hp (145kW)
Performance:	Maximum road speed: 100km/h (60mph); fording: 1m (3.3ft); gradient: 60 percent; vertical obstacle: 0.6m (2ft)

Spartan

The Alvis Spartan is a member of the Scorpion family and entered service with the British Army in 1978. It has specialised roles, such as carrying Javelin surface-to-air missiles (SAMs) or Royal Engineer assault teams. It has a three-man crew and room in the back for four fully equipped troops, though the vehicle has no firing ports. Flotation screens can be fitted around the top of the hull, which, when erected, makes the Spartan fully amphibious (in the water it is propelled by its tracks). The newest production models incorporate a number of improvements, including an upgraded suspension system and a more fuel-efficient Perkins diesel engine. By the end of 1995, a total of 960 Spartan vehicles had been built. As shown above, it can be fitted with a Milan anti-tank weapon.

Country of origin:	United Kingdom
Crew:	3 + 4
Weight:	8172kg (17,978lb)
Dimensions:	length 5.125m (16ft 9in); width 2.24m (7ft 4in); height 2.26m (7ft 5in)
Range:	483km (301 miles)
Armour:	classified
Armament:	one 7.62mm machine gun; one Milan missile launcher
Powerplant:	one Jaguar six-cylinder petrol engine developing 190hp (142kW)
Performance:	maximum road speed 80km/h (50mph); fording 1.067m (3ft 6in); vertical obstacle 0.5m 1ft 7in); trench 2.057m (6ft 9in)

M901

The 1970s and 1980s saw many military forces combining APCs with ATGW weapons systems. In the United States, the enormously successful M113A1 APC received its ATGW upgrade in the mid-1970s, and the M901 entered production in 1978. The vehicle body is the standard APC model, but mounted with the two-tube M27 TOW 2 cupola on the roof. The M901 must come to a stop before it can fire, though it only takes 20 seconds for the TOW system to target and fire. Two TOW missiles are pre-loaded and 10 more are carried internally. Reloading only takes around 40 seconds, the rear of the cupola sinking down to the hull for the convenience and protection of the crew.

Country of origin:	United States
Crew:	4 or 5
Weight:	11,794kg (26,005lb)
Dimensions:	Length: 4.88m (16.01ft); width: 2.68m (8.79ft); height: 3.35m (10.99ft)
Range:	483km (300 miles)
Armour:	(Aluminium) 44mm (1.73in)
Armament:	1 x TOW 2 ATGW system
Powerplant:	1 x Detroit Diesel 6V-53N 6-cylinder diesel, developing 215hp (160kW)
Performance:	Maximum road speed: 68km/h (42mph); fording: amphibious; gradient: 60 percent; vertical obstacle: 0.61m (2ft); trench: 1.68m (5.51ft)

Wiesel TOW

The Wiesel was specifically designed to be air-portable, and consequently weighs in at only 2750kg (6063lb) and measures a mere 3.26m (10.69ft) in length. It was mainly designed to carry the Hughes TOW 1 ATGW weapon, and so give air-landed units immediate anti-armour support. Eight TOW missiles are carried on board, with two set for immediate use. The TOW 1 is the standard ATGW used by over 20 nations worldwide. It is a wire-guided missile with a range of up to 3750m (12,300ft) and has the ability to defeat most MBT armour using High-Explosive Anti-tank (HEAT) warheads. Because of its small size and low weight, the Wiesel can reach speeds of 80km/h (50mph) even in off-road environments.

Country of origin:	West Germany
Crew:	3
Weight:	2750kg (6063lb)
Dimensions:	Length: 3.26m (10.7ft); width: 1.82m (5.97ft); height: 1.89m (6.2ft)
Range:	200km (125 miles)
Armour:	Not available
Armament:	1 x TOW 1 ATGW system
Powerplant:	1 x Volkswagen Type 069 5-cylinder turbo diesel, developing 98hp (73kW)
Performance:	Maximum road speed: 80km/h (50mph); gradient: 60 percent; vertical obstacle: 0.4m (1.3ft); trench: 1.5m (4.9ft)

VBL

By definition, the Panhard Véhicule Blindé Léger (Lightly Armoured Vehicle) is technically an armoured scout car, but tank-hunting capabilities were a major part of its design brief. A single Anti-tank Guided Weapon (ATGW) is mounted on the roof and operated by the crew member using a roof hatch. The ATGW is usually a MILAN, but TOW and HOT missile systems are also used. Other armament includes a 7.62mm (0.3in) GPMG as standard, and a Mistral SAM launcher as an option. The VBL is fully amphibious and features lightweight steel armour 11.5mm (0.45in) thick. The driver has night-vision devices and the ability to control tyre pressure from a central console.

Country of origin:	France
Crew:	3
Weight:	3550kg (7828lb)
Dimensions:	Length: 3.87m (12.69ft); width: 2.02m (6.63ft); height: 1.7m (5.58ft)
Range:	600km (370 miles)
Armour:	(Steel) 11.5mm (0.45in)
Armament:	1 x MILAN ATGW; 1 x 7.62mm (0.3in) GPMG
Powerplant:	1 x Peugeot XD3T 4-cylinder turbo diesel, developing 105hp (78kW) at 4150rpm
Performance:	Maximum road speed: 95km/h (59mph); fording: 0.9m (2.9ft); gradient: 50 percent; trench: 0.5m (1.6ft)

Centauro

The Centauro is officially described as a tank hunter. Its armour, however, is light compared to an MBT, and a Centauro crew would rarely tackle an enemy tank in open battle. On top of an IVECO chassis is an OTOBREDA turret armed with a 105mm (4.13in) gun. This weapon is capable of penetrating over 700mm (27.56in) of armour at a range of around 2000m (6550ft) using armour-piercing fin-stabilized discarding-sabot (APFSDS) rounds. Gun handling and targeting are assisted by laser range-finding and a fully computerized fire control system like that used on the Ariete MBT. As an 8x8 vehicle, the Centauro has good off-road mobility assisted by hydropneumatic suspension and central tyre-pressure regulation.

Country of origin:	Italy
Crew:	4
Weight:	25,000kg (55,100lb)
Dimensions:	Length (with gun): 8.55m (28.05ft); width: 2.95m (9.68ft); height: 2.73m (8.96ft)
Range:	800km (500 miles)
Armour:	Steel (details classified)
Armament:	1 x 105mm (4.13in) gun; 1 x 7.62mm (0.3in) coaxial MG; 1 x 7.62mm (0.3in) AA MG; 2 x 4 smoke grenade launchers
Powerplant:	1 x Iveco MTCA 6-cylinder turbo diesel, developing 520hp (388kW)
Performance:	Maximum speed: 108km/h (67mph); fording: 1.5m (4.9ft); gradient: 60 percent; vertical obstacle: 0.55m (1.8ft); trench: 1.2m (3.9ft)

Panzerjäger 90

The MOWAG Piranha APC has produced many specialist variants since it entered production in 1976. In 1989, an ATGW launcher version was introduced in the Piranha's 6x6 configuration, and acted as a replacement for the Swiss Army's 106mm (4.17in) recoilless rifle carriers. Called the Panzerjäger 90, the first versions were armed with a single Tube-Launched Optically Tracked Wire-Guided (TOW) 2 ATGW, but subsequent versions have received a turret-mounted twin TOW launcher. The commander of the vehicle can stand between the two launchers via a hatch, though the missiles can be launched with all crew inside the vehicle. The TOW 2 missile has a range of 4000m (13,100ft) and armour penetration of 800mm (31.5in) in its latest models.

Country of origin:	Switzerland
Crew:	5
Weight:	11,000kg (24,300lb)
Dimensions:	Length: 6.23m (20.44ft); width: 2.5m (8.2ft); height: 2.97m (9.74ft)
Range:	600km (370 miles)
Armour:	10mm (0.39in)
Armament:	1 x 76.2mm (3in) cannon; 1 x 7.62mm (0.3in) coaxial MG
Powerplant:	1 x Detroit Diesel 6V-53T 6-cylinder diesel, developing 215hp (160kW)
Performance:	Maximum road speed: 102km/h (63mph); fording: amphibious; gradient: 60 percent; vertical obstacle: 0.5m (1.6ft)

Vickers Light Tank

Originally based on the Carden-Loyd tankette of the 1920s, the Vickers light tanks were developed in the 1930s. Mobile and fast across country, the Vickers was widely used in the 1930s for policing the British Empire and in the early years of World War II. However, World War II combat experience proved them to be virtually useless. Their thin armour was easily pierced and their machine-gun armament was utterly inadequate on the battlefield. Lack of equipment forced the British to use them in combat rather than for reconnaissance, as they were designed to be used, and the consequences were disastrous. Attempts to convert them into anti-aircraft tanks failed, although the Germans managed to employ some captured vehicles as anti-tank gun carriers.

Country of origin:	United Kingdom
Crew:	3
Weight:	4877kg (10,729lb)
Dimensions:	length 3.96m (13ft); width 2.08m (6ft 10in); height 2.235m (7ft 6in)
Range:	range 201km (215 miles)
Armour:	10-15mm (0.4-0.6in)
Armament:	one 7.7mm/12.7mm machine gun
Powerplant:	one Meadows ESTL six-cylinder petrol engine developing 88hp (66kW)
Performance:	maximum road speed 51.5km/h (32mph); fording 0.6m (2ft); vertical obstacle – ; trench –

T-37

The origins of the T-37 are to be found in the 1931 purchase by the USSR of a number of British Carden-Loyd amphibious tanks. The Soviets were duly impressed but realised that the tank was unsuited to fulfil all their requirements. Their version of the British design eventually became the T-37. The first production models appeared in late 1933. A small vehicle with a crew of just two, their buoyancy stemmed from pontoons attached to either side of the hull. Designed mainly for reconnaissance, and with only light armour and armament, they nevertheless were used in a combat role following the German invasion in 1941, where they fared badly and were replaced as quickly as possible. A few were retained for use as light tractors.

Country of origin:	USSR
Crew:	2
Weight:	3200kg (7040lb)
Dimensions:	length 3.75m (12ft 3.6in); width 2.10m (6ft 10.7in); height 1.82m (5ft 11.7in)
Range:	185km (115 miles)
Armour:	3-9mm (0.1-0.4in)
Armament:	one 7.62mm machine gun
Powerplant:	one GAZ AA petrol engine developing 40hp (29.8kW)
Performance:	maximum speed 56.3km/h (35mph); fording amphibious; vertical obstacle 0.787m (2ft 7in); trench 1.879m (6ft 2in)

T-40

The T-40 was designed to replace the T-37, whose manifold deficiencies had become painfully apparent by 1938. To speed development, the design included as many automobile components as possible. Flotation tanks were fitted at the rear, giving the vehicle a rather bulky appearance. The T-40 was equipped with very thin armour and fared poorly as a result during the fighting in Finland in 1939. It was thus decided to dispense with the amphibious characteristics and use the vehicle as a land tank. This proved an impractical conversion and its use was minimal after that, seeing some service with armoured formations as a reconnaissance vehicle during 1941 against the Germans. Only around 225 T-40s were ever built, as light tanks were given low priority at that time.

Country of origin:	USSR
Crew:	2
Weight:	5900kg (12,980lb)
Dimensions:	length 4.11m (13ft 5.8in); width 2.33m (7ft 7.7in); height 1.95m (6ft 4.8in)
Range:	360km (224 miles)
Armour:	8-14mm (0.3-0.55in)
Armament:	one 12.7mm machine gun
Powerplant:	one GAZ-202 petrol engine developing 70hp (52.2kW)
Performance:	maximum speed 44km/h (27.3mph); fording amphibious; vertical obstacle 0.70m (2ft 3.6in); trench 3.12m (10ft 2.8in)

T-70 Light Tank

The Soviet military had spent a great deal of time and effort in the development of a series of light tanks during the 1930s. The T-70 was the culmination of this effort at the time of the German invasion of Russia in June 1941. Reasonably armoured, the T-70's armament was of limited use against heavier tanks, especially as the commander of the tank had to operate the gun single-handed, thus reducing his combat effectiveness. Its service record was unremarkable, mainly being used for reconnaissance and close infantry support. Over 8000 were produced up to 1943, but despite the numbers, the T-70 was at best only an adequate combat tank. It was certainly better than the tank it superseded, the T-60, but was outgunned by the German panzers in 1941–42.

Country of origin:	USSR
Crew:	2
Weight:	9367kg (20,608lb)
Dimensions:	length 4.29m (14ft 0.9in); width 2.32m (7ft 7.3in); height 2.04m (6ft 8.3in)
Range:	360km (223.7 miles)
Armour:	10-60mm (0.39-2.36in)
Armament:	one 45mm gun; one 7.62mm machine gun
Powerplant:	two GAZ-202 petrol engines delivering a total of 140hp (104kW)
Performance:	maximum road speed 45km/h (28mph); fording not known; vertical obstacle 0.70m (2ft 3.6in); trench 3.12m (10ft 2.8in)

Light Tank M3

Having followed the battles of 1940 on the European mainland closely, the American military realised that its main light tank, the M2, was obsolete, and that a more heavily armoured version was required. The result was the M3 which entered full-scale production in 1941, and nearly 6000 were built. Many were passed to the Soviet Red Army and to British forces where they were known as Stuarts. Their reliability and mobility were impressive and they were popular with crews, being used in all theatres of the war. Obsolete as a combat tank by 1944, many were converted to command and reconnaissance vehicles with the turrets removed and extra machine guns added instead. Variants included mine-clearing, flame-throwing and anti-aircraft versions.

Country of origin:	United States
Crew:	4
Weight:	12,927kg (28,440lb)
Dimensions:	length 4.54m (14ft 10.75in); width 2.24m (7ft 4in); height 2.30m (7ft 6.5in)
Range:	112.6km (70 miles)
Armour:	15-43mm (0.59-1.69in)
Armament:	one 37mm gun; two 7.7mm machine guns
Powerplant:	one Continental W-970-9A six-cylinder radial petrol engine developing 250hp (186.5kW)
Performance:	maximum road speed 58km/h (36mph); fording 0.91m (3ft 0in); vertical obstacle 0.61m (2ft); trench 1.83m (6ft 0in)

Light Tank Mk VII Tetrarch

When the prototype of the Tetrarch, known at the time as the Purdah, appeared in 1938, it was received without enthusiasm as it had no outstanding attributes. Like other light tanks, it fared badly in combat in the early years of the war, being poorly armed and armoured and lacking a specified purpose. It was withdrawn quickly, although some were passed on to the Soviet Union (where it was greeted with a similar lack of enthusiasm). However, it was given new life as an airborne tank and the Hamilcar glider was specifically designed to carry it. Fitted with a more powerful armament, the tank landed with British airborne forces on D-Day, but proved no match for enemy armour and its role was later assumed by the American M22 Locust.

Country of origin:	United Kingdom
Crew:	3
Weight:	7620kg (16,764lb)
Dimensions:	length overall 4.305m (14ft 1.5in); length of hull 4.115m (13ft 6in); width 2.31m (7ft 7in); height 2.121m (6ft 11.5in)
Range:	224km (140 miles)
Armour:	4-16mm (0.16-0.63in)
Armament:	one 2-pounder gun; one coaxial 7.92mm machine gun
Powerplant:	one Meadows 12-cylinder petrol engine developing 165hp (123kW)
Performance:	maximum road speed 64km/h (40mph); maximum cross-country speed 45km/h (28mph); fording 0.914m (3ft 0in); trench 1.524m (5ft)

Light Tank M24 Chaffee

By 1942 it was evident that the 37mm gun was inadequate for the needs of America's light tanks, and indeed as a main armament of any tank. Attempts to install larger weapons in M5 tanks failed and so a new tank was designed by Cadillac, the first being ready by late 1943. Known as the Chaffee, the M24 entered full service with the US Army in late 1944, too late in the war to make a big impression. It was in Korea that the M24 realised its full combat value, with the agility for reconnaissance, but well-armed for battle. Its biggest contribution was in its concept. It was designed to be part of a combat family of vehicles, all using the same chassis, including self-propelled guns and anti-aircraft tanks. The tank remained in service with some nations until recently.

Country of origin:	United States
Crew:	5
Weight:	18,370kg (40,414lb)
Dimensions:	length 5.49m (18ft); width 2.95m (9ft 8in); height 2.48m (8ft 1.5in)
Range:	161km (100 miles)
Armour:	12-38mm (0.47-1.5in)
Armament:	one 75mm gun; two 7.62mm machine guns; one 12.7mm gun on turret; one 51mm smoke mortar
Powerplant:	two Cadillac Model 44T24 V-8 petrol engines developing 110hp (82kW) each
Performance:	maximum road speed 56km/h (35mph); fording 1.02m (3ft 4in); vertical obstacle 0.91m (3ft); trench 2.44m (8ft)

PT-76

The PT-76 was designed in the immediate period after World War II. For many years it was the standard reconnaissance vehicle of the Soviet Red Army, before being replaced by heavier T-62s, and was exported to more than 25 countries, seeing action in the 1967 Six-Day War, Vietnam and Angola. Intended as an amphibious tank, its armour was only sufficient to withstand small-arms fire, in order to keep the weight to a minimum. The tank was equipped with bilge pumps and water jets to allow it to move efficiently through water and could travel up to 65km (40 miles) in this fashion. The chassis was used for a number of other vehicles, including the BTR-50 Armoured Personnel Carrier and the FROG missile launcher. Though old, it is still in service with a number of countries.

Country of origin:	USSR
Crew:	3
Weight:	14,000kg (30,800lb)
Dimensions:	length 7.625m (25ft 0.25in); width 3.14m (10ft 3.7in); height 2.255m (7ft 4.75in)
Range:	260km (160 miles)
Armour:	5-17mm (0.19-0.66in)
Armament:	one 76mm gun; one coaxial 7.62mm machine gun; one 12.7mm anti-aircraft machine-gun
Powerplant:	one V-6 six-cylinder diesel engine developing 240hp (179kW)
Performance:	maximum road speed 44km/h (27mph); fording amphibious; vertical obstacle 1.10m (3ft 7.3in); trench 2.80m (9ft 2in)

AMX-13

The AMX-13 was designed immediately after the end of World War II. Production began in 1952 and continued until the 1980s. Its design included an automatic loader in the turret bustle which included two revolver-type magazines, each holding six rounds of ammunition. The tank was widely exported, proving particularly popular with developing nations such as Chile, Djibouti and Nepal, as well as Israel, the Netherlands and Switzerland. One interesting feature is the oscillating turret in which the gun is fixed in the upper part, which in turn pivots on the lower part. The AMX-13 was extensively modified and used as the basis for a complete family of vehicles, from self-propelled guns and howitzers to engineer vehicles, recovery vehicles, bridgelayers and infantry fighting vehicles.

Country of origin:	France
Crew:	3
Weight:	15,000kg (33,000lb)
Dimensions:	length 6.36m (20ft 10.3in); width 2.50m (8ft 2.5in); height 2.30m (7ft 6.5in)
Range:	400km (250 miles)
Armour:	10-40mm (0.4-1.57in)
Armament:	one 75mm gun; one 7.62mm machine gun
Powerplant:	one SOFAM eight-cylinder petrol engine developing 250hp (186kW)
Performance:	maximum road speed 60km/h (37mph); fording 0.60m (1ft 11.7in); vertical obstacle 0.65m (2ft 1.7in); trench 1.60m (5ft 3in)

Schützenpanzer SPz 11-2 kurz

The SPz kurz is actually a German version of a French vehicle, the Hotchkiss SP 1A. During the 1950s, Hotchkiss produced tracked armoured vehicles intended for the French Army, though ultimately the army placed no orders. West Germany, however, was at this time seeking to develop its armoured military forces. After testing the Hotchkiss prototypes, the German Army received 2374 Hotchkiss vehicles between 1958 and 1962. Redesignated the SPz 11-2, it featured an all-welded hull of APC type, with twin doors in the rear and escape hatch underneath. The SPz kurz was a reconnaissance vehicle variant of the 11-2, with the small turret carrying a Hispano-Suiza 20mm (0.78in) cannon.

Country of origin:	West Germany
Crew:	5
Weight:	8200kg (18,100lb)
Dimensions:	Length: 4.51m (14.8ft); width: 2.28m (7.23ft); height: 1.97m (6.46ft)
Range:	400km (250 miles)
Armour:	15mm (0.59in)
Armament:	1 x Hispano-Suiza 820/L35 20mm (0.78in) cannon; 3 x smoke grenade launchers
Powerplant:	1 x Hotchkiss 6-cylinder petrol, developing 164hp (122kW) at 3900rpm
Performance:	Maximum speed: 58km/h (36mph); fording: 1m (3.3ft); gradient: 60 percent; vertical obstacle: 0.6m (2ft); trench: 1.5m (4.9ft)

M551 Sheridan

The M551 was developed following a 1959 requirement for a air-portable tank to equip the US Army's airborne divisions. Between 1965 and 1970, 1700 vehicles were produced by General Motors and saw service in South Korea, Europe and Vietnam. It was in the latter that the M551's deficiencies were revealed when it proved highly susceptible to landmines, although its ability to fire canister ammunition was effective in beating off mass guerrilla attacks. As a result, it was withdrawn from most frontline units in the late 1970s, although many were modified by the National Training Center to resemble Soviet vehicles and used for training purposes. The main armament consisted of a 152mm weapon that fired a wire-guided Shilelagh missile.

Country of origin:	United States
Crew:	4
Weight:	15,830kg (34,826lb)
Dimensions:	length 6.299m (20ft 8in); width 2.819m (9ft 3in); height (overall) 2.946m (9ft 8in)
Range:	600km (310 miles)
Armour:	40-50mm (1.57-2in)
Armament:	one 152mm gun/missile launcher; one coaxial 7.62mm machine gun; one 12.7mm anti-aircraft machine gun
Powerplant:	one six-cylinder Detroit 6V-53T diesel, developing 300hp (224kW)
Performance:	maximum road speed 70km/h (43mph); fording amphibious; vertical obstacle 0.838m (2ft 9in); trench 2.54m (8ft 4in)

Scorpion

The first prototype of the Alvis Scorpion, officially named Combat Vehicle Reconnaissance (Tracked), appeared in 1969, following a British Army requirement for a tracked reconnaissance vehicle to replace the Saladin armoured car. It entered service in 1972 and was exported to countries all over the world, particularly Belgium, where it was produced under licence. It saw action in the Falklands in 1982, where its flotation screens giving amphibious capability were particularly useful during the landings. The Scorpion proved its worth in both reconnaissance and in high-speed advances, but it has now been retired from British service. The Scorpion chassis has been used for a complete range of tracked vehicles, such as the Sultan, Spartan and Scimitar.

Country of origin:	United Kingdom
Crew:	3
Weight:	8073kg (17,760lb)
Dimensions:	length 4.794m (15ft 8.75in); width 2.235m (7ft 4in); height 2.102m (6ft 10.75in)
Range:	644km (400 miles)
Armour:	12.7mm (0.5in)
Armament:	one 76mm gun; one coaxial 7.62mm machine gun
Powerplant:	one Jaguar 4.2-litre petrol engine developing 190hp (142kW)
Performance:	maximum road speed 80km/h (50mph); fording 1.067m (3ft 6in); vertical obstacle 0.50m (1ft 8in); trench 2.057m (6ft 9in)

Scimitar

The Scimitar is a variant of the Scorpion FV101 tracked reconnaissance vehicle, one of the CVR(T) family of light armoured vehicles developed for the British Army. Entering service in 1978, it was intended mainly for a fire support role. The powerful RARDEN cannon is able to penetrate all light armoured vehicles, and the side armour of most main battle tanks. Its own armour protection is minimal, though, being barely sufficient to resist small-arms fire. The Scimitar can be fitted with night-vision sights, laser rangefinder and computerised fire-control system. The original Jaguar petrol engine has now been replaced by a diesel unit in British service. Amphibious capability is provided by a collapsible flotation screen, and the vehicle is propelled in the water by its tracks.

Country of origin:	United Kingdom
Crew:	3
Weight:	7800kg (17,160lb)
Dimensions:	length 4.8m (15ft 9in); width 2.24m (7ft 4in); height 2.1m (6ft 11in)
Range:	644km (402 miles)
Armour:	12.7mm (0.5in)
Armament:	one 30mm Rarden gun; one 12.7m machine gun
Powerplant:	one Jaguar 4.2-litre petrol engine developing 190hp (142kW)
Performance:	maximum road speed 80km/h (50mph); fording 1.067m (3ft 6in); vertical obstacle 0.50m (1ft 8in); trench 2.057m (6ft 9in)

Wiesel

The Wiesel was developed to a requirement for an air-portable light armoured tracked vehicle for use by airborne troops. Prototypes were built by Porsche and deliveries began at the end of the 1980s – a total of 345 vehicles will be delivered to the German Army (210 will be armed with a wire-guided anti-tank weapon). There are two main versions, one armed with a conventional cannon (complete with 20 rounds of ready use ammunition), the other with a missile launcher. Its compact nature, necessary for air transport, makes it very difficult to detect the Wiesel on the battlefield. A whole host of variants are possible such as ambulance, anti-aircraft (equipped with Stinger surface-to-air missiles), armoured personnel carrier, command vehicle and recovery vehicle.

Country of origin:	West Germany
Crew:	3
Weight:	2750kg (6050lb)
Dimensions:	length 3.265m (10ft 8.5in); width 1.82m (5ft 11.7in); height 1.875m (6ft 1.8in)
Range:	200km (124 miles)
Armour:	classified
Armament:	one 20mm cannon or a Hughes anti-tank missile launcher
Powerplant:	one five-cylinder turbocharged diesel engine developing 86hp (64kW)
Performance:	maximum road speed 80km/h (50mph); vertical obstacle 0.4m (1ft 4in); trench 1.20m (3ft 11in)

Stingray

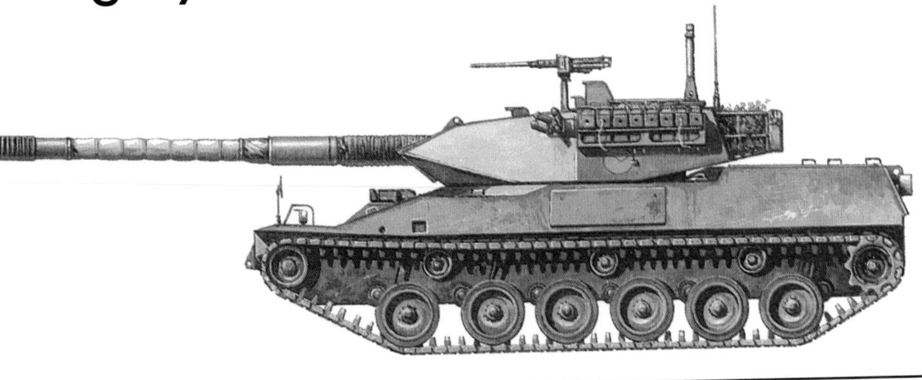

The prototype of the Stingray was unveiled in 1984 by Cadillac Gage, who had foreseen the need for a light tank with good mobility and firepower which was simple to operate and maintain. Wherever possible, proven parts from other vehicles have been adapted to save development costs. The Stingray comes equipped with laser rangefinder, stabilisation devices for the gun, nuclear, biological and chemical (NBC) protection and has the firepower of a main battle tank. Its drawback is its light armour. The Stingray has performance and power at a much lower unit cost when compared to a main battle tank. It is in service with a number of countries such as Taiwan and Thailand, and there is now an upgraded Stingray II available.

Country of origin:	United States
Crew:	4
Weight:	19,051kg (41,912lb)
Dimensions:	length 9.35m (30ft 8in); width 2.71m (8ft 11in); height 2.54m (8ft 4in)
Range:	483km (300 miles)
Armour:	classified
Armament:	one 105mm rifled gun; one coaxial 7.62mm machine gun; one 7.62mm anti-aircraft machinegun
Powerplant:	one Diesel Model 8V-92 TA diesel engine developing 535hp (399kW)
Performance:	maximum road speed 69km/h (43mph); fording 1.22m (4ft); vertical obstacle 0.76m (2ft 6in); trench 1.69m (5ft 7in)

Close Combat Vehicle – Light

The CCV-L was designed as a private venture by the FNC Corporation, manufacturer of the M113 and Bradley Armoured Fighting Vehicles, and was intended for the US Army's Light Divisions. When the prototype appeared in 1985, it created interest because it only required a three-man crew, allowed for by an automatic loading system for the main armament. This gave a rate of fire of 12 round per minute. The CCV-L borrowed parts from various other vehicles, such as the M113 Armoured Personnel Carrier, in order to reduce development time. The CCV-L has a hull of all-welded aluminium construction with bolt-on steel to enhance ballistic protection. Additional armour can be applied to the outside of the tank if required, including explosive reactive armour. It has yet to find a buyer, however.

Country of origin:	United States
Crew:	3
Weight:	19,414kg (42,710lb)
Dimensions:	length 9.37m (30ft 9in); width 2.69m (8ft 10in); height 2.36m (7ft 9in)
Range:	483km (300 miles)
Armour:	classified
Armament:	one 105mm gun
Powerplant:	one Detroit Diesel Model 6V-92 TA 6-cylinder diesel engine developing 552hp (412kW)
Performance:	maximum road speed 70km/h (43.5mph); fording 1.32m (4ft 4in); vertical obstacle 0.76m (2ft 6in); trench 2.13m (7ft)

Churchill AVRE

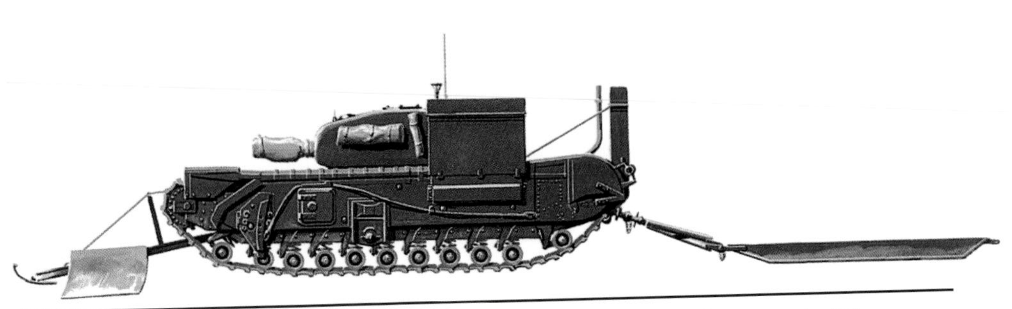

The Churchill (Assault Vehicle Royal Engineers) AVRE was borne out of the failure of the 1942 Dieppe raid where engineers were prevented from clearing obstacles by enemy fire. The tank was developed to transport engineers to the required spot and give protection, as well as carrying a heavy demolition weapon (special fittings were placed on the sides at the front for attaching devices). With a stripped interior to give extra storage space and a mortar capable of firing a heavy demolition charge, they performed excellently during their first action, clearing the way for the Normandy landings on D-Day (6 June 1944). They remained in service with the British Army until the 1960s but the concept was so successful that AVREs are still used, the current model being the Chieftain AVRE.

Country of origin:	United Kingdom
Crew:	6
Weight:	38,000kg (83,600lb)
Dimensions:	length 7.67m (25ft 2in); width 3.25m (10ft 8in); height 2.79m (9ft 2in)
Range:	193km (120 miles)
Armour:	16-102mm (0.6-4in)
Armament:	one Petard 290mm spigot mortar; one 7.92mm Besa machine-gun
Powerplant:	one Bedford Twin-Six petrol engine developing 350hp (261kW)
Performance:	maximum road speed 24.9km/h (15.5mph); fording 1.016m (3ft 4in); vertical obstacle 0.76m (2ft 6in); trench 3.048m (10ft)

Churchill AVRE Fascine- and Mat-Layer

The fascine-layer was developed from a technique used in ancient times and resurrected during World War I to allow tanks and other vehicles to cross ditches or soft ground, generally using bundles of brushwood to fill gaps or mats made of bundles of chespaling or hessian, linked up and laid out behind the tank using a roller mechanism. The tank was a standard Churchill AVRE with the devices attached to the front. The Bobbin Carpet used a hessian mat to cover wire obstacles and allow troops forward to assault the defences. The bobbins were carried well above the ground. When required the weighted free end of the carpet was dropped to the ground, the bobbin automatically unwinding itself as the tank rolled forward. This was first used during the 1942 Dieppe raid.

Country of origin:	United Kingdom
Crew:	5
Weight:	42,000kg (92,400lb)
Dimensions:	length 7.442m (24ft 5in); width 2.438m (8ft); height 5.49m (18ft)
Range:	130km (81.25 miles)
Armour:	16-102mm (0.6-4in)
Armament:	one Petard 290mm spigot mortar; one 7.92mm Besa machine gun
Powerplant:	one Bedford twin-six petrol engine developing 350hp (261kW)
Performance:	maximum road speed 20km/h (12.5mph); maximum cross-country speed about 12.8km/h (8mph); fording 1.016m (3ft 4in); vertical obstacle 0.76m (2ft 6in); trench 3.048m (10ft)

Churchill AVRE with Log Carpet

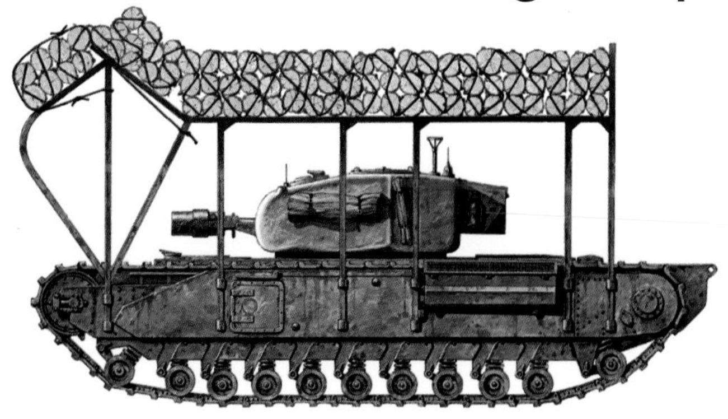

A similar arrangement was developed using linked logs. The roadway was laid under the front tracks and was pulled from its carrying frame as the AVRE moved forward. Like the Bobbin Carpet, the Log Carpet was intended to be a temporary measure only. After World War II, flexible metal roadways were developed to replace these earlier devices. The log carpet itself consisted of 100 152mm (6in) diameter logs, each 4.26m (14ft) long, bound together with wire rope. A removable steel frame was fitted above the AVRE superstructure carrying the looped mat, which was released over the front of the vehicle by detonating a light charge. The vehicle was one of a number developed for laying tracks over marshy ground or barbed wire for wheeled vehicles and infantry.

Country of origin:	United Kingdom
Crew:	5
Weight:	40,727kg (89,600lb)
Dimensions:	length 7.442m (24ft 5in); width 2.438m (8ft); height 3.454m (11ft 4in) – log carpet mounted above tank
Range:	144.8km (90 miles)
Armour:	16-102mm (0.6-4in)
Armament:	one Petard 290mm spigot mortar; one 7.92mm Besa machine gun
Powerplant:	one Bedford twin-six petrol engine developing 350hp (261kW)
Performance:	maximum road speed 20km/h (12.5mph); maximum cross-country speed about 12.8km/h (8mph); fording 1.016m (3ft 4in); vertical obstacle 0.76m (2ft 6in); trench 3.048m (10ft)

ARK

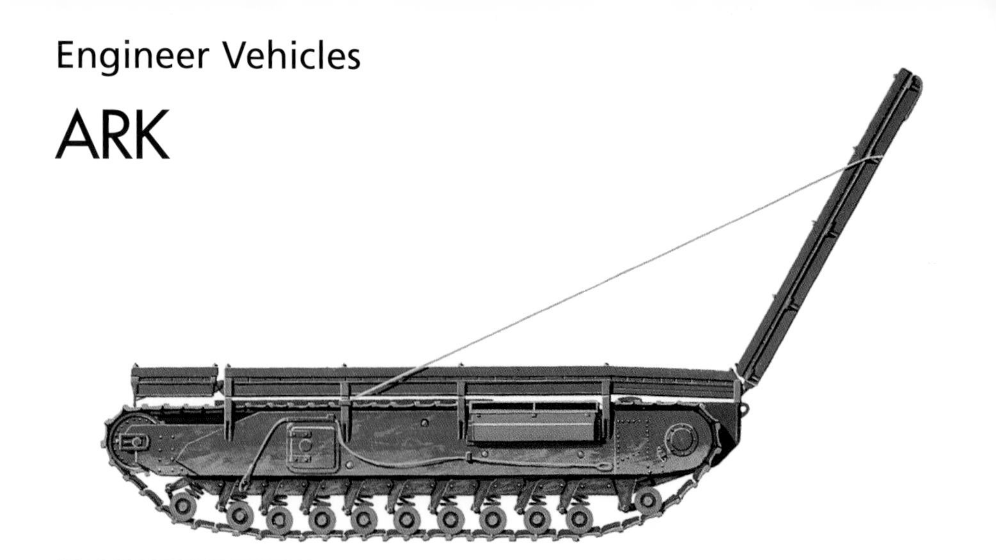

The British Army produced its first bridging tank at the end of World War I and experimented throughout the inter-war period, seeing the need to have vehicles to facilitate the crossing of obstacles. The first Armoured Ramp Carrier, the ARK Mk I, appeared in 1943. This was a converted Churchill tank with the turret removed and a blanking plate welded over the aperture and timbered trackways across the top. The ARK could be driven into ditches or against obstacles and when the two folding ramps were lowered it could be used as a bridge for other vehicles. Variants included the Churchill Woodlark, which used rockets to open up the ramps and put them into position, and the Churchill Great Eastern which used a raised ramp system, but neither was very successful.

Country of origin:	United Kingdom
Crew:	4
Weight:	38,385kg (84,450lb)
Dimensions:	length 7.442m (24ft 5in); width 2.43m (8ft); height 2.13m (7ft)
Range:	144km (90 miles)
Armour:	16mm (0.6in)
Armament:	none
Powerplant:	one Bedford twin-six petrol engine developing 350hp (261kW)
Performance:	maximum road speed 20km/h (12.5mph); maximum cross-country speed about 12.8km/h (8mph); fording 1.016m (3ft 4in); vertical obstacle 0.76m (2ft 6in); trench 3.048m (10ft)

Sherman Crab Mine-Clearing Flail

Invented by a South African, the concept of using flails to clear mines was developed in the UK culminating in the development of the Crab, usually fitted to Sherman tanks. Some 43 chains were mounted on a revolving drum powered by the main tank engine. Further developments included the addition of barbed wire-cutting disks and a contour-following device to allow the flails to operate effectively over rough ground. The Crab carried the standard Sherman armament and could thus be used in a combat role if the need arose. The drive for the rotor was taken by roller chain from the tank propeller shaft, through an aperture in the hull off-side armour, to a carden shaft. The drive from this shaft was taken by another carden shaft to a spiral bevel double reduction gear on the off-side end of the rotor.

Country of origin:	United Kingdom
Crew:	5
Weight:	31,818kg (70,000lb)
Dimensions:	length 8.23m (27ft); width 3.5m (11ft 6in); height 2.7m (9ft)
Range:	62km (100 miles)
Armour:	15-76mm (0.59-2.99in)
Armament:	one 75mm gun; one 7.62mm machine gun
Powerplant:	one Ford GAA V-8 petrol engine developing 500hp (373kW)
Performance:	maximum road speed 46km/h (28.75mph); fording 0.9m (3ft); vertical obstacle 0.6m (2ft); trench 2.26m (7ft 5in)

Bergepanther

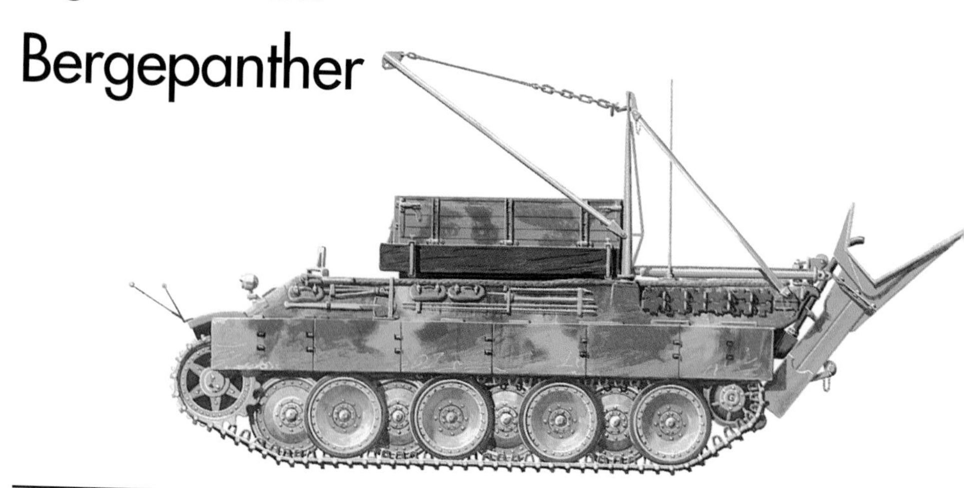

With the advent of the heavier Tiger and Panther tanks, standard German recovery vehicles such as the SdKfz 9/1 proved inadequate. The Panther tank was therefore used as the basis for a new heavy recovery vehicle. The Bergepanther first appeared in 1943. The Panther's turret was removed and replaced by an open superstructure containing a winch. A large anchor at the back dug into the ground to give the vehicle extra stability when winching. There was also an open machine-gun mounting on the front of the vehicle for self-defence. Bergepanthers entered full service in the spring of 1944, concentrated in the heavy tank battalions, and by the end of the war almost 300 had been produced. It proved to be the best recovery vehicle of World War II.

Country of origin:	Germany
Crew:	5
Weight:	42,000kg (92,400lb)
Dimensions:	length 8.153m (26ft 9in); width 3.276m (10ft 9in); height 2.74m (9ft)
Range:	169km (105 miles)
Armour:	8-40mm (0.3-1.57in)
Armament:	one 20mm cannon and one 7.92mm machine gun
Powerplant:	one Maybach HL210 P.30 petrol engine developing 642hp (478.7kW)
Performance:	maximum road speed 32km/h (20mph); fording 1.70m (5ft 7in); vertical obstacle 0.91m (3ft 0in); trench 1.91m (6ft 3in)

M32

Though developed in 1943 as a combat tank-recovery vehicle, the M32 remained in service in the United States and then abroad into the late 1950s. The hull and chassis are instantly recognizable as those of the M4 Sherman tank. The Sherman was converted into an M32 by removing the turret and replacing it with an A-frame crane and a winch with a 27,210kg (60,000lb) pull capacity. A single 12.7mm (0.5in) Browning M2 HB machine gun was also mounted on the superstructure for crew defence against infantry attack, though some could also be seen with 81mm (3.19in) mortars. Approximately 1500 M32s were produced during World War II.

Country of origin:	United States
Crew:	6
Weight:	28,000kg (61,700lb)
Dimensions:	Length: 5.93m (19.46ft); width: 2.68m (8.79ft); height: 2.74m (8.99ft)
Range:	300km (190 miles)
Armour:	(Steel) 76mm (2.99in)
Armament:	1 x 12.7mm (0.5in) Browning M2 HB machine gun; 1 x 81mm (3.19in) mortar
Powerplant:	1 x Continental R975-C1 9-cylinder petrol, developing 350hp (261kW) at 2400rpm
Performance:	Maximum speed: 40km/h (25mph); fording: 1.22m (4ft); gradient: 58 percent; vertical obstacle: 0.61m (2ft); trench: 1.88m (6.17ft)

Sherman BARV

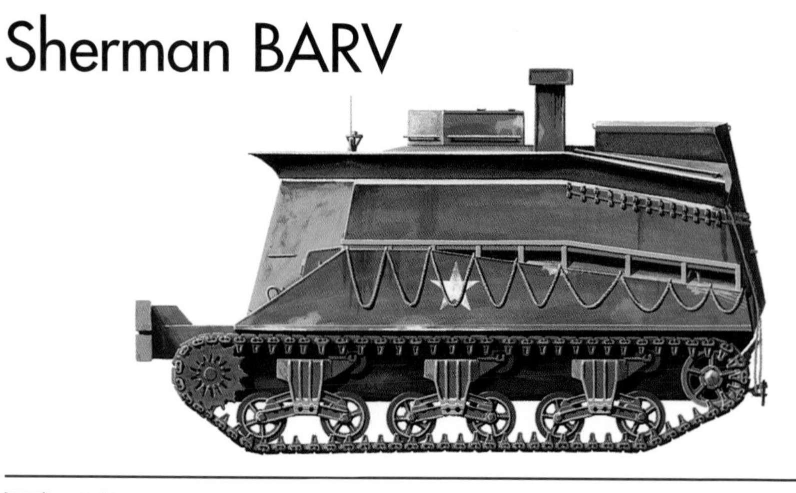

The BARV was developed during the planning for the D-Day landings when it was deemed prudent to have deep-wading recovery vehicles available to rescue vehicles stranded in the water. Trials in December 1943 were successful, and by D-Day there were 55 ready for action, the rough weather giving them plenty of work to do. The BARV was in essence a standard Sherman, but with the turret replaced by a tall superstructure with extensive waterproofing. The crew generally included a diver for securing towing cables. The BARV could either tow or push but suffered a little from the lack of a winch. The BARV was eventually christened the Sea Lion during a long post-war service record. It was standard procedure for the crew to be issued with life jackets, and for one of their number to be a diver.

Country of origin:	United States
Crew:	5
Weight:	unknown
Dimensions:	length 6.2m (20ft 4in); width 2.68m (8ft 9in); height 2.97m (9ft 9in)
Range:	136-160km (85-100 miles)
Armour:	12mm – 62mm (0.4in – 2.4in)
Armament:	none
Powerplant:	twin General Motors 6-71 engines
Performance:	maximum road speed 47km/h (29mph); fording amphibious; vertical obstacle 0.61m (2ft); trench 2.26m (7ft 5in)

Sherman T15E1

The attempt to mechanize mine clearance led to the production of a huge range of vehicles during World War II. US M4 Sherman tanks in particular were converted into several mine-clearing variants. First came the Mine Exploder T1E3. This utilized two large rollers extended to the front of the vehicle on side arms which detonated mines on contact. Many other versions later arrived, such as the Mine Resistant Vehicle T15E1. The basis of the T15E1 was simply a turretless M4 tank laden with extra body and belly armour. It was intended to detonate mines by driving over them, but the concept was as impractical as it sounds. No T15E1s were actually tested in combat.

Country of origin:	United States
Crew:	5
Weight:	33,200kg (73,200lb)
Dimensions:	Length: 5.9m (19.36ft); width: 2.75m (9.02ft); height: 2.04m (6.69ft)
Range:	270km (170 miles)
Armour:	Not applicable
Armament:	None
Powerplant:	2 x General Motors 6-cylinder petrol, developing 500hp (373kW)
Performance:	Maximum road speed: 29km/h (18mph)

M48 AVLB

The M48 Armoured Vehicle-Launched Bridge (AVLB) was a variant of the M48 MBT. Basically the chassis was exactly the same as that of the tank, but the turret was removed and replaced with a hydraulically operated scissor bridge. The bridge itself was 19.2m (63ft) long and 4.01m (13.16ft) wide. Laying the bridge took only three minutes, retracting it took between 10 and 30 minutes. The actual width of obstacle the bridge could span was 18.28m (59.97ft). The M48 was used extensively by the US Army but was also exported to several other countries. Earlier models were recognizable by two 12.7mm (0.5in) Browning machine guns, each mounted in a turret. Later models were unarmed.

Country of origin:	United States
Crew:	2
Weight:	55,205kg (121,727lb)
Dimensions:	Length: 11.28m (37ft); width: 4m (13.12ft); height: 3.9m (12.79ft)
Range:	500km (310 miles)
Armour:	120mm (4.72in) maximum
Armament:	None
Powerplant:	1 x Continental AVDS-1790-2A 12-cylinder diesel, developing 750hp (559kW) at 2400rpm
Performance:	Maximum road speed: 48km/h (30mph); fording: 1.22m (4ft); gradient: 60 percent; vertical obstacle: 0.9m (2.95ft); trench: 2.59m (8.5ft)

Centurion AVRE

In the 1960s, the Centurion Mk V Assault Vehicle Royal Engineers (AVRE) replaced the World War II-vintage Churchill AVRE as the main combat engineer vehicle of the British Army. Based on the Centurion main battle tank, the AVRE carries a heavy demolition gun for blasting enemy fortifications and a dozer blade for removing obstacles. The vehicle is also capable of laying down tracks for wheeled vehicles to help them across muddy ground, and can carry a fascine-layer to cope with anti-tank ditches. Later models were fitted with mine-clearing ploughs at the front of the hull, which were used to rip up the ground and push any anti-tank mines to one side. In addition, the tank can tow a two-wheeled trailer carrying the Giant Viper mine-clearance system. A deep-fording system was developed but not used.

Country of origin:	United Kingdom
Crew:	5
Weight:	51,809kg (113,979lb)
Dimensions:	length 8.69m (28ft 6in); width 3.96m (13ft 0in); height 3m (9ft 10in)
Range:	177km (110 miles)
Armour:	17-118mm (0.66-4.6in)
Armament:	one 165mm demolition gun; one 7.62mm co-axial machine gun; one 7.62mm anti-aircraft machine gun
Powerplant:	one Rolls-Royce Meteor Mk IVB 12-cylinder petrol engine developing 650hp (484.7kW)
Performance:	maximum road speed 34.6km/h (21.5mph); fording 1.45m (4ft 9in); vertical obstacle 0.94m (3ft 1in); trench 3.35m (11ft 0in)

M88A1

Developed in the early 1960s, the M88 Armoured Recovery Vehicle was produced until 1964, with roughly 1000 vehicles entering service with the US Army and US Marine Corps. Its chief role was MBT recovery. It was equipped with an A-frame boom, two winches and a dozer blade. The boom could pull up to 25 tons when the dozer was set into the ground to stabilize the vehicle, and could lift just under eight tons. The two winches were located at the front of the hull, one capable of pulling 23,000kg (50,700lb) and the other 13,600kg (30,000lb). A Browning M2HB 12.7mm (0.5in) machine gun was mounted on top of the crew compartment for anti-aircraft use.

Country of origin:	United States
Crew:	4
Weight:	50,803kg (112,020lb)
Dimensions:	Length: 8.27m (27.13ft); width: 3.43m (11.25ft); height: 2.92m (9.58ft)
Range:	450km (280 miles)
Armour:	Not applicable
Armament:	1 x 12.7mm (0.5in) Browning M2HB MG
Powerplant:	1 x Continental AVDS-1790-2DR 12-cylinder diesel, developing 980hp (730kW) at 2800rpm
Performance:	Maximum road speed: 42km/h (26mph); fording: 1.63m (5.35ft); gradient: 60 percent; vertical obstacle: 1.06m (3.48ft); trench: 2.62m (8.59ft)

M728

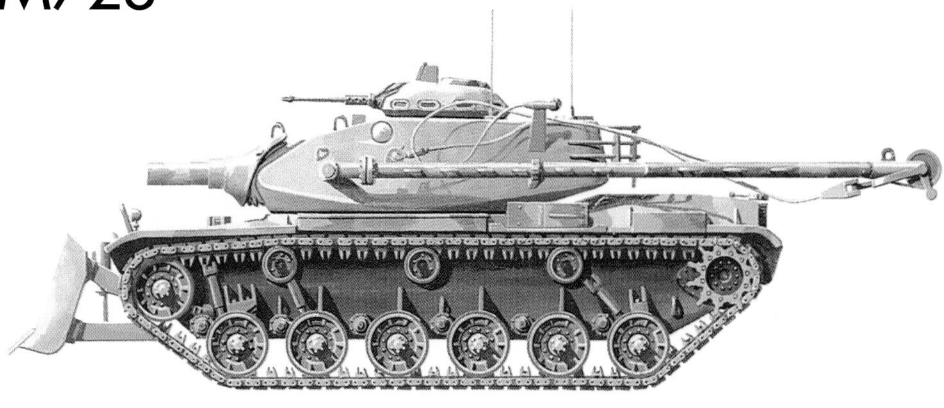

Following the development of the M60 main battle tank, a decision was taken to create a combat engineer vehicle based on the same chassis. The M728 was finally accepted for service in 1963 as the standard combat engineer vehicle for the US Army. The two vehicles were very similar. The M60's 105mm gun was replaced by a demolition-charge launcher and a hydraulically operated dozer blade added, together with a winch, which was mounted on an A-frame. The A-Frame was laid flat over the top of the vehicle when travelling. Night-vision equipment (as well as a searchlight) and a nuclear, biological and chemical (NBC) defence system were standard. The vehicle could be equipped for deep-fording. In addition to the US Army, the vehicle saw service with Singapore and Saudi Arabia.

Country of origin:	United States
Crew:	4
Weight:	53,200kg (117,040lb)
Dimensions:	length (travelling) 8.92m (29ft 3in); width (overall) 3.71m (12ft 2in); height (travelling) 3.20m (10ft 6in)
Range:	451km (280 miles)
Armour:	classified
Armament:	one 165mm demolition gun; one 7.62mm machine gun
Powerplant:	one Teledyne Continental AVDS-1790-2A 12-cylinder diesel engine developing 750bhp (559.3kW)
Performance:	maximum road speed 48.3km/h (30mph); fording 1.22m (4ft); vertical obstacle 0.76m (2ft 6in); trench 2.51m (8ft 3in)

PMP Floating Bridge

The PMP bridge entered service with the USSR in the 1960s, and was soon in use in most Warsaw Pact armies. Originally mounted on the Kr AZ-214 truck chassis, it was later transferred to the Kr AZ-255. The truck was backed up to the shore and the bridge rolled off into the water where it unfolded automatically. The full set consisted of 32 river pontoons, four shore pontoons and 12 bridging boats, the whole structure spanning some 389m (1275ft). The pontoons could also be used to form a ferry to be pushed across by boats. The PMP was exported outside of the Warsaw Pact on a significant scale, notably being used by the Egyptian Army to cross the Suez Canal during the Yom Kippur War of 1973. Note that the specifications below relate to the river pontoon bridge.

Country of origin:	USSR
Crew:	3
Weight:	6676kg (14,687lb)
Dimensions:	length (open) 6.75m (22ft 1.75in); width (open) 7.10m (23ft 3.5in); depth (open) 0.915m (3ft 0in)
Range:	–
Armour:	none
Armament:	none
Powerplant:	–
Performance:	–

M578

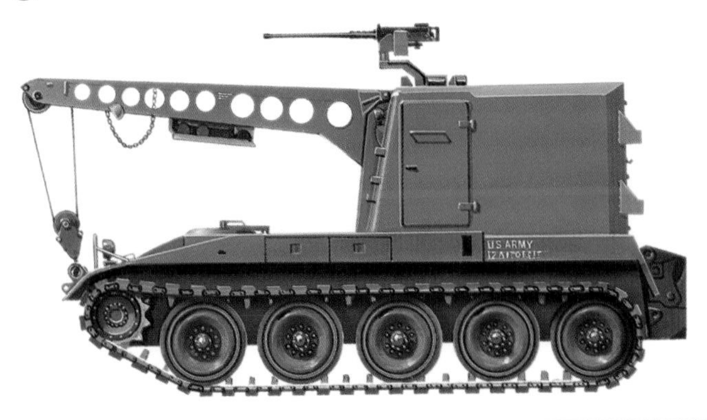

The M578 was developed specifically as a support vehicle for the M107 175mm (6.89in) and the M110 203mm (8in) self-propelled howitzers. A vehicle was required to assist with the frequent barrel changes required by these weapons, and the M578 filled the brief. The M578 was constructed using the same chassis and basic turret design as the howitzers themselves, the key differences being a hydraulically powered crane replacing the gun and a hydraulic stabilizing blade fitted to the rear hull. Despite the M107 and M110 now being out of service, the M578 continues in use as a Light Armoured Recovery Vehicle (LARV), and saw service in the first Gulf War of 1991.

Country of origin:	United States
Crew:	3
Weight:	24,300kg (53,600lb)
Dimensions:	Length: 6.42m (21.06ft); width: 3.15m (10.33ft); height: 2.92m (9.58ft)
Range:	725km (450 miles)
Armour:	Not available
Armament:	1 x 12.7mm (0.5in) Browning M2 HB MG
Powerplant:	1 x General Motors 8V-71T 8-cylinder diesel, developing 405hp (302kW) at 2300rpm
Performance:	Maximum road speed: 55km/h (34mph); fording: 1.07m (3.51ft); gradient: 60 percent; vertical obstacle: 1.02m (3.35ft); trench: 2.36m (7.74ft)

TMM Bridge

The TMM truck-mounted treadway bridge consists of four spans, launched over the rear of a 6 x 6 Kr AZ-214 or Kr AZ 255B truck chassis. Each span is extended vertically and supported by cables until it reaches its final position, at which point trestle legs are swung into place. The truck then disconnects and drives off to pick up the next span. The basic unit has a span of around 40m (131ft 3in), but more spans can be added if necessary. The bridge takes 45-60 minutes to erect. One disadvantage of the system is that it relies on legs which must be kept level – if the depth of water cannot be ascertained, problems may arise. There is nothing sophisticated about the TMM system, but it is cheap, easy to operate and can be produced in mass numbers if need be.

Country of origin:	USSR
Crew:	3
Weight:	19,500kg (42,900lb)
Dimensions:	length (with bridge) 9.30m (30ft 6.1in); width (with bridge) 3.20m (10ft 6in); height (with bridge) 3.15m (10ft 4in)
Range:	530km (329 miles)
Armour:	none
Armament:	none
Powerplant:	one YaMZ M206B six-cylinder water-cooled diesel engine developing 205hp (152.9kW)
Performance:	maximum road speed 55km/h (34.2mph); fording 1.0m (3ft 3in); vertical obstacle 0.4m (1ft 4in); trench no capability

MDK-2M

The MDK-2M is a powerful ditch-digging machine introduced into Soviet forces in 1965. Its tracked chassis belongs to the AT-T heavy artillery tractor, but fitted with a hydraulically operated dozer blade at the front and a rotary-head circular ditching machine at the rear. Using eight cutting heads, the ditcher can move an average of 400 to 500 cubic metres (14,100 to 17,700 cubic feet) of soil each hour, and in a single pass can cut a trench 3.5m (11.5ft) wide by 1.7m (5.6ft) deep. The excavated soil is channelled away from the trench down a tube while the dozer blade cuts out the shape of the floor and walls. The MDK-2M is operated by only two crew members.

Country of origin:	USSR
Crew:	2
Weight:	28,000kg (61,700lb)
Dimensions:	Length: 8m (26.25ft); width: 3.4m (11.15ft); height: 3.95m (12.96ft)
Range:	500km (310 miles)
Armour:	Not applicable
Armament:	Not applicable
Powerplant:	1 x Model V-401 12-cylinder diesel, developing 414hp (309kW)
Performance:	Maximum road speed: 35km/h (22mph)

4KH7FA SB20 Greif ARV

The Greif ARV was developed from the chassis of the Jadgpanzer SK105 Light Tank/Tank Destroyer. This was developed by Sauer-Werke in the mid-1960s and featured a heavily armoured steel hull capable of stopping 20mm (0.78in) cannon ammunition across its frontal sections. Greif ARV production began in 1976 and combined the SK105's mobility and armour protection with a new superstructure designed for engineering processes. It has a hydraulic crane with a 6500kg (14,300lb) lift capacity and a frontal winch which can pull a 20,000kg (44,100lb) load. The winch has 100m (328ft) of cable. Other engineering equipment such as welding gear is stored internally.

Country of origin:	Austria
Crew:	4
Weight:	19,800kg (43,700lb)
Dimensions:	Length: 6.7m (21.98ft); width: 2.5m (8.2ft); height: 2.3m (7.55ft)
Range:	625km (390 miles)
Armour:	(Steel) 25mm (0.98in) maximum
Armament:	1 x 12.7mm (0.5in) MG
Powerplant:	1 x Steyr 7FA 6-cylinder turbo diesel, developing 320hp (239kW) at 1900rpm
Performance:	Maximum road speed: 67km/h (42mph); fording: 1m (3.3ft); gradient: 75 percent; vertical obstacle: 0.8m (2.6ft); trench: 2.41m (7.91ft)

Pionierpanzer 1

The Pionierpanzer 1 is an Armoured Engineer Vehicle (AEV) variant of the Leopard 1 MBT family. Produced by MaK it relies on the same chassis and powerplant as the Leopard's Armoured Recovery Vehicle variant, though instead of the ARV's spare powerplant the Pionierpanzer is fitted with a spiral earth-boring device. The earth-borer is capable of drilling a hole up to 2m (6.6ft) deep and 700mm (27.56in) wide. For major engineering work, the Pionierpanzer 1 has a large dozer blade at the front with optional scarifiers for lifting road surfaces. Significant quantities of explosives can also be stored inside the hull for use in demolition work.

Country of origin:	Germany
Crew:	4
Weight:	40,800kg (90,000lb)
Dimensions:	Length: 7.98m (26.18ft); width (with dozer blade): 3.75m (12.3ft); height: 2.69m (8.83ft)
Range:	800km (500 miles)
Armour:	40mm (1.57in) maximum
Armament:	1 x 7.62mm (0.3in) MG; 1 x 7.62mm (0.3in) anti-aircraft MG
Powerplant:	1 x MTU MB838 10-cylinder multi-fuel, developing 830hp (619kW)
Performance:	Maximum road speed: 65km/h (40mph); fording: 2.1m (6.9ft); gradient: 60 percent; vertical obstacle: 1.15m (3.77ft); trench: 3m (9.8ft)

Entpannungspanzer 65

The Entpannungspanzer 65 (Entp. Pz. 65) is constructed using the chassis of the Swiss Pz.68 MBT, the turretless superstructure designed for engineering and ARV work. Its main recovery tool is an A-frame winch system which can lift up to 15,000kg (33,100lb). The pulling weight of the 120m (394ft) main winch is 25,000kg (55,100lb), though this rises to 75 tons if block and tackle are used. A 240m (787ft) auxiliary winch can draw light weights of up to 500kg (1100lb). Welding equipment and an air compressor are stored internally. Because of its MBT derivation, the Entp. Pz. 65 retains armour over the frontal section of the crew compartment up to 60mm (2.36in) in depth.

Country of origin:	Switzerland
Crew:	5
Weight:	38,000kg (83,800lb)
Dimensions:	Length: 7.6m (24.93ft); width: 3.06m (10.04ft); height: 3.25m (10.66ft)
Range:	300km (190 miles)
Armour:	(Steel) 60mm (2.36in) maximum
Armament:	1 x 7.5mm (0.28in) MG; 8 x smoke dischargers
Powerplant:	1 x MTU MB 837 8-cylinder diesel, developing 704hp (525kW) at 2200rpm
Performance:	Maximum road speed: 55km/h (34mph); fording: 1.2m (3.9ft); gradient: 70 percent; vertical obstacle: 0.75m (2.46ft); trench: 2.6m (8.5ft)

Chieftain AVLB

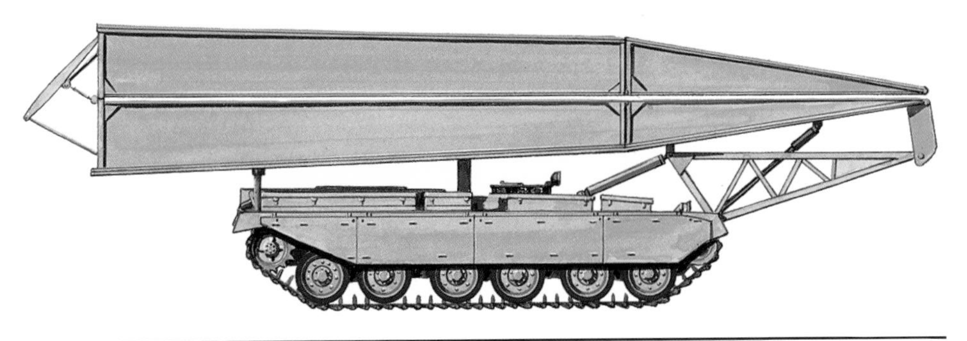

The Chieftain Armoured Vehicle Launched Bridge (AVLB) remains one of the British Army's main mobile bridge-laying systems, although they are now being phased out of service and replaced with a Challenger-tank-based system. Some 37 are in service in the UK, while another 14 are in service with the Iranian Army. The AVLB is essentially a Chieftain MBT chassis mounted with one of two bridge types. The No.8 Class 60 bridge is 24m (78.7ft) long and 4.16m (13.65ft) wide. The No.9 bridge is 13.5m (44.3ft) long and the same width. Both bridges are transported on the AVLB in a hinged double section connected to the front of the hull. They are laid by a hydraulic system pulling them over the front of the vehicle, and can bridge gaps roughly 1.5m (4.9ft) shorter than their length.

Country of origin:	United Kingdom
Crew:	3
Weight:	53,300kg (117,500lb)
Dimensions:	Length: 13.74m (45.08ft); width: 4.16m (13.65ft); height: 3.92m (12.86ft)
Range:	400km (250 miles)
Armour:	Steel (details classified)
Armament:	2 x 7.62mm (0.3in) GPMG
Powerplant:	1 x Leyland L50 12-cylinder multi-fuel, developing 750hp (559kW) at 2100rpm
Performance:	Maximum road speed: 48km/h (30mph); fording: 1.07m (3.51ft); gradient: 60 percent; vertical obstacle: 0.91m (2.98ft)

BgBv 82

The Bärgnings Bandvagn (BgBv 82) is a versatile ARV developed in the late 1960s and produced entirely in 1973, when the total production of 24 vehicles was completed. It is still in service today, and is unusual since it was an original design rather than one adapted from an existing vehicle. The hull is all-welded steel, and its three-man crew sit at the front of the vehicle in an armoured cab topped with a 20mm (0.78in) cannon. Two-thirds of the hull is open, and mounts a HM 20 winch and a Hiab-Foco 9000 lifting crane. The former can pull 20,000kg (44,100lb), while the crane can lift 5500kg (12,100lb).The BgBv 82 is also fully amphibious to suit Sweden's wet terrain.

Country of origin:	Sweden
Crew:	4
Weight:	26,300kg (58,000lb)
Dimensions:	Length: 7.2m (23.62ft); width: 3.2m (10.49ft); height: 2.45m (8.04ft)
Range:	480km (300 miles)
Armour:	Classified
Armament:	1 x 20mm (0.78in) cannon; 6 x smoke dischargers
Powerplant:	1 x Volvo-Penta THD-100C 6-cylinder turbo diesel, developing 310hp (231kW) at 2200rpm
Performance:	Maximum road speed: 56km/h (35mph); fording: amphibious; gradient: 60 percent; vertical obstacle: 0.6m (2ft); trench: 2.5m (8.2ft)

IMR

The IMR was introduced into service with the Red Army in the 1970s and was essentially a T-55 tank with the standard turret replaced by a crane and an armoured cupola. A pincer device was fitted for removing trees and a front-mounted dozer blade were standard. An unditching beam was also carried, to be fitted to the tracks in order to improve traction if the vehicle became stuck (an idea pioneered by the British in World War I). Like most vehicles based on the T-55 chassis, the IMR could lay its own smoke screen. The vehicle was very limited by Western standards, carrying no demolition charge or mine-laying equipment, but the Soviets had other vehicles to perform these tasks. The IMR saw service with most Warsaw Pact countries and the former Yugoslavia.

Country of origin:	USSR
Crew:	2
Weight:	34,000kg (74,800lb)
Dimensions:	length 10.60m (34ft 9.3in); width 3.48m (11ft 5in); height 2.48m (8ft 1.6in)
Range:	400km (249 miles)
Armour:	up to 203mm (8in)
Armament:	none
Powerplant:	one Model V-55 V-12 diesel engine developing 580hp (432.5kW)
Performance:	maximum road speed 48km/h (29.8mph); fording 1.4m (4ft 7in); vertical obstacle 0.8m (2ft 7.5in); trench 2.7m (8ft 10.3in)

SIBMAS ARV

The basis of the SIBMAS Armoured Recovery Vehicle is the SIBMAS APC developed in the mid-1970s by B.N. Constructions Ferroviaires et Métalliques. This capacious vehicle could carry 16 passengers and was also converted to various anti-tank configurations. An ARV variant was produced in the early 1980s to fulfil an order from the Malaysian military. It added a winch, crane and rear spades to the APC. The winch can pull 20,000kg (44,100lb) and the crane has a lift capacity of 10,500kg (23,150lb). Stabilizing spades are fitted at the front and rear of the hull. Twenty-four of the ARVs have been produced, mainly for the Malaysian market.

Country of origin:	Belgium
Crew:	5
Weight:	16,500kg (36,400lb)
Dimensions:	Length: 7.63m (25.03ft); width: 2.54m (8.33ft); height: 3.2m (10.49ft)
Range:	800km (500 miles)
Armour:	Not disclosed
Armament:	1 x 7.62mm (0.3in) MG
Powerplant:	1 x MAN D2566 MK 6-cylinder turbo diesel, developing 320hp (239kW) at 1900rpm
Performance:	Maximum road speed: 100km/h (62mph); fording: amphibious; gradient: 70 percent; vertical obstacle: 0.6m (2ft); trench: 1.5m (4.9ft)

SMT-1

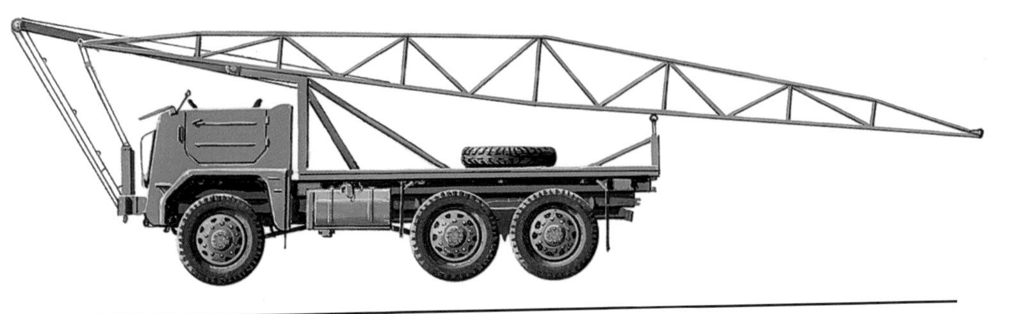

The SMT-1 is a portable bridge system introduced into the Polish armed forces in the mid-1970s. Total length of the bridge is 11m (36ft). When deployed, it is supported on trestles which can be adjusted to give the bridge surface a 3.5m (11.5ft) ground clearance. The bridge is mounted on a heavily modified Star 66 two-ton 6x6 truck. Its cab has no roof, which allows the truck to safely deploy and retract the bridge as it is pulled over the front of the vehicle by winch cables, though it has the drawback of not providing much weather protection for the crew. Once in place, the bridge can safely support 40 tons of traffic at any one moment, though the bridge itself only weighs 2.3 tons.

Country of origin:	Poland
Crew:	3
Weight:	9600kg (21,200lb)
Dimensions:	Length: 11.97m (39.27ft); width: 3.3m (10.82ft); height: 3.15m (10.33ft)
Range:	500km (310 miles)
Armour:	Not applicable
Armament:	None
Powerplant:	1 x S-47 6-cylinder petrol, developing 103hp (77kW)
Performance:	Maximum road speed: 50km/h (31mph)

Chieftain AVRE

The Chieftain AVRE has replaced the Centurion Mk 5 AVRE, which was used by the British Army since the 1960s. It is similar to a standard Chieftain MK 5 main battle tank in terms of its chassis and engine. The main difference is that the gun turret is removed and replaced with an armoured 'penthouse', on top of which is situated the commander's cupola. The vehicle carries three large hampers for storing equipment and a dozer blade or mine plough is fitted at the front. In addition, the vehicle carries a crane capable of lifting 3.6 tonnes (3.5 tons). At the back there is a winch capable of pulling 10.1 tonnes (10 tons). Around 50 of these vehicles are currently in service with the British Army. The illustration above shows the AVRE optimised for maxi-pipe fascines and trackway.

Country of origin:	United Kingdom
Crew:	3
Weight:	51,809kg (113,979lb)
Dimensions:	length: 7.52m (24.8ft); width: 3.663m (11.8ft); height: 2.89m (9.4ft)
Range:	500km (300 miles)
Armour:	classified
Armament:	one 7.62mm machine gun; 2 x 6 smoke dischargers (front); 2 x 4 smoke dischargers (rear)
Powerplant:	one Leyland L60 (No.4 Mk 8) 12-cylinder diesel engine, developing 750hp (559kW)
Performance:	maximum road speed 48km/h (28.8mph); fording 1.067m (3ft 6in); vertical obstacle 0.9m (3ft); trench 3.15m (10ft 4in)

AMX-30 Tractor

The AMX-30 EBG was based on the AMX-30 main battle tank chassis and designed to carry out a number of roles, including laying mines and clearing battlefield obstacles, by means of a hydraulically operated dozer blade mounted at the front of the vehicle. In addition, the teeth of the dozer blade can be used to dig up roads, thus making them impassable to enemy wheeled vehicles. At the rear is a winch for recovering damaged vehicles. Also, the vehicle has a powerful demolition-charge launcher for destroying bunkers and other fortifications. Standard equipment includes night vision, nuclear, biological and chemical (NBC) defence system and a deep-fording kit to provide some amphibious capability. The AMX-30 tractor is integral to the movement of French armoured forces on the battlefield.

Country of origin:	France
Crew:	3
Weight:	38,000kg (83,600lb)
Dimensions:	length 7.90m (25ft 11in); width 3.50m (11ft 5.8in); height 2.94m (9ft 7.7in)
Range:	500km (311 miles)
Armour:	80mm (3.14in)
Armament:	one 7.62mm machine gun; one 142mm demolition-charge launcher
Powerplant:	one Hispano-Suiza HS 110-2 12-cylinder multi-fuel engine developing 700hp (522.0kW)
Performance:	maximum road speed 65km/h (40.4mph); fording 2.50m (8ft 2.4in); vertical obstacle 0.9m (2ft 11.4in); trench 2.9m (9ft 6.2in)

AMX-30 Bridge

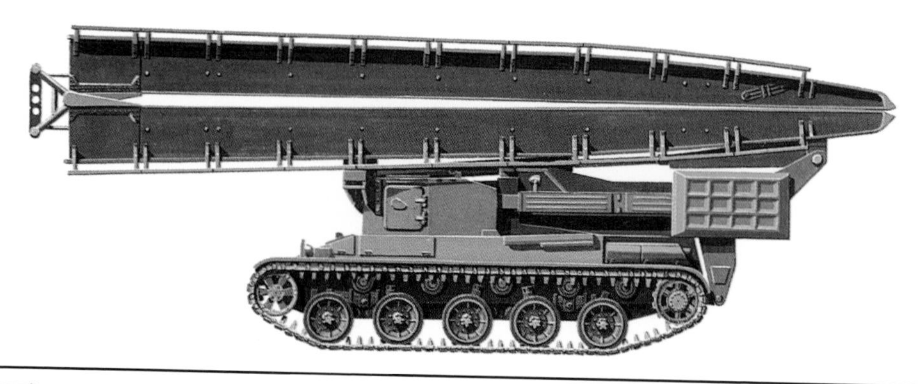

The prototype of the AMX-30 bridgelayer was built in the mid-1960s, but delays meant that the vehicle did not enter production until the mid-1970s. Based on the AMX-30 tank chassis, with an almost identical layout, the scissors bridge was laid hydraulically over the rear of the vehicle. It took around five minutes to erect and a similar time to recover the bridge. The bridge span was 20m (65ft 7in). A nuclear, biological and chemical (NBC) defence system and night-vision capability were installed as standard. The vehicle was designed to operate in tandem with the AMX-30 tank, and has no armament of its own, relying on accompanying vehicles for protection. The major disadvantage was that the bridge is erected vertically and thus can easily be seen by enemy forces.

Country of origin:	France
Crew:	3
Weight:	42,500kg (93,500lb)
Dimensions:	length (with bridge) 11.40m (37ft 4.8in); width (with bridge) 3.95m (12ft 11.5in); height (with bridge) 4.29m (14ft 0.9in)
Range:	600km (373 miles)
Armour:	80mm (3.14in)
Armament:	none
Powerplant:	one Hispano-Suiza HS-110 12-cylinder multi-fuel diesel engine developing 700hp (522.0kW)
Performance:	maximum road speed 50km/h (31.1mph); fording 1.0m (3ft 4in); vertical obstacle 0.93m (3ft 0.6in); trench 2.9m (9ft 6.2in)

Ural-375E KET-L

The Ural-375E KET-L is a recovery vehicle based on a modified Ural-375D truck chassis. It is equipped with two main winches. A rear winch is capable of pulling 15 tons, and the frontal winch can pull five tons. The KET-L is also fitted with a jib crane which has a 2.4m (7.9ft) reach and a lift capacity of 1.5 tons. The crane is used for towing other vehicles, as the KET-L has no dedicated towing hook. Cross-country, the KET-L can tow vehicles up to five tons, though on-road, the tow weight is 10 tons. During recovery operations, vehicles up to 13.5 tons can be retrieved by the static vehicle without using its anchor plate. Tools carried include oxyacetylene cutters and two sections of timber to place beneath the wheels in muddy operations.

Country of origin:	USSR
Crew:	1 + 2
Weight:	12,400kg (27,300lb)
Dimensions:	Length: 8.25m (27.07ft); width: 2.69m (8.83ft); height: 2.68m (8.79ft)
Range:	570km (350 miles)
Armour:	Not applicable
Armament:	None
Powerplant:	1 x ZIL-375 8-cylinder petrol, developing 180hp (134kW)
Performance:	Maximum road speed: 75km/h (47mph)

Biber

The first production vehicles were completed by Krupp in 1975, based on the chassis of the Leopard 1 main battle tank. The hull of the Biber AVLB was virtually identical to that of the tank. However, with the AVLB the turret was replaced by a two-part aluminium bridge, capable of spanning a 20m (65ft 7in) gap. A support blade was fitted to the front, to be lowered before the bridge was laid, but this was also useful for levelling surfaces on either side of the gap. One of the main advantages of the Biber was that its bridge was laid horizontally rather than vertically, which made for much better concealment. The Biber carried four electrically operated smoke dischargers to provide extra cover for its operations, but otherwise relied on other armoured vehicles for protection.

Country of origin:	West Germany
Crew:	2
Weight:	with bridge 45,300kg (99,660lb)
Dimensions:	length (with bridge) 11.82m (38ft 9.4in); width (with bridge) 4.0m (13ft 1.5in); height (with bridge) 3.57m (11ft 8.6in)
Range:	550km (342 miles)
Armour:	70mm (2.75in)
Armament:	none
Powerplant:	one MTU MB 838 Ca.M500 10-cylinder multi-fuel engine developing 830hp (618.9kW)
Performance:	maximum road speed 62km/h (38.5mph); fording 1.2m (3ft 11in); vertical obstacle 0.7m (2ft 3.6in); trench 2.5m (8ft 2.4in)

Pionierpanzer Dachs 2

The Pionierpanzer Dachs 2 is the update of the earlier Pionierpanzer 1. The Dachs 2 has a digging bucket at the end of its telescopic arm rather than the spiral drill fitted on its predecessor. Though developed and primarily used in Germany, the Dachs 2 has exported well, and is currently in service with Belgium, the Netherlands, Italy and Canada. Its chassis is that of the Leopard 1 MBT. During transit, the telescopic arm is laid down along the right-hand side of the hull. At the front, a dozer blade acts as a minesweeping shield. The Dachs 2 has several specialist features. Its digger can be operated by remote control, and it has onboard tools for splitting concrete and steel girders.

Country of origin:	West Germany
Crew:	3
Weight:	43,000kg (94,800lb)
Dimensions:	Length: 9.01m (29.56ft); width: 3.25m (10.66ft); height: 2.57m (8.43ft)
Range:	650km (400 miles)
Armour:	Not available
Armament:	1 x 7.62mm (0.3in) MG
Powerplant:	1 x MTU MB838 CaM5000 10-cylinder diesel, developing 818hp (610kW)
Performance:	Maximum road speed: 62km/h (39mph)

Skorpion

The Skorpion is an automated and self-propelled minelaying system. Its uses the standard chassis of the US M548 tracked cargo-carrying vehicle, but mounts a rack of mine dispensers. Each dispenser unit consists of five tubes, each tube holding 20 mines, and there are six units in total. The mines can be anti-personnel or anti-tank, though the vehicle is typically used to dispense AT-2 anti-tank mines. They are ejected to either side of the rear of the vehicle from the dispensers. The mines can be fitted with delay fuses to activate the mine only once the minelaying team have retreated. In five minutes, the Skorpion can sow a minefield 1500x50m (4900 x 160ft).

Country of origin:	West Germany
Crew:	2
Weight:	12,000kg (26,500lb)
Dimensions:	Length: 5.85m (19.19ft); width: 2.87m (9.42ft); height: 3.17m (10.4ft)
Range:	600km (370 miles)
Armour:	Not applicable
Armament:	1 x minelaying system; 1 x 7.62mm (0.3in) MG
Powerplant:	1 x Detroit Diesel 6V-53N 6-cylinder petrol, developing 202hp (151kW)
Performance:	Maximum road speed: 40km/h (25mph)

FV106 Samson

The FV106 Samson Armoured Recovery Vehicle entered production in 1978 and further extended the Scorpion family of vehicles. Its chassis is directly borrowed from the Scorpion Combat Vehicle Reconnaissance (CVR), and its hull is that of the FV103 Spartan Armoured Personnel Carrier. As an ARV, the Samson is entirely unarmed. At the rear of the hull is a heavy-duty winch and two anchor spades which extend to the ground during lifting operations. Side racks contain timber for various field applications. The winch has 229m (751ft) of wire cable and a pull capacity of 12 tons, though the Samson requires a 4:1 snatch block to pull weights greater than itself. The winch is powered directly from the Samson's main engine. A diesel engine has now been fitted to UK examples.

Country of origin:	United Kingdom
Crew:	3
Weight:	8740kg (19,300lb)
Dimensions:	Length: 4.78m (15.68ft); width: 4.78m (15.68ft); height: 2.55m (8.37ft)
Range:	483km (300 miles)
Armour:	Classified
Armament:	1 x 7.62mm (0.3in) MG
Powerplant:	1 x Jaguar J60 N01 Mk100B 6-cylinder petrol, developing 195hp (145kW) at 4750rpm
Performance:	Maximum road speed: 55km/h (34mph); fording: 1.07m (3.51ft); gradient: 70 percent; vertical obstacle: 0.5m (1.6ft); trench: 2.06m (6.76ft)

Combat Engineer Tractor

The Combat Engineer Tractor (CET) was designed by the British Army to fulfil the Royal Engineers' requirement for a vehicle combining elements of an armoured vehicle and an earthmover. Between 1978 and 1981, a total of 181 vehicles were built to undertake a variety of roles such as vehicle recovery, clearing obstacles and preparing river banks for vehicle crossings. Mounted on the roof is a rocket-propelled anchor which could be fired into the earth to enable the vehicle to winch itself out if it became stuck. The CET has full amphibious capability and when afloat is powered by twin water jets. The hull is made of all-welded aluminium armour, which is supplied by Alcan. The vehicle saw extensive service during the 1982 Falklands Conflict and was exported to India.

Country of origin:	United Kingdom
Crew:	2
Weight:	18,000kg (39,600lb)
Dimensions:	length 7.54m (24ft 9in); width 2.90m (9ft 6in); height 2.67m (8ft 9in)
Range:	322km (200 miles)
Armour:	classified
Armament:	one 7.62mm machine gun
Powerplant:	one Rolls-Royce C6TFR six-cylinder inline diesel engine developing 320hp (238.6kW)
Performance:	maximum road speed 56km/h (35mph); fording 1.83m (6ft 0in); vertical obstacle 0.61m (2ft); trench 2.06m (6ft 9in)

KrAZ-260

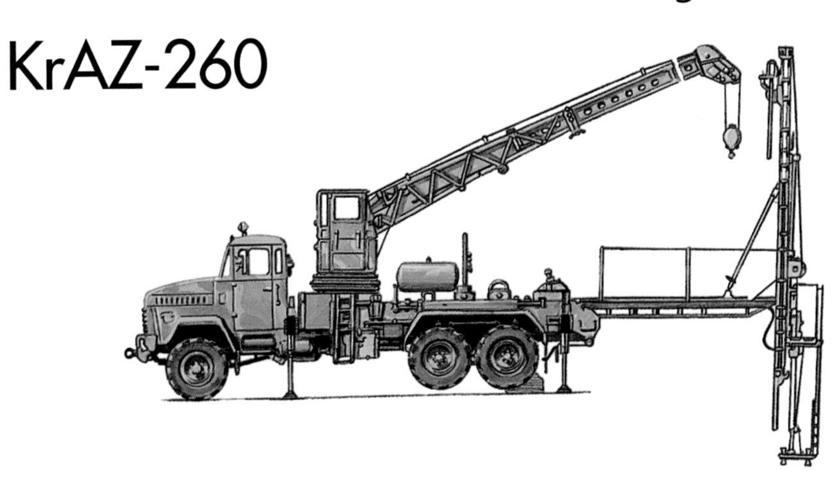

The KrAZ-260 was introduced in 1979 as a replacement amongst Russian forces for the KrAZ-255B, a 6x6 truck with an eight-ton load capacity and a 12-ton winch capacity. In basic format, the KrAZ-260 shows little change. The load weight, however, is upgraded to nine tons and 12.25 tons can be pulled with the front-mounted winch. Like the earlier vehicle, the KrAZ-260 has the option of locking the suspension when using the winch. The basic cargo body is an open bed with hinged tailgate. Weather protection is provided by a metal frame and canvas cover. The KrAZ comes in the usual range of variants and was first seen towing a 2A36 152mm (5.98in) howitzer in 1976.

Country of origin:	USSR
Crew:	1 + 2
Weight:	12,250kg (27,000lb)
Dimensions:	Length: 9m (29.53ft); width: 2.72m (8.92ft); height: 2.98m (9.78ft)
Range:	700km (430 miles)
Armour:	None
Armament:	None
Powerplant:	1 x YaMZ-238L 8-cylinder diesel, developing 287hp (214kW)
Performance:	Maximum road speed: 80km/h (50mph)

BREM-1

The BREM-1 entered production in 1984, and utilized the chassis of the T72 MBT to create a powerful battlefield recovery and engineering vehicle. At the hull front is a hydraulically powered bulldozer blade which doubles as a frontal stabilizer when the BREM-1 is using its crane. The crane itself can lift 12 tons of weight, while the BREM's winch has a pull capacity of 25 tons or 100 tons (101 tonnes) with special adaptation. An auxiliary winch is also fitted. As a recovery vehicle, the only armament is one 12.7mm (0.5in) NSVT heavy machine gun. In Russian forces, the BREM-1 is steadily being replaced by the more modern BREM-80U, which is developed from the T-80 MBT.

Country of origin:	USSR
Crew:	3
Weight:	41,000kg (90,400lb)
Dimensions:	Length: 7.98m (26.18ft); width: 3.46m (11.35ft); height: 2.43m (7.97ft)
Range:	700km (450 miles)
Armour:	Not available
Armament:	1 x 12.7mm (0.5in) NSVT MG
Powerplant:	1 x 12-cylinder diesel, developing 839hp (626kW)
Performance:	Maximum road speed: 60km/h (37mph)

MAN/Krupp Leguan

The MAN/Krupp Leguan bridge-laying vehicle entered production in 1988, and brought together the vehicle expertise of MAN and the engineering know-how of Krupp. Unlike many military bridge layers, the Leguan is based upon a truck rather than an MBT. The chassis is that of a standard MAN-ÖAF 36.422 VFAE 8x8 heavy truck. Its cab, however, is slung lower to accommodate the 26m (85.3ft) 10-ton folding bridge which occupies the rear cargo area. The bridge can be deployed and recovered in only eight minutes, and with a 60-ton weight capacity it can handle most MBT and heavy goods traffic. The vehicle is mainly in use with the armed forces of Norway and Singapore.

Country of origin:	West Germany
Crew:	2
Weight:	35,600kg (78,500lb)
Dimensions:	Length: 15.3m (50.19ft); width: 4.01m (13.16ft); height: 4m (13.12ft)
Range:	600km (370 miles)
Armour:	Not applicable
Armament:	None
Powerplant:	1 x MAN D 2866LD/422 diesel, developing 412hp (307kW)
Performance:	Maximum road speed: 72km/h (45mph)

Bergepanzer 3 Buffalo ARV

The Bergepanzer 3 (BPz 3) was produced between 1992 and 1997 and is currently in service with both German and Dutch armed forces. It is based on the chassis of the Leopard 2 MBT. The chassis choice was necessitated by the introduction of the Leopard 2 itself, which placed demands on ARVs not met by any existing vehicle. Yet the Buffalo can accomplish more than just vehicle rescue. It is capable of major earthworks using its forward dozer blade, and its crane can hoist objects weighing up to 35 tons. Welding and cutting gear are standard on board equipment. The BPz 3 has replaced the US M88 ARV amongst Leopard 2 armoured units in Germany.

Country of origin:	Germany
Crew:	3
Weight:	54,300kg (120,000lb)
Dimensions:	Length: 9.07m (29.76ft); width: 3.54m (11.61ft); height: 2.73m (8.96ft)
Range:	650km (400 miles)
Armour:	Not available
Armament:	1 x 7.62mm (0.3in) MG
Powerplant:	1 x MTU MB873 Ka-501 12-cylinder turbo diesel, developing 1500hp (1119kW)
Performance:	Maximum road speed: 68km/h (42mph)

MAN FSG

The MAN FSG is an ingenious temporary road-surface layer produced as a joint development for the French Army and the German Federal Armed Forces. It is designed to lay an aluminium road surface 50m (160ft) long and 4.2m (13.8ft) wide over muddy, snow-covered or eroded terrain. One of its main applications is to create a solid drive surface on riverbanks during fording operations. In the German Army, the road system is laid in flat hinged sections from the back of an all-wheel-drive SX90 truck, whereas in the French Army, a Renault 6x6 TRM 10000 is used. In both cases, the two-man crew are able to either lay or retract the road surface in 10 to 20 minutes.

Country of origin:	Germany
Crew:	2
Weight:	27,500kg (60,600lb)
Dimensions:	Length: 11.45m (37.58ft); width: 2.99m (9.81ft); height: 3.52m (11.55ft)
Range:	800km (500 miles)
Armour:	Not applicable
Armament:	None
Powerplant:	1 x 8-cylinder diesel, developing 355hp (265kW)
Performance:	Maximum road speed: 80km/h (50mph)

FSB 2000

The FSB 2000 is a folding float-bridge system deployed from the back of a 6x6 or 8x8 truck, in this case an 8x8 MAN mil gl A1. The truck itself is a popular vehicle with a six-cylinder turbo diesel and a payload of around seven tons. To deploy the bridge, the vehicle positions itself close to a riverbank and slides the hinged bridge sections down a ramp into the water on rollers. Several sections can be interconnected and a 100m (328ft) bridge can be constructed in under an hour. Independent sections can be towed by tug boats to make an amphibious crossing. The FSB system has exported widely, and versions are currently in use with the US Army.

Country of origin:	Germany
Crew:	1 + 2
Weight:	(bridge system) 4800kg (10,600lb)
Dimensions:	(bridge system) Length: 6.7m (21.98ft); width: (folded) 3.03m (9.94ft); height: 1.27m (4.17ft)
Range:	Not applicable
Armour:	Not applicable
Armament:	None
Powerplant:	1 x MAN diesel, developing 248hp (185kW)
Performance:	Maximum road speed: 90km/h (56mph); fording: 1.2m (3.9ft)

BAT-2

The BAT-2 is one of a large series of Ukrainian vehicles based upon the tracked chassis of the MT-T artillery tractor. It is a general engineer vehicle, but one ideally suited to earth-shifting or obstacle-clearing operations, using its large V-shaped hydraulically powered articulating dozer blade. A boom crane with a two-ton lifting capacity enables the BAT-2 to undertake vehicle recovery missions. The BAT-2 is also fitted with a ripping device, designed mainly for tearing up frost-hardened ground, a necessity in the harsh Ukrainian winters. The cab is fully armoured to protect the crew and features NBC systems for enhanced battlefield survivability.

Country of origin:	Ukraine
Crew:	2 + 8
Weight:	39,700kg (87,500lb)
Dimensions:	Length: 9.64m (31.63ft); width: 4.2m (13.78ft); height: 3.69m (12.11ft)
Range:	500km (310 miles)
Armour:	Not applicable
Armament:	None
Powerplant:	1 x V-64-4 12-cylinder multi-fuel diesel, developing 700hp (522kW)
Performance:	Maximum road speed: 60km/h (37mph); fording: 1.3m (4.3ft); vertical obstacle: 0.8m (2.6ft)

Challenger ARRV

The Challenger Armoured Repair and Recovery Vehicle (ARRV) is, as its name suggests, based upon the Challenger MBT. Like the earlier Chieftain ARRV, the Challenger model uses two Rotzler winches and an Atlas crane. Pulling and lifting capacities are 68 tons for the main winch, 20 tons for the auxiliary winch, and 43 tons for the crane. The front dozer blade can be used as either a stabilizing blade or applied to earth-moving projects. In the latter role, the Challenger ARRV can move 229 cubic metres (8100 cubic feet) of earth an hour. The vehicle is also fitted with night-vision devices and armed with a 7.62mm (0.3in) FN MAG machine gun.

Country of origin:	United Kingdom
Crew:	3
Weight:	62,000kg (136,700lb)
Dimensions:	Length: 9.59m (31.46ft); width: 3.51m (11.52ft); height: 3m (9.84ft)
Range:	450km (280 miles)
Armour:	Chobham/steel (details classified)
Armament:	1 x 7.62mm (0.3in) FN MAG MG
Powerplant:	1 x Perkins CV12 TCA 1200 12-cylinder petrol, developing 1200hp (895kW) at 2300rpm
Performance:	Maximum road speed: 60km/h (37mph); fording: 1.07m (3.51ft); gradient: 58 percent; vertical obstacle: 0.9m (2.9ft); trench: 2.8m (9.2ft)

Faun ATF 70-4

Faun has made a successful business of supplying military logistical vehicles, particular a family of mobile lifting machines. The ATF 70-4 is an All-Terrain Mobile Crane system, its 8x8 drive giving it excellent cross-country mobility. Its telescopic lifting arm has a weight capacity of 70 tons and when fully extended, has a total reach of 40.5m (133ft). The lifting gear has its own separate motor to ensure maximum traction, and the vehicle itself develops enough power to negotiate 73 percent gradients. The ATF 70-4 has hydropneumatic suspension with levelling adjustment which allows it to maintain a solid lifting base during recovery operations.

Country of origin:	Germany
Crew:	2
Weight:	48,000kg (105,800lb)
Dimensions:	Length (with crane): 12.87m (42.22ft); width: 2.75m (9.02ft); height: 3.73m (12.24ft)
Range:	400km (250 miles)
Armour:	Not applicable
Armament:	Not applicable
Powerplant:	1 x Mercedes-Benz 8-cylinder diesel, developing 375hp (280kW)
Performance:	Maximum road speed: 78km/h (48mph)

Keiler Mine-Clearing System

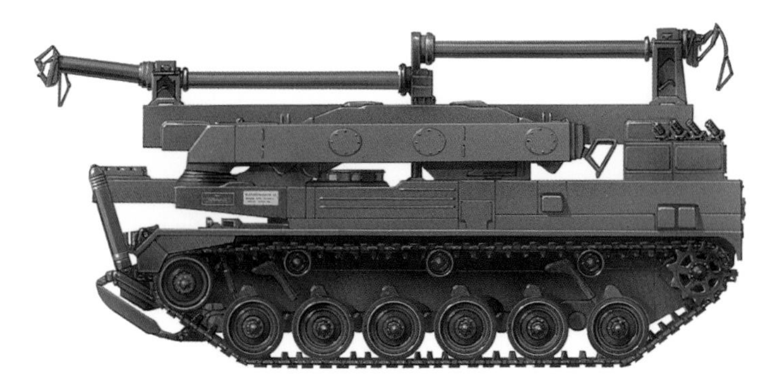

The Keiler Mine-Clearing System began production in 1996 under the Rheinmetall Landsysteme GmbH company. The system uses an M-48 cast-steel armoured hull. A carrier arm extends from the front with 24 mine-clearing flails (known, from their shape, as 'elephant's feet'). With the flails in motion, the Keiler can clear a track through a minefield up to 250mm (9.84in) deep, 4.7m (15.4ft) wide and 120m (400ft) long in less than 10 minutes. The mines are either detonated by the flails or wrenched from the ground and flung aside. The Keiler's 100 percent clearance rate has placed it in heavy demand with UN and NATO mine-clearance units operating in war zones.

Country of origin:	Germany
Crew:	2
Weight:	5300kg (11,687lb)
Dimensions:	Length (clearance arm retracted): 7.83m (25.69ft); width: 3.76m (12.34ft); height: 3.75m (12.3ft)
Range:	350km (220 miles)
Armour:	Not available
Armament:	Not available
Powerplant:	1 x MTU MB871 Ka-501 8-cylinder diesel, developing 1086hp (810kW)
Performance:	Maximum road speed: 50km/h (31mph)

M9 ACE

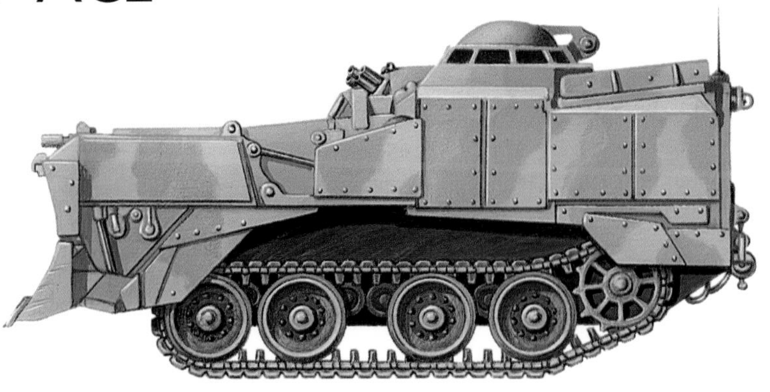

Though the M9's role is purely as an earthmover, it is one of a new generation of sophisticated engineer vehicles. Unusually for an earthmover, it is fully amphibious and propels itself through water at speeds of 4.8km/h (3mph) using its tracks. The crew sit in the rear of the vehicle and a large apron/dozer blade is located at the front. This is deployed by using hydraulic rotary actuators to lower the front of the vehicle. When driving, shock-absorbing accumulators in the chassis give a smooth ride over most terrains up to a maximum speed of 48km/h (30mph). The driver's position has chemical/biological protection and the vehicle is armoured against small-arms fire and shell splinters.

Country of origin:	United States
Crew:	3
Weight:	16,327kg (36,001lb)
Dimensions:	Length: 6.25m (20.51ft); width: 3.2m (10.5ft); height: 2.7m (8.86ft)
Range:	322km (200 miles)
Armour:	Not available
Armament:	None
Powerplant:	1 x Cummins V903C 8-cylinder diesel, developing 220hp (164kW)
Performance:	Maximum road speed: 48km/h (30mph)

Vickers-Carden-Loyd Type 31

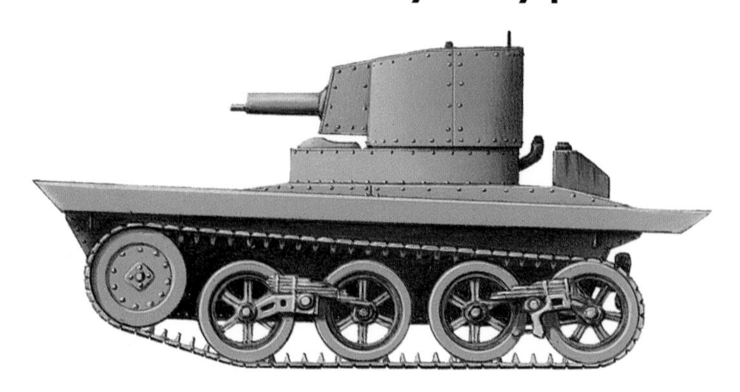

The Vickers-Carden-Loyd amphibious vehicle was the brainchild of J.V. Carden and V. Loyd, employees of the British Vickers works. During the late 1920s, they designed a series of light tanks for the British Army, one of which became the Vickers-Carden-Loyd Type 31 – the world's first operational amphibious tank. The Type 31 was basically a Vickers four-ton light tank fitted with a pontoon-shaped watertight hull. The vehicle floated by virtue of buoyant mudguards. Power came from a propeller at the rear of the hull which gave a top speed of 10km/h (6mph). Directional control was provided by a rudder. The Type 31 sold only on the export market, particularly to the Far East, and it inspired other nations to build their own.

Country of origin:	United Kingdom
Crew:	2
Weight:	3100kg (6800lb)
Dimensions:	Length: 3.96m (12.99ft); width: 2.08m (6.82ft); height: 1.83m (6ft)
Range:	260km (160 miles)
Armour:	(Steel) 9mm (0.35in) maximum
Armament:	1 x 7.7mm (0.31in) MG
Powerplant:	1 x Meadows 6-cylinder petrol, developing 56hp (42kW)
Performance:	Maximum road speed: 64km/h (39mph); maximum water speed: 10km/h (6mph)

Land-Wasser-Schlepper

In 1936 the German Army contracted Rheimetall to build a special tractor for amphibious operations, which could tow behind it a cargo trailer also capable of floating. The Land-Wasser-Schlepper was essentially a motor tug fitted with tracks, capable of carrying up to 20 passengers. Its ungainly appearance belied its effective performance. However, it was rather cumbersome on land and suffered from a lack of armour. Even though designed for the calm waters of inland Europe, the project was pursued with enthusiasm while the invasion of England looked possible. After this was cancelled, interest waned and the project was cancelled in turn. Nevertheless, a pre-production series of seven vehicles was produced and some of them went on to serve on the Eastern Front after 1941.

Country of origin:	Germany
Crew:	3 + 20
Weight:	13,000kg (28,600lb)
Dimentions:	length 8.60m (28ft 2.6in); width 3.16m (10ft 4.4in); height 3.13m (10ft 3.3in)
Range:	240km (149 miles)
Armour:	unknown
Armament:	none
Powerplant:	one Maybach HL 120 TRM V-12 engine developing 265hp (197.6kW)
Performance:	maximum road speed 40km/h (24.85mph); maximum water speed unloaded 12.5km/h (7.8mph); fording amphibious

Type 2 Ka-Mi

Development of the Type 2 began in the 1930s, with efforts to turn the Type 95 Kyu-Go light tank into an amphibious vehicle by adding flotation tanks. The unwieldy results prompted the designers to fit pontoons to the tank to provide buoyancy, retaining the main components of the tank. The new Type 2, as it was designated, went into production in 1942. The most commonly used Japanese amphibious tank, it contained several innovations including radio and telephone intercom system for the crew, as well as an onboard mechanic. It was used mainly for infantry support and often as just a land-based pillbox for island defence by 1944. This diminished their tactical effectiveness, and too few were built by the Japanese war machine to give this impressive design the impact it deserved.

Country of origin:	Japan
Crew:	5
Weight:	with pontoons 11,301kg (24,862lb); without pontoons 9571kg (21,056lb)
Dimensions:	length with pontoons 7.417m (24ft 4in); length without pontoons 4.826m (15ft 10in); width 2.79m (9ft 1.8in); height 2.337m (7ft 8in)
Range:	land radius 199.5km (125 miles); water radius 149.6km (93 miles)
Armour:	6-12mm (0.23-0.47in)
Armament:	one 37mm anti-tank gun; two 7.7mm machine gun
Powerplant:	one six-cylinder air-cooled diesel engine developing 110hp (82kW)
Performance:	maximum land speed 37km/h (23mph); maximum water speed 9.65km/h (6mph); fording amphibious

Schwimmwagen Type 166

The Schwimmwagen Type 166 was an amphibious light vehicle developed by Volkswagen in the early 1940s. It was meant to provide German infantry and airborne units with an amphibious version of the excellent Kübelwagen. A bulbous flotation body was added to the Kübelwagen and a chain-driven propeller (which had to be lowered prior to entering the water) situated at the rear of the hull. The front wheels acted as the rudder. With its maximum load of four men, the Schwimmwagen had an on-water speed of 11km/h (7mph). Of the 14,625 Schwimmwagens produced during WWII, most ended up serving on the Eastern Front, though small numbers went to North Africa.

Country of origin:	Germany
Crew:	1 + 3
Weight:	910kg (2007lb)
Dimensions:	Length: 3.82m (12.53ft); width: 1.48m (4.86ft); height: 1.61m (5.28ft)
Range:	520km (320 miles)
Armour:	Not applicable
Armament:	None
Powerplant:	1 x VW 4-cylinder petrol, developing 25hp (19kW)
Performance:	Maximum road speed: 80km/h (50mph); maximum water speed: 11km/h (7mph)

DUKW

Universally known as the 'Duck', the DUKW first appeared in 1942. In essence it was a derivative of the GMC 6 x 6 truck with a boat-shaped hull for buoyancy. The simple design made it easy to operate and maintain and over 21,000 were built before the end of World War II, seeing service with all Allied forces. Designed to carry supplies from ships to the beach, it could in fact travel much farther inland, carrying troops or even light artillery. A number of weapons-carrying versions were produced, including the Scorpion, which could be used as a rocket launcher. Despite limited load-carrying capability and temperamental performance in rough seas, the DUKW was a sturdy and reliable vehicle and has often been described as an Allied war-winner.

Country of origin:	United States
Crew:	2
Weight:	9097kg (20,013lb)
Dimensions:	length 9.75m (32ft 0in); width 2.51m (8ft 2.9in); height 2.69m (8ft 10in)
Range:	120km (75 miles)
Armour:	none
Armament:	basic version – none.
Powerplant:	one GMC Model 270 engine developing 91.5hp (68.2kW)
Performance:	maximum land speed 80km/h (50mph); maximum water speed 9.7km/h (6mph); fording amphibious

Ford GPA

The Ford General Purpose Amphibious (GPA) had its origins in a National Defense Research Committee (NDRC) project in 1941 which sought to develop an amphibious 0.25-ton amphibious vehicle. A collaborative effort by the Marmon-Herrington Company, the boat builders Sparkman & Stephens and the Ford Motor Company resulted in the Ford GPA, an amphibious version of the Willys Jeep. The GPA did not achieve the Jeep's status. Production had been rushed to meet the needs of US invasion forces in North Africa and Italy, and only 12,778 out of the 50,000 ordered were built. It was too small to be a useful seagoing craft, and most went to the Russians under the Lend-Lease agreement.

Country of origin:	United States
Crew:	1 + 3
Weight:	1647kg (3632lb)
Dimensions:	Length: 4.62m (15.16ft); width: 1.63m (5.35ft); height: 1.73m (5.68ft)
Range:	Not available
Armour:	None
Armament:	None
Powerplant:	1 x GPA-6005 4-cylinder petrol, developing 54hp (40kW)
Performance:	Maximum road speed: 105km/h (65mph); maximum water speed: 8km/h (5mph)

LVT 2

The LVT 2 was an improvement on the LVT 1, which was a civil design intended for use in the Florida swamps and not really suited for combat. The new vehicle used the engine and transmission of the M3 Light Tank. Initially the engine was mounted at the rear which restricted cargo space, but this was soon solved by moving the engine to the front in later versions. Steering and brake systems were also problematic for inexperienced crews. These vehicles were used widely in the early Pacific campaigns, from Guadalcanal onwards. They also saw action in northwest Europe during the latter stages of the war. Some versions had rocket-launchers, flame-throwers and light cannon, but their main role was to carry ashore the first wave of a landing force.

Country of origin:	United States
Crew:	3
Weight:	17,509kg (38,519lb)
Dimensions:	length 7.95m (26ft 1in); width 3.25m (10ft 8in); height 3.023m (9ft 11in)
Range:	road radius 241km (150 miles); water radius 120.7km (75 miles)
Armour:	12mm (0.47in)
Armament:	one 0.5in and two 0.3in machine-guns
Powerplant:	two Cadillac petrol engines developing a total of 220hp (164.1kW)
Performance:	maximum land speed 27.3km/h (17mph); maximum water speed 9.7km/h (6mph); fording amphibious

LVT (A)

The LVT (A) was an ordinary LVT adapted to mount an M3 light tank turret with a 37mm gun. The intention was that this vehicle should provide fire-support during the initial stages of an amphibious landing, giving a significant punch in the battles to establish a beachhead. It was common for LVT (A)s to fire their 37mm guns while still in the water, a waste considering the amount of naval gunfire which usually accompanied an amphibious landing. However, the 37mm gun proved to be too light for this task and so a 75mm howitzer was installed, mounted in the turret of the M8 Howitzer Motor Carriage. The LVT (A) was used extensively along with the rest of the LVT family during the island-hopping operations in the Pacific in World War II, as well as in parts of northwest Europe with British forces.

Country of origin:	United States
Crew:	2
Weight:	10,800kg (23,760lb)
Dimensions:	length 7.95m (26ft 1in); width 3.25m (10ft 8in); height 3.023m (9ft 11in)
Range:	road radius 241km (150 miles); water radius 120.7km (75 miles)
Armour:	up to 67mm (2.63in)
Armament:	one 37mm cannon (later 75mm howitzer); one 7.62mm machine gun
Powerplant:	two Cadillac petrol engines developing a total of 220hp (164.1kW)
Performance:	maximum land speed 27.3km/h (17mph); maximum water speed 9.7km/h (6mph); fording amphibious

LVT 4

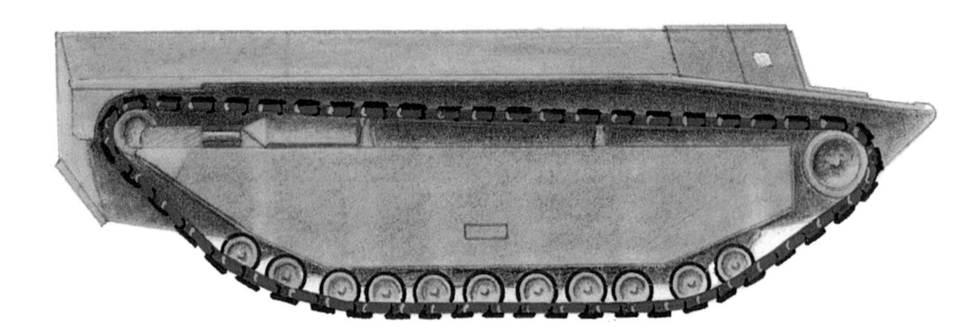

The LVT 4 was an improved LVT 2 with the engine moved forward and a ramp added at the rear for easier loading and unloading, giving the LVT 4 the capability to carry cargo such as jeeps and artillery. This was the most prolific of the series with over 8000 produced, four times as many as the LVT 2. Like the LVT 2, the LVT 4 was developed from the pre-war Roebling tractor, used in the Florida Everglades. Propelled in the water by its tracks, one problem was that the flotation chambers gave the vehicle a high silhouette and thus made it an easier target. The British Army received a number of LVTs, designating them as the Buffalo, and these were used for river-crossings in the final stages of the war in Europe, particularly the crossing of the River Rhine in March 1945.

Country of origin:	United States
Crew:	3
Weight:	17,509kg (38,519lb)
Dimensions:	length 7.95m (26ft 1in); width 3.25m (10ft 8in); height 3.023m (9ft 11in)
Range:	road radius 241km (150 miles); water radius 120.7km (75 miles)
Armour:	12mm (0.47in)
Armament:	one 0.5in and two 0.3in machine-guns
Powerplant:	two Cadillac petrol engines developing a total of 220hp (164.1kW)
Performance:	maximum land speed 27.3km/h (17mph); maximum water speed 9.7km/h (6mph); fording amphibious

DD Sherman

The Duplex Drive (DD) Sherman was born from a British concept, designed to allow tanks to float in water during amphibious operations. Development began in 1941, with a collapsible fabric screen and rubber air tubes being fitted to a boat-shaped platform welded onto a Sherman tank. The tank was powered in the water by two rear propellers. Once in shallow water, the screen could be collapsed and the tank was ready for conventional use. The vehicle was rather slow and could only be used in fairly calm waters. However, the Sherman's main gun proved very useful in supporting amphibious landings, in particular those on D-Day in June 1944, and the tank was a nasty surprise for the Germans, whose attempts to develop a similar concept had failed.

Country of origin:	United States
Crew:	5
Weight:	32,284kg (71,025lb)
Dimensions:	length 6.35m (20ft 10in); width 2.81m (9ft 3in); height 3.96m (13ft)
Range:	240km (149 miles)
Armour:	12-51mm (0.47-2in)
Armament:	one 75mm gun; two 0.3in machine guns
Powerplant:	one Ford GAA V-8 petrol engine developing 400 or 500hp (335.6 or 373kW)
Performance:	maximum water speed four knots; fording amphibious; vertical obstacle 0.61m (2ft 0in); trench 2.26m (7ft 5in)

Terrapin Mk 1

The Terrapin was the British equivalent of the American DUKW, although never produced on the same scale. It did make a useful contribution, though, during the latter stages of the war, particularly during its first action, being used to open up the water approaches to Antwerp in 1944. The Terrapin had a number of defects, though. Its two engines each drove one side of the vehicle, thus if one engine broke down the Terrapin tended to swing round violently. The centrally located engines split the cargo compartment in two, preventing large loads such as guns or vehicles being carried. Rather slow and easily swamped in rough waters, the Terrapin was adequate but further development was abandoned due to the large numbers of American DUKWs available, an altogether machine.

Country of origin:	United Kingdom
Crew:	2
Weight:	12,015kg (26,411lb)
Dimensions:	length 7.01m (23ft); width 2.67m (8ft 9in); height 2.92m (9ft 7in)
Range:	240km (150 miles)
Armour:	8mm (0.31in)
Armament:	none
Powerplant:	two Ford V-8 petrol engines each developing 85hp (63.4kW)
Performance:	maximum land speed 24.14km/h (15mph); maximum water speed 8km/h (5mph); fording amphibious

LVT-3

The LVT-3 was introduced at the tail end of World War II. A good design, however, ensured that it was used heavily by the US Marine Corps and Navy in the immediate post-war era. It was a spacious vehicle which could carry 30 infantry or 14,000kg (30,900lb) of cargo. The space was achieved by locating the two Cadillac engine units, bilge pumps, transmissions and fume extractors in two side sponsons. An additional advantage was that a rear loading ramp could be fitted (earlier LVTs were loaded/unloaded over the side of the hull). The LVT-3 was armed with one 12.7mm (0.5in) and two 7.62mm (0.3in) machine guns. Armoured panels were available for additional protection.

Country of origin:	United States
Crew:	3 + 30
Weight:	17,050kg (37,595lb)
Dimensions:	Length: 7.33m (24.05ft); width: 3.23m (10.59ft); height: 3.38m (11.09ft)
Range:	Road: 241km (150 miles); water: 121km (75 miles)
Armour:	None (see text)
Armament:	1 x 12.7mm (0.5in) MG; 2 x 7.62mm (0.3in) MGs
Powerplant:	2 x Cadillac petrol, developing 220hp (164kW)
Performance:	Maximum road speed: 27km/h (17mph); maximum water speed: 10km/h (6mph)

BAV-485

The BAV-485 was inspired by the US DUKW amphibious vehicle used by Soviet troops during World War II under the Lend-Lease agreement. The chassis was based on that of the ZIL-151 6x6 truck, later the ZIL-157, and the body lines were modelled directly on the DUKW. In most senses, however, the BAV-485 was an improvement on the US vehicle. It had a drop-down tailgate at the rear of the cargo compartment, and could carry 25 fully equipped troops or 2500kg (5500lb) of cargo. A later model, the BAV-485A, even had a central tyre-pressure regulation system installed (though some DUKWs also had a similar system). In all models, amphibious propulsion came from a single propeller at the rear of the hull.

Country of origin:	USSR
Crew:	2
Weight:	9650kg (21,278lb)
Dimensions:	Length: 9.54m (31.29ft); width: 2.5m (8.2ft); height: 2.66m (8.73ft)
Range:	530km (330 miles)
Armour:	Not applicable
Armament:	1 x 12.7mm (0.5in) DShKM MG (optional)
Powerplant:	1 x ZIL-123 6-cylinder petrol, developing 110hp (82kW)
Performance:	Maximum road speed: 60km/h (37mph); maximum water speed: 10km/h (6mph); gradient: 60 percent; vertical obstacle: 0.4m (1.3ft)

GAZ-46 MAV

The GAZ-46 imitated the Ford GPA 4x4 amphibious jeep. For troop carrying, three soldiers sat on the rear bench seat, while the driver and commander had individual seats in the front. A fold-down windscreen provided some protection against water spray during amphibious operations. No armament was mounted on the vehicle. Though it was used almost entirely for reconnaissance duties, cargo transportation to a weight of 500kg (1100lb) was possible. The chassis came from the GAZ-67B 4x4 light vehicle and later the GAZ-69. A single three-blade propeller was mounted under the rear of the hull and driven off the engine, and a trim vane had to be fitted prior to entering the water.

Country of origin:	USSR
Crew:	1 + 4
Weight:	2480kg (5470lb)
Dimensions:	Length: 5.06m (16.6ft); width: 1.74m (5.7ft); height: 2.04m (6.69ft)
Range:	500km (310 miles)
Armour:	Not available
Armament:	None
Powerplant:	1 x M-20 4-cylinder petrol, developing 55hp (41kW)
Performance:	Maximum road speed: 90km/h (56mph); maximum water speed: 9km/h (5.5mph); gradient: 60 percent

GT-S

During World War II, experiments with oversnow/amphibious cars and personnel carriers were mostly unsuccessful. The GT-S was the first fully amphibious 'oversnow' vehicle of the post-war era and had the genuine ability to move from deep snow to water without any preparation. As with all oversnow vehicles, its tracks were very wide – 300mm (11.81in) – and ground pressure was only 0.24kg/sq cm (3.4lb/sq in). The wide tracks also propelled it in the water to speeds of 4km/h (2.5mph). The GT-S was a tough and reliable vehicle. It could carry 11 soldiers or 1000kg (2200lb) of cargo. A later variant, the GT-SM, was simply a bigger vehicle and had six road wheels instead of the GT-S' five.

Country of origin:	USSR
Crew:	1 + 11
Weight:	4600kg (10,100lb)
Dimensions:	Length: 4.93m (16.17ft); width: 2.4m (7.87ft); height: 1.96m (6.43ft)
Range:	400km (250miles)
Armour:	Not available
Armament:	None
Powerplant:	1 x GAZ-61 6-cylinder petrol, developing 85hp (63kW)
Performance:	Maximum road speed: 35km/h (22mph); maximum water speed: 4km/h (2.5mph); gradient: 60 percent; vertical obstacle: 0.6m (2ft)

K-61

The K-61 was a popular amphibious transporter developed shortly after World War II and exported widely throughout the Eastern Bloc and communist-allied Middle Eastern countries. It is little more than an amphibious chassis mounted with a spacious all-steel cargo/troop area. On-water propulsion is provided by two propellers at the rear of the hull, and amphibious speed is 10km/h (6mph). The great advantage of the K-61 is its carrying capacity. Up to 60 fully armed troops or 5000kg (11,000lb) of cargo can be transported on water, though only 3000kg (6600lb) of cargo on land. The K-61 has also been used as an amphibious weapons platform for mortars, AA guns and howitzers.

Country of origin:	USSR
Crew:	2
Weight:	14,550kg (32,083lb)
Dimensions:	Length: 9.15m (30ft); width: 3.15m (10.33ft); height: 2.15m (7.05ft)
Range:	260km (160 miles)
Armour:	Not available
Armament:	Various (see text)
Powerplant:	1 x YaAZ M204VKr 4-cylinder diesel, developing 135hp (101kW)
Performance:	Maximum road speed: 36km/h (22mph); maximum water speed: 10km/h (6mph); gradient: 40 percent; vertical obstacle: 0.65m (2.13ft)

LVTP-5

The Landing Vehicle, Tracked, Personnel, Mark 5 (LVTP-5) made a number of departures from previous LVT designs. It had an inverted V-shaped bow to improve its hydrodynamics, and the bow was lowered to allow troop or vehicle entry/exit (roof hatches provided other routes of access). Up to 34 fully equipped infantry could be transported inside, and were protected by the large hull constructed with 6mm (0.24in) armour plate. The LVTP-5 was propelled through the water by its tracks, and could maintain water speeds of 11km/h (7mph). Its driver sat in a cupola on top of the forward hull. The LVTP-5 was costly to maintain and prone to mechanical failure, and it was replaced in the 1970s by the LVTP-7.

Country of origin:	United States
Crew:	3 + 34
Weight:	37,422kg (82,516lb)
Dimensions:	Length: 9.04m (29.66ft); width: 3.57m (11.71ft); height: 2.91m (9.55ft)
Range:	306km (190 miles)
Armour:	(Steel) 6mm (0.24in)
Armament:	1 x 7.62mm (0.3in) MG
Powerplant:	1 x Continental 12-cylinder petrol, developing 810hp (604kW) at 2400rpm
Performance:	Maximum road speed: 48km/h (30mph); maximum water speed: 11km/h (7mph)

Gillois PA

The Gillois PA was named after the French General, J. Gillois. In the mid-1950s, Gillois began work on developing various amphibious bridging and ferry systems with the German engineering company, EWK. The result was the Gillois-EWK. The title 'Gillois PA' refers to 'Pont Amphibian', the Gillois' specific bridging configuration. The Gillois vehicle has a large inflatable flotation chamber on each side. Each chamber has nine watertight sections to prevent flooding if part of the chamber is damaged. In bridging operations, the PA transports an 8 x 4m (26.25 x 13.12ft) bridge slab which is swivelled through 90 degrees to connect with other bridge units to form a floating highway.

Country of origin:	France
Crew:	4
Weight:	26,915kg (59,425lb)
Dimensions:	Length: 11.86m (38.91ft); width: 3.2m (10.49ft); height: 3.99m (13.09ft)
Range:	780km (480 miles)
Armour:	Not applicable
Armament:	None
Powerplant:	1 x Deutz V12 diesel, developing 220hp (164kW)
Performance:	Maximum road speed: 64km/h (40mph); maximum water speed: 12km/h (7mph)

LARC-5

The LARC-5 was developed to a US Army requirement for a vehicle capable of transporting cargo from ship to shore and then inland to supply bases. Around 950 were built between 1962 and 1968. The LARC-5 was a fairly basic vehicle with no proper suspension and power steering on the front wheels only. It could carry just under 4.5 tonnes (4.3 tons) of cargo or 20 fully equipped troops between the cabin at the front and the engine at the rear. It was exported to Australia, West Germany and Argentina, seeing action with the latter in the Falklands conflict. The influence of the World War II-vintage DUKW can clearly be seen – testimony to the excellence of the original vehicle. The good range of the LARC-5 is indicative of the more mobile nature of modern warfare when compared to World War II.

Country of origin:	United States
Crew:	1 + 2
Weight:	14,038kg (30,883lb)
Dimensions:	length 10.668m (35ft 0in); width 3.149m (10ft 4in); height 3.034m (9ft 11.4in)
Range:	402km (250miles)
Armour:	none
Armament:	none
Powerplant:	one V8 diesel engine developing 300hp (224kW)
Performance:	maximum road speed 48.2km/h (30mph); maximum water speed 16km/h (10mph); fording amphibious; vertical obstacle about 0.5m (1ft 7.7in); trench not applicable

PTS

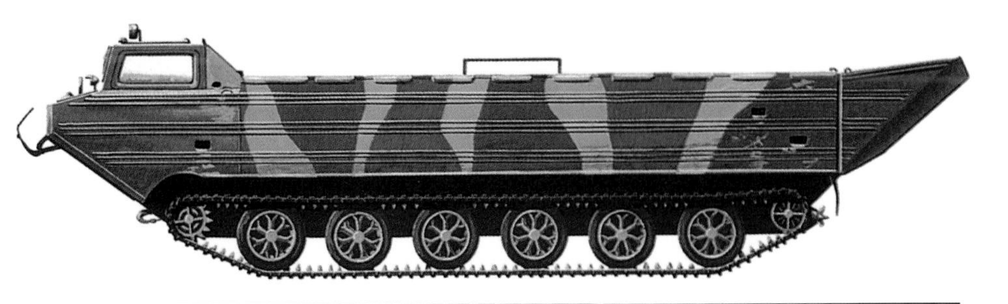

The PTS entered service with the Soviet Red Army in the mid-1960s. On water, the PTS could carry up to 10 tonnes (9.8 tons) of equipment or 70 men, but the drawback was that the position of the exhaust pipes on top of the cargo compartment tended to allow fumes to blow back onto the troops behind – a potentially fatal flaw. The PTS was the first Soviet amphibious vehicle to have a fully enclosed crew compartment. A PKP boat-shaped trailer was specially developed for the PTS. A variant was used by Poland which mounted a rocket-propelled mine-clearing system in the rear. The PTS was used by most Warsaw Pact countries, Iraq, Syria and also Egypt, which used it to good effect during the Yom Kippur War, during the crossing of the Suez Canal.

Country of origin:	USSR
Crew:	2
Weight:	22,700kg (49,940lb)
Dimensions:	length 11.50m (37ft 8.8in); width 3.30m (10ft 10in); height 2.65m (8ft 8.3in)
Range:	300km (186miles)
Armour:	6-10mm (0.23-0.39in)
Armament:	none
Powerplant:	one V-54P diesel engine developing 359hp (261kW)
Performance:	maximum road speed 42km/h (26mph); maximum water speed 10.6km/h (6.5mph); fording amphibious; vertical obstacle 0.65m (2ft 1.6in); trench 2.5m (8ft 2.4in)

M2 and M3

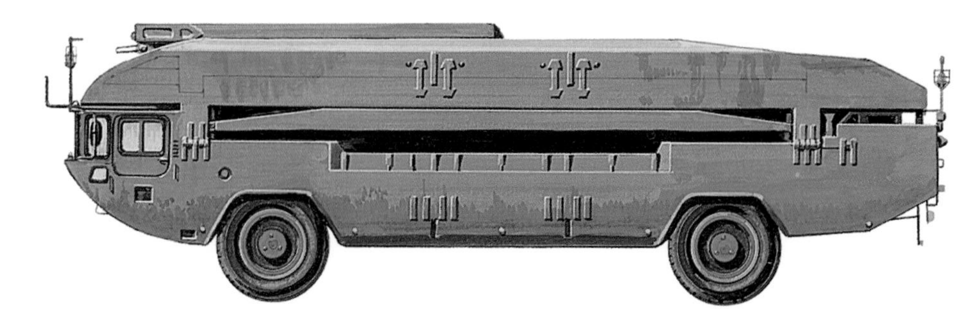

The EWK M2 vehicle entered production in 1968 and improved greatly on EWK's earlier Gillois design for the French Army. Aluminium side pontoons replaced the Gillois' inflatable versions, and actually functioned as part of the floating-bridge structure. The M2's water-drive gave a slightly better amphibious speed than that of the Gillois and also made it more stable in heavy currents. Over 350 M2s were produced and still serve today, but in 1996 the more advanced M3 came onto the market. Eight M3s operated by 24 soldiers can build a bridge 100m (330ft) long in only 15 minutes, 50 percent faster than was possible with the M2. Both the M2 and M3 have enjoyed excellent export sales.

Country of origin:	West Germany
Crew:	3
Weight:	25,300kg (55,800lb)
Dimensions:	Length: 12.82m (42.06ft); width: 3.35m (10.99ft); height: 3.93m (12.89ft)
Range:	725km (450 miles)
Armour:	Not applicable
Armament:	None
Powerplant:	2 x Deutz BF8 LC513 8-cylinder diesel, developing 362hp (270kW)
Performance:	Maximum road speed: 80km/h (50mph); maximum water speed: 13km/h (8mph)

LVTP7

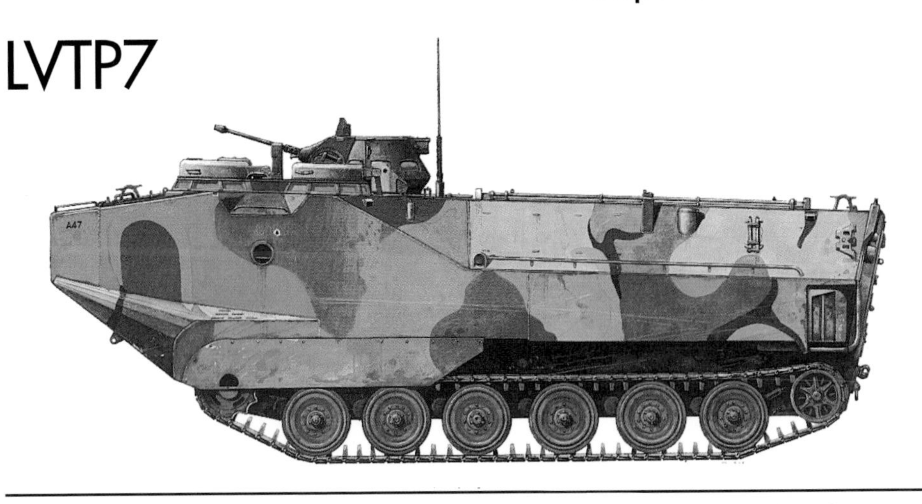

In 1971, FMC completed the first production model of the LVTP7 designed specifically for the US Marine Corps. With an aluminium hull and propelled either by twin-waterjets or its tracks, the vehicle was capable of carrying up to 25 fully equipped troops, forming an important element in US power projection capabilities. The vehicle could be loaded alongside ships through an opening in the roof hatch, although troops usually exited through the rear. The vehicle was widely exported, notably to Argentina where it took part in the Falklands invasion in 1982. It also saw service on peacekeeping duties in Lebanon. Variants included a command vehicle and recovery vessel, and some vehicles in US Marine Corps service have been fitted with Enhanced Applique Armour for extra protection.

Country of origin:	United States
Crew:	3 + 25
Weight:	22,837kg (50,241lb)
Dimensions:	length 7.943m (26ft 0.7in); width 3.27m (10ft 8.7in); height 3.263m (10ft 8.5in)
Range:	482km (300miles)
Armour:	45mm (1.8in)
Armament:	one 12.7mm machine gun; optional 40mm grenade launcher
Powerplant:	one Detroit-Diesel Model 8V-53T engine, developing 400hp (298kW)
Performance:	maximum road speed 64km/h (40mph); maximum water speed 13.5km/h (8.5mph); fording amphibious; vertical obstacle 0.914m (3ft 0in); trench 2.438m (8ft)

Type 6640A

As the largest manufacturer of wheeled vehicles in Italy, it was no surprise that Fiat was chosen to build an amphibious vehicle, following a requirement for the Italian Home Office for a civil protection and fire-fighting vehicle. The hull was constructed of aluminium for lightness and the vehicle could carry a maximum payload of 2.14 tonnes (two tons). A winch was provided at the rear for cargo loading. Once afloat, the vehicle could be powered either by its wheels or by a propeller, the rudder being coupled to the steering wheel. The Type 6640A bore a striking resemblance, as do many modern amphibious vehicles, to the American DUKW of World War II. Production ended in the early 1980s. Like most modern Italian amphibious vehicles, the Type 6640A was well built.

Country of origin:	Italy
Crew:	2
Weight:	6950kg (15,290lb)
Dimensions:	length 7.30m (23ft 11.4in); width 2.50m (8ft 2.4in); height 2.715m (8ft 10.9in)
Range:	750km (466 miles)
Armour:	4mm (0.16in)
Armament:	none
Powerplant:	one six-cylinder diesel engine developing 117hp (87kW)
Performance:	maximum road speed 90km/h (56mph); maximum water speed with propeller 11km/h (6.8mph) or with wheels 5km/h (3.1mph); fording amphibious; vertical obstacle 0.43m (1ft 5in); trench not applicable

AAAVR7A1

The Armoured Amphibian Assault Vehicle Recovery 7A1 (AAAVR7A1) emerged from the FMC Corporation as a prototype in 1979, and entered production in 1983. Its main role is recovering damaged vehicles or making engineering repairs on or from amphibious landing zones. It can also carry 21 combat-equipped troops or 4500kg (10,000lb) of cargo. For recovery operations, it uses a hydraulic crane with a 2700kg (6000lb) breaking strength and a crane winch with a 10,400kg (23,000lb) capacity. Also stored on board are a Miller Maxtron 300 welder, a portable generator and an air compressor. The AAAVR7A1 has either a 12.7mm (0.5in) Browning M2 HB or a 7.62mm (0.3in) M60 fitted for defence.

Country of origin:	United States
Crew:	5
Weight:	23,601kg (52,040lb)
Dimensions:	Length: 7.94m (26ft); width: 3.27m (10.73ft); height: 3.26m (10.7ft)
Range:	480km (300 miles)
Armour:	Not available
Armament:	1 x 12.7mm (0.5in) Browning M2 HB or 7.62mm (0.3in) M60
Powerplant:	1 x Cummins VT400 8-cylinder multi-fuel, developing 399hp (298kW)
Performance:	Maximum road speed: 72km/h (45mph); maximum water speed: 13km/h (8mph)

CAMANF

For many years, the Brazilian Marines relied on American DUKWs of World War II vintage for transportation from offshore boats to the beach. By the 1970s, these were becoming difficult to maintain. BVEI began work on a replacement in 1975, and the first production vehicles were delivered towards the end of the decade. The CAMANF is in essence a 6 x 6 F-7000 Ford chassis fitted with a watertight body. It is virtually identical to the DUKW with minor modifications, such as a stronger bow to cope with rougher water, to suit regional requirements. The payload is officially five tonnes (4.9 tons), but this is much reduced in rough waters. The Brazilians made the correct decision in selecting a tried and trusted design, and although the CAMANF is unexceptional, it is a reliable amphibian.

Country of origin:	Brazil
Crew:	3
Weight:	13,500kg (29,700lb)
Dimensions:	length 9.50m (31ft 2in); width 2.50m (8ft 2.4in); height 2.65m (8ft 8.3in)
Range:	430km (267miles)
Armour:	6-10mm (0.23-0.39in)
Armament:	one 12.7mm anti-aircraft machine gun
Powerplant:	one 190hp (142kW) Detroit-Diesel Model 40-54N diesel engine
Performance:	maximum road speed 72km/h (45mph); maximum water speed 14km/h (8.7mph); fording amphibious; vertical obstacle 0.40m (1ft 3.7in); trench not applicable

EKW Bison

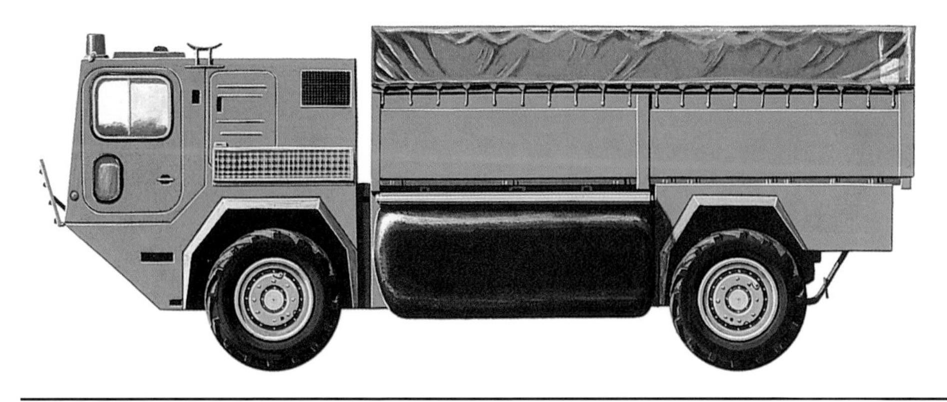

Developed originally as a civilian truck for use in underdeveloped regions, the EKW Bison 4 x 4 was first seen in public in 1982, having been adopted for military use. Fully amphibious, the Bison is equipped with side flotation bags and two propellers (which can be traversed through 360 degrees for maximum manoeuvrability), as well as automatically activated bilge pumps. For land use, the Bison has power-assisted steering and a tyre-pressure regulation system for rough terrain, a feature which Soviet designers have been particularly fond of since the end of World War II. The Bison has a fully enclosed forward control cab with the engine to the rear. The engine itself is coupled to a fully automatic transmision with six forward and one reverse gear.

Country of origin:	West Germany
Crew:	2
Weight:	16,000kg (35,200lb)
Dimensions:	length 9.34m (30ft 7.7in); width 2.50m (8ft 2.4in); height to cab roof 2.964m (9ft 8.5in)
Range:	900km (559miles)
Armour:	none
Armament:	none
Powerplant:	one V8 air-cooled diesel engine developing 320hp (239kW)
Performance:	maximum road speed 80km/h (49.7mph); maximum water speed 12km/h (7.4mph); fording amphibious; vertical obstacle not available; trench not applicable

Pegaso VAP 3550/1

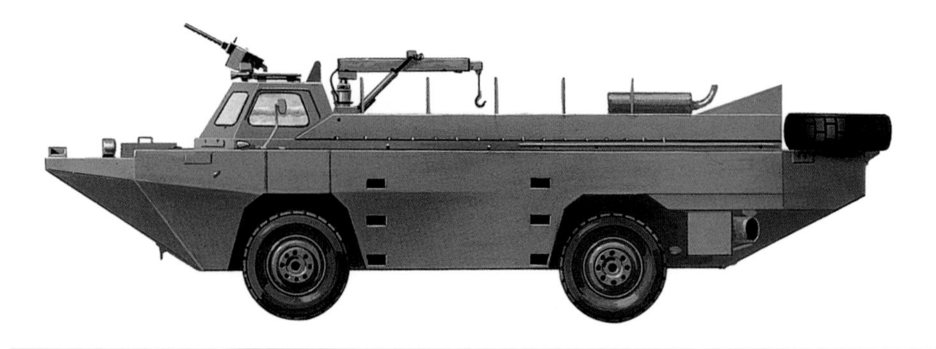

The Pegaso VAP 3550/1 was developed for use by the Spanish marines, but also serves marine forces in Egypt and Mexico. It was designed to be launched offshore from a Landing Ship Tank (LST) craft and transport men and equipment to the landing beachhead. The hull is separated into watertight compartments to reduce the danger of sinking if part of the hull is holed. Eighteen troops or 3000kg (6600lb) of cargo are transported in the front of the vehicle. A hydraulic crane is fitted at the rear for off-loading cargo and a 4500kg (9900lb) winch is set in the front bows. Two waterjets provide amphibious propulsion and two bilge pumps keep the craft free from leaks.

Country of origin:	Spain
Crew:	3 + 18
Weight:	12,500kg (27,550lb)
Dimensions:	Length: 8.85m (29.04ft); width: 2.5m (8.2ft); height: 2.5m (8.2ft)
Range:	800km (500 miles)
Armour:	(Steel) 6mm (0.24in)
Armament:	1 x 7.62mm (0.3in) MG (export versions only)
Powerplant:	1 x Pegaso 9135/5 6-cylinder turbo diesel, developing 190hp (142kW)
Performance:	Maximum road speed: 87km/h (54mph); maximum water speed: 10km/h (6mph); gradient: 60 percent

Arisgator

Purpose-designed amphibious vehicles are very expensive to make. The Italian company Aris developed a far cheaper alternative by fitting a flotation kit to the US M113A2 armoured personnel carrier. (Though the M113 is itself amphibious, its performance in the water is generally poor.) The flotation kit has front and rear sections. At the front, a bow-shaped bolt-on section gives buoyancy and improves handling in turbulent waters. Two tail sections contain the propeller units. The only other modifications to the original M113 vehicle are redirected air intakes and exhaust pipes and better sealing around joints and hatches. The Arisgator is still in the trial and development stage, though orders with the Italian forces are likely.

Country of origin:	Italy
Crew:	2 + 11
Weight:	c.12,000kg (26,500lb)
Dimensions:	Length: 6.87m (22.54ft); width: 2.95m (9.68ft); height: 2.05m (6.73ft)
Range:	550km (340 miles)
Armour:	38mm (1.49in)
Armament:	1 x 12.7mm (0.5in) Browning M2 HB MG
Powerplant:	1 x Detroit 6V-53N 6-cylinder diesel, developing 215hp (160kW) at 2800rpm
Performance:	Maximum road speed: 68km/h (42mph)

EFV

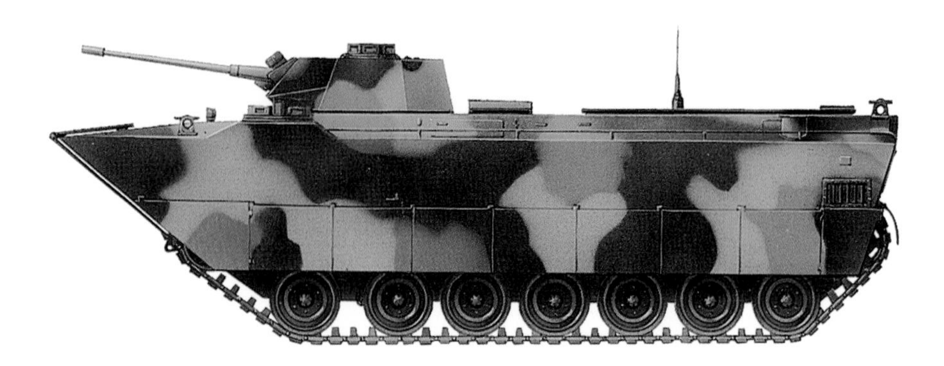

The Expeditionary Fighting Vehicle (EFV) – formerly known as the Advanced Amphibious Assault Vehicle (AAAV) – represents the pinnacle of amphibious-vehicle technology. It is due to come into production in 2008, its primary client being the US Marine Corps. The EFV is entirely self-deploying. Seventeen combat-ready Marines can be carried across water at 47km/h (30mph), propelled by high-power waterjets. A hydraulic trim vane is lowered when entering the water. On land, the EFV will travel at 72km/h (45mph), fast enough to keep up with main battle tanks. It has full NBC systems and computerized fire control and its armour is resistant to 12.7mm (0.5in) machine-gun fire. Armament consists of a Bushmaster II 30mm (1.18in) cannon firing high-explosive or armour-piercing rounds.

Country of origin:	United States
Crew:	3 + 17
Weight:	33,525kg (73,922lb)
Dimensions:	Length: 9.01m (29.56ft); width: 3.66m (12ft); height: 3.19m (10.47ft)
Range:	480km (300 miles)
Armour:	Details classified
Armament:	1 x Bushmaster II 30mm (1.18in) cannon; 1 x 7.62mm (0.3in) MG
Powerplant:	1 x MTU MT883 12-cylinder multi-fuel, developing 2702hp (2015kW)
Performance:	Maximum road speed: 72km/h (45mph); maximum water speed: 47km/h (30mph); gradient: 60 percent; vertical obstacle: 0.9m (3ft); trench: 2.4m (8ft)

Renault Char TSF

The Renault Char TSF was derived from the FT 17 light tank. Most sources credit the FT 17 with being the 'most successful' of the World War I tanks, and it was still found in action as late as 1944 in the next world war. Its design was visually unusual, with a conventional top turret facing forwards while the rear of the hull formed a secondary turret facing backwards. Variants of the FT 17 included a 75mm (2.95in) self-propelled gun version, a bridge layer, and the TSF. The TSF was a radio-command vehicle. It was unarmed with a fixed casemate and a ER10 station radio installed. Crewed by three men, its role was to provide mobile battlefield communications amongst infantry and armoured units.

Country of origin:	France
Crew:	3
Weight:	7000kg (15,400lb)
Dimensions:	Length: 5m (16.4ft); width: 1.74m (5.7ft); height: 2.5m (8.2ft)
Range:	60km (37 miles)
Armour:	(Steel) 16mm (0.63in)
Armament:	None
Powerplant:	1 x Renault 4-cylinder petrol, developing 35hp (26kW)
Performance:	Maximum road speed: 8km/h (5mph)

Carden-Loyd Mk VI

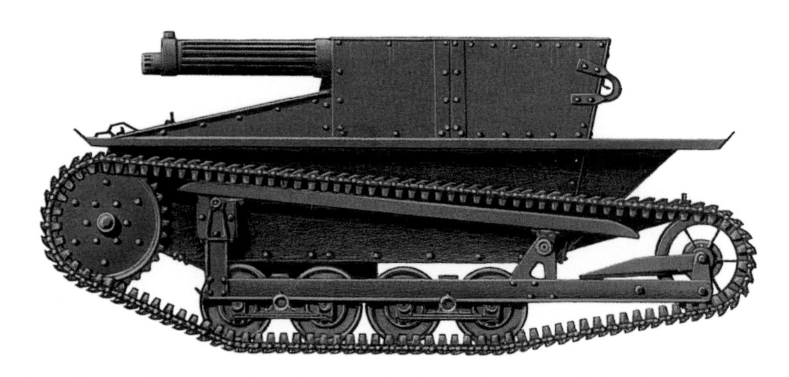

Carden-Loyd tankettes were an unsuccessful inter-war experiment in providing armoured mobile machine-gun carriers for pairs of infantrymen. The first tankette was produced in 1925, a small tracked vehicle big enough for one man only, subsequently topped with a flimsy shield and a Hotchkiss machine gun to form the Carden-Loyd Mk I. Several variations were then produced, focusing mainly on experiments with track and suspension configurations. In 1926, a two-man version was produced which became the Vickers machine-gun-armed Carden-Loyd Mk IV in 1928. Two more versions emerged and achieved some sales abroad, but the vehicles were tactically impractical and had no future past the mid-1930s.

Country of origin:	United Kingdom
Crew:	2
Weight:	1600kg (3500lb)
Dimensions:	Length: 2.47m (8.1ft); width: 1.7m (5.58ft); height: 1.22m (4ft)
Range:	160km (100 miles)
Armour:	9mm (0.35in) maximum
Armament:	1 x 7.7mm (0.303in) Vickers MG
Powerplant:	1 x Ford T 4-cylinder petrol, developing 40hp (30kW)
Performance:	Maximum road speed: 45km/h (28mph)

Renault UE

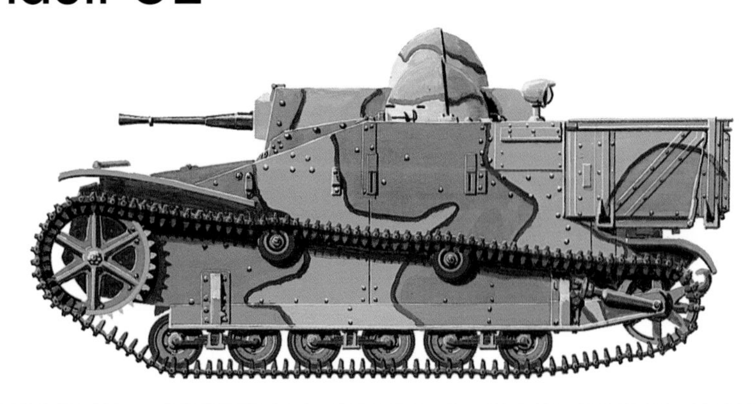

The Renault UE or 'Universal Carrier' was indebted in design to the British Carden-Loyd tankettes developed between the wars. With a two-man crew and a 38hp (28kW) Renault 85 engine, it could pull 600kg (1300lb) of trailer-mounted ammunition or weaponry or carry 350kg (775lb) of materials in its rear storage compartment. Thus laden, it travelled at a respectable 48km/h (30mph), powered by a Renault 85 four-cylinder petrol engine. Each crew member had a rounded dome cover to provide overhead protection. Following the German occupation of France in 1940, the Germans pressed the Renault UE into service and used it for ammunition carriage or for airfield security patrols.

Country of origin:	France
Crew:	2
Weight:	3300kg (7300lb)
Dimensions:	Length: 2.94m (9.64ft); width: 1.75m (5.74ft); height: 1.24m (4.07ft)
Range:	125km (80 miles)
Armour:	Not available
Armament:	None
Powerplant:	1 x Renualt 85 4-cylinder petrol, developing 38hp (28kW)
Performance:	Maximum road speed: 48km/h (30mph)

Saurer RR-7

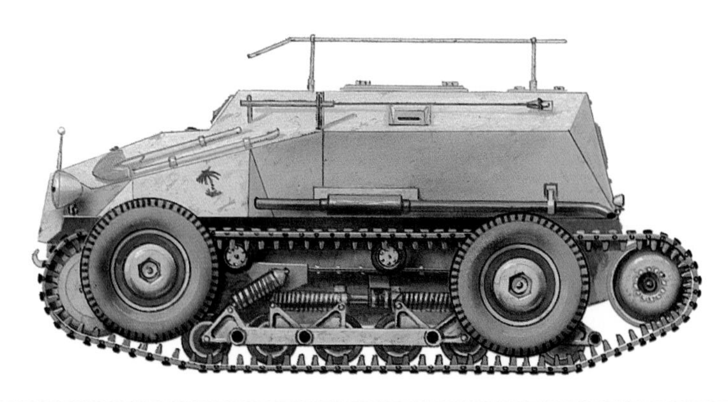

The RR-7 was developed by Saurer in 1937 as an artillery tractor for the Austrian Army. Distinctively, it used a wheel-and-track design, the wheels lowered to take over from the tracks when travelling on road surfaces. The design worked well, and 12 RR-7s entered service. After Austria was absorbed by Germany in the Anschluss of 1938, the German Panzer divisions found a different use for the RR-7. It was converted into an armoured observation post and given the designation SdKfz 254. Artillery observers would ride in the SdKfz 254 to the battlefront and direct fire for mobile artillery batteries. The SdKfz 254 saw service in the Balkans, Russia and North Africa and production reached 128 vehicles.

Country of origin:	Austria
Crew:	5
Weight:	6420kg (14,156lb)
Dimensions:	Length: 4.5m (14.76ft); width: 2.47m (8.1ft); height: 2.33m (7.64ft)
Range:	240km (150 miles)
Armour:	(Steel) 15mm (0.59in)
Armament:	None
Powerplant:	1 x Saurer CRDv 4-cylinder diesel, developing 70hp (52kW)
Performance:	Maximum road speed: 60km/h (37mph)

SdKfz 265 kleiner Panzerbefehlswagen

The concept of the 'command tank' came about following the realisation that the leaders of massed panzer formations would not only have to travel in tanks themselves, but the vehicles would have to carry extra equipment and personnel to assist the commander in his duties. In 1938, the PzKpfw I training tank was converted. The rotating hull was changed to a box superstructure to give more space and allow room for map boards and paperwork (though even then the space was not voluminous). More powerful radios were installed and a signaller added to the crew. Around 200 conversions were made, and the tank first saw action in the Polish campaign in September 1939, later being used in France and North Africa, before being replaced by conversions of larger tanks.

Country of origin:	Germany
Crew:	3
Weight:	5800kg (12,768lb)
Dimensions:	length 4.445m (14ft 7in); width 2.08m (6ft 9.9in); height 1.72m (5ft 7.7in)
Range:	290km (180 miles)
Armour:	6-13mm (0.24-0.5in)
Armament:	one 7.92mm machine gun
Powerplant:	one Maybach NL38TR petrol engine developing 100hp (74.6kW)
Performance:	maximum road speed 40km/h (25mph); fording 0.85m (2ft 10in); vertical obstacle 0.42m (1ft 5in); trench 1.75m (5ft 9in)

Wasp Mk IIC

The Wasp was a flamethrower vehicle developed in the United Kingdom in the early 1940s. It was basically a Universal Carrier vehicle fitted with a flame-throwing device. Two fuel tanks and nitrogen pressure cylinders were fitted into the rear of the hull. The driver and co-driver sat in the front, a flamethrower nozzle jutting out of the front armoured wall. Aiming the flamethrower was a crude process of simply pointing the vehicle at the target, which could be engaged at about 100m (330ft). The Wasp Mk IIC was a Canadian variant. It added an extra crew member, the space acquired by reducing fuel capacity and relocating some fuel to a tank behind the hull.

Country of origin:	Canada/United Kingdom
Crew:	3
Weight:	3850kg (8500lb)
Dimensions:	Length: 3.65m (11.97ft); width: 2.03m (6.66ft); height: 1.58m (5.18ft)
Range:	180km (110 miles)
Armour:	(Steel) 10mm (0.39in) maximum
Armament:	1 x flamethrower; 1 x 7.7mm (0.303in) MG
Powerplant:	1 x Ford 9-cylinder petrol, developing 59hp (44kW)
Performance:	Maximum road speed: 48km/h (29mph)

Fiat-Ansaldo L3/35Lf

In 1929, the Italian Army purchased 25 British Carden Lloyd Mk VI tankettes for use in mountainous terrain. Subsequently, Fiat-Ansaldo produced their own version, the Carro Veloce 29 (CV 29), which began an entire series of Italian tankettes. In 1938, the variants numbered CV 3/33 and 3/35 were redesignated as L3. The most basic L3s were armed with a Breda 13.2mm (0.52in) machine gun, but the L3/35Lf flame-thrower version became the most prevalent of the L3 series. The flamethrower barrel extended from the left of the barbette, and the L3/35Lf had its own internal flame-liquid tank. L3s served extensively in North Africa and during the later Italian campaign.

Country of origin:	Italy
Crew:	2
Weight:	3300kg (7300lb)
Dimensions:	Length: 3.2m (10.5ft); width: 1.42m (4.66ft); height: 1.3m (4.27ft)
Range:	120km (75 miles)
Armour:	Not available
Armament:	1 x flame-thrower
Powerplant:	1 x Fiat 4-cylinder petrol, developing 40hp (30kW)
Performance:	Maximum road speed: 42km/h (26mph)

Canal Defence Light

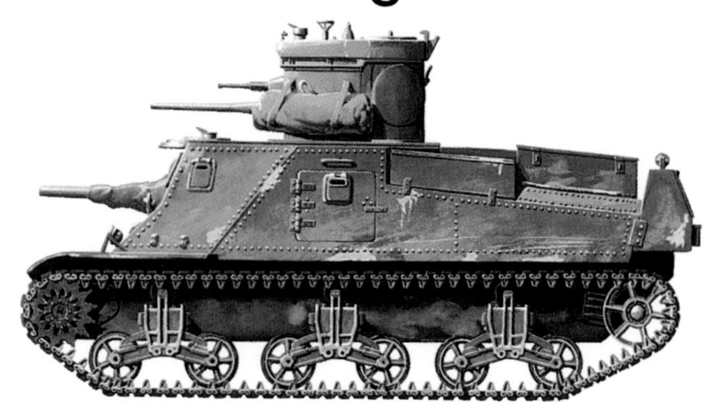

The basic idea behind the the Canal Defence Light (a name chosen to preserve secrecy) was to replace the turret of a tank with a powerful searchlight to illuminate battlefields at night. The idea was first mooted in the mid-1930s, and by late 1939 a turret was ready for production. Initially attached to Matilda II tanks and then Grants, some 300 turrets were ordered. Two British brigades were equipped, one in the UK and one in North Africa. The light was positioned behind a shutter which was opened and closed to provide a flickering impression. Somehow, the opportunity to use the CDL never arose and they were confined to providing light for night river crossings and the like. This was probably just as well, for similar Russian experiments proved disastrous in battle.

Country of origin:	United Kingdom
Crew:	3 or 4
Weight:	26,000kg (57,200lb)
Dimensions:	length 5.61m (18ft 5in); width 2.59m (8ft 6in); height 2.51m (8ft 3in)
Range:	257km (160 miles)
Armour:	12-38mm (0.47-1.5in)
Armament:	one 7.92mm Besa machine gun
Powerplant:	two Leyland E148/E149 diesel engines each developing 95hp (70.8kW)
Performance:	maximum road speed 24km/h (15mph); fording 1.02m (3ft 4in); vertical obstacle 0.61m (2ft); trench 1.91m (6ft 3in)

M29C Weasel

The M28 Weasel was developed for use by Allied commandos and special forces soldiers in northern European theatres. It was envisaged that raids against German heavy water plants in Norway could be conducted using small and fast oversnow vehicles. Even when that threat receded in 1942 after Norwegian partisan raids, production continued and the vehicles found use as light cargo carriers in Europe, the Pacific and Alaska. A fully amphibious version, the M29C, became the most popular version with over 15,000 units produced. The M29C had excellent mobility over snow, mud and soft sand, and could transport loads of 900kg (1990lb). After the war, some Scandinavian countries adapted the Weasel for civilian use.

Country of origin:	United States
Crew:	1 + 3
Weight:	1800kg (4000lb)
Dimensions:	Length: 4.79m (15.72ft); width: 1.7m (5.58ft); height: 1.82m (5.97ft)
Range:	280km (170 miles)
Armour:	None
Armament:	None
Powerplant:	1 x Studebaker Champion 6-170 6-cylinder petrol, developing 65hp (48kW) at 3600rpm
Performance:	Maximum road speed: 58km/h (36mph); maximum water speed: 6km/h (4mph); fording: amphibious

AMX VTT/TB

The chassis of the AMX-13 light tank yielded a bewildering number of variants. Most prolific were the series of vehicles based upon the AMX VCI mechanized infantry combat vehicle, developed from the late 1950s onwards. The standard VCI was converted into, amongst other vehicles, an 81mm (3.19in) mortar vehicle, a battery command post, an ENTAC missile launcher, a Roland SAM vehicle, a TOW anti-tank missile vehicle, a combat engineer vehicle and an ambulance vehicle – this being the AMX VTT/TB. The VTT/TB was more of a battlefield rescue vehicle than an ambulance, as it had no facilities for advanced medical care. It could carry four sitting and three stretchered patients as well as two orderlies and the two-man crew of the vehicle.

Country of origin:	France
Crew:	2 + 9
Weight:	14,300kg (31,500lb)
Dimensions:	Length: 5.7m (18.7ft); width: 2.67m (8.76ft); height: 1.92m (6.29ft)
Range:	350km (220 miles)
Armour:	(Steel) 30mm (1.18in) maximum
Armament:	None
Powerplant:	1 x SOFAM 8Gxb 8-cylinder petrol, developing 250hp (186kW) at 3200rpm
Performance:	Maximum road speed: 60km/h (37mph); fording: 1m (3.3ft); gradient: 60 percent; vertical obstacle: 1m (3.3ft); trench: 1.6m (5.3ft)

The M114 was a command and reconnaissance derivative of the M113 armoured personnel carrier and served in the US Army from 1964 to 1982. It was a simple aluminium armoured hull on a tracked chassis, though unlike in the M113, the crew compartment was given over to communications equipment. Armament was a central feature of the vehicle. At first, M114s were armed with manually operated machine guns, but by the late 1960s the commander had a remote-controlled 12.7mm (0.5in) or even a 20mm (0.78in) Hispano-Suiza cannon fitted to a cupola in front of his hatch. The M114 was phased out from the late 1970s after disappointing off-road performance during the Vietnam war.

Country of origin:	United States
Crew:	3 or 4
Weight:	6930kg (15,280lb)
Dimensions:	Length: 4.46m (14.63ft); width: 2.33m (7.64ft); height: 2.16m (7.09ft)
Range:	440km (270 miles)
Armour:	(Aluminium) 37mm (1.46in)
Armament:	1 x 12.7mm (0.5in) MG or 1 x 20mm (0.78in) Hispano-Suiza cannon; 1 x 7.62mm (0.3in) MG
Powerplant:	1 x Chevrolet 283-V8 8-cylinder petrol, developing 160hp (119kW)
Performance:	Maximum road speed: 58km/h (36mph); fording: amphibious; gradient: 60 percent; vertical obstacle: 0.5m (1.6ft); trench: 1.5m (4.9ft)

M577

The M577 is one of the many variants of the ubiqitous M113 armoured personnel carrier. Its official designation is M577 Carrier, Command Post. The troop compartment is filled with communications and observation equipment which allows it to perform a multitude of command roles, including directing fire, acting as a centre of mobile communications and radio-listening, and operating as a tactical liaison vehicle. An external generator provides power for all the electronics, but in the latest versions of the M577 a hand-pump generator may be used to keep vital systems functioning in case of power failure. When at a standstill, a purpose-designed tent can be fitted to the outside of the vehicle to increase work space for the crew.

Country of origin:	United States
Crew:	5
Weight:	11,513kg (25,386lb)
Dimensions:	Length: 4.86m (15.94ft); width: 2.68m (8.79ft); height: 2.68m (8.79ft)
Range:	595km (370 miles)
Armour:	(Aluminium) 12–38mm (0.47–1.5in)
Armament:	1 x 7.62mm (0.3in) MG
Powerplant:	1 x GMC Detroit 6-cylinder diesel, developing 215hp (160kW) at 2800rpm
Performance:	Maximum road speed: 68km/h (42mph); fording: amphibious; gradient: 60 percent; vertical obstacle: 0.61m (2ft); trench: 1.68m (5.51ft)

M113A1G

The M113A1G is a German version of the US M113 armoured personnel carrier, a variant of which is a mortar-carrier. The troop compartment is converted to hold a 120mm (4.72in) mortar, reducing total personnel capacity to five. The mortar is fired directly out of an open space in the rear of the hull roof, and can hit targets 6200m (20,300ft) away. A 7.62mm (0.3in) machine gun provides a local defensive capability. The on-board store of mortar ammunition is 60 shells while the machine gun has 2400 rounds of 7.62mm (0.3in) ammunition. The Federal German Armed Forces have produced over 4000 M113A1G vehicles in other variants which include radar vehicles, ambulances and ATGW carriers.

Country of origin:	West Germany
Crew:	5
Weight:	12,800kg (28,200lb)
Dimensions:	Length: 4.86m (15.94ft); width: 2.68m (8.79ft); height: 1.85m (6.07ft)
Range:	480km (300 miles)
Armour:	35mm (1.38in) maximum
Armament:	1 x 120mm (4.72in) mortar;1 x 7.62mm (0.3in) MG
Powerplant:	1 x Detroit 6V-53N 6-cylinder diesel, developing 212hp (158kW) at 2800rpm
Performance:	Maximum road speed: 68km/h (42mph); fording: amphibious; gradient: 60 percent; vertical obstacle: 0.6m (2ft); trench: 1.68m (5.51ft)

ABRA/RATAC

The ABRA/RATAC vehicle is a German M113 armoured personnel carrier converted to use the sophisticated RATAC artillery observation radar. RATAC is a French-designed system which can detect or calculate the positions of active artillery from the flight or burst of shells or through simple radar detection of the artillery piece's location. When fitted into the ABRA vehicle, the RATAC is deployed on a vertical telescopic pole 7.2m (23.6ft) high. In this position, the system can detect an artillery piece up to 18km (11 miles) away. In addition, it can monitor aerial targets up to 20km (12 miles) away. Once a target has been detected, the ABRA communications system relays the precise coordinates back to fire-control.

Country of origin:	West Germany
Crew:	3 or 4
Weight:	13,000kg (28,700lb)
Dimensions:	Length: 4.86m (15.94ft); width: 2.7m (8.86ft); height: 7.16m (23.49ft)
Range:	300km (190 miles)
Armour:	Aluminium 12–38mm (0.47–1.5in)
Armament:	None
Powerplant:	1 x GMC Detroit 6V-53N 6-cylinder diesel, developing 215hp (160kW) at 2800rpm
Performance:	Maximum road speed: 68km/h (42mph); fording: amphibious; gradient: 60 percent; vertical obstacle: 0.61m (2ft); trench: 1.68m (5.51ft)

Bv 202

The Bv 202 entered production in 1961, made by the Bolinder-Munktell company. Only with the advent of the Bv 206 in 1981 did production of the Bv 202 cease. It was a double-unit vehicle, the front unit containing engine and crew, the rear unit carrying either a cargo load of 800 to 900kg (1800 to 2000lb) or 10 fully equipped soldiers. Unlike the later Bv 206, the rear unit was unheated with only a tarpaulin cover. Consequently winter travel in the Bv 202 could be icy, particularly during water crossings (the Bv 202 was fully amphibious). Later the rear unit was offered in a fully enclosed and heated version. Bv 202s have seen service across the world, and were used heavily by the British during the 1982 Falklands War.

Country of origin:	Sweden
Crew:	2 + 10
Weight:	2900kg (6400lb)
Dimensions:	Length: 6.17m (20.24ft); width: 1.76m (5.77ft); height: 2.21m (7.25ft)
Range:	400km (250 miles)
Armour:	None
Armament:	None
Powerplant:	1 x Volvo B18 4-cylinder diesel, developing 91hp (68kW)
Performance:	Maximum road speed: 39km/h (24mph); fording: amphibious; gradient: 60 percent; vertical obstacle: 0.5m (1.6ft)

Green Archer

The Green Archer is not a vehicle, but a mortar-detecting radar system. Germany, the Netherlands and the United Kingdom all developed an interest in the system in the mid-1960s. Both the Germans and the Dutch mounted the radar on modified M113 vehicles, whereas the British used the indigenous FV432 armoured personnel carrier to form the FV436 Self-Propelled Mortar-Locating Radar System, Green Archer. By detecting the firing and detonation of a shell, the radar could compute the location of an enemy mortar at ranges of up to 30km (18.6 miles). The main modification to the vehicles was the rerouting of the exhaust systems to avoid interference with the radar. Almost all these systems have now been replaced.

Country of origin:	West Germany/United Kingdom/Netherlands
Crew:	4
Weight:	11,900kg (26,200lb)
Dimensions:	Length: 4.86m (15.94ft); width: 2.7m (8.86ft); height: 4.32m (14.17ft)
Range:	480km (300 miles)
Armour:	(Aluminium) 12–38mm (0.47–1.5in)
Armament:	1 x 7.62mm (0.3in) MG
Powerplant:	1 x Detroit Diesel 6V-53N 6-cylinder diesel, developing 215hp (160kW) at 2800rpm
Performance:	Maximum road speed: 68km/h (42mph); fording: amphibious; gradient: 60 percent; vertical obstacle: 0.61m (2ft); trench: 1.68m (5.51ft)

Lynx CR

The Lynx Command and Reconnaissance Vehicle was based heavily upon the M113A1 armoured personnel carrier. The main similarities were in the all-welded aluminium hull and tracked configuration. Amphibious properties were also the same. The troop compartment, however, was occupied with communications equipment and troop carrying was restricted to the three-man crew. Armament consisted of a single 12.7mm (0.5in) Browning M2 HB at the front and a single 7.62mm (0.3in) Browning M1919 at the rear, both pintle-mounted. The Lynx was adopted in modified versions in Canada and the Netherlands. The Netherlands version had a 25mm (0.98in) Oerlikon cannon turret fitted.

Country of origin:	United States
Crew:	3
Weight:	8775kg (19,300lb)
Dimensions:	Length: 4.6m (15.09ft); width: 2.41m (7.91ft); height: 1.65m (5.41ft)
Range:	525km (325 miles)
Armour:	Aluminium (details not available)
Armament:	1 x 12.7mm (0.5in) MG; 1 x 7.62mm (0.3in) MG
Powerplant:	1 x Detroit Diesel GMC 6V53 6-cylinder diesel, developing 215hp (160kW) at 2800rpm
Performance:	Maximum road speed: 70km/h (43mph); fording: amphibious; gradient: 60 percent; vertical obstacle: 0.61m (2ft); trench: 1.47m (4.82ft)

Sultan

The Sultan is part of a group of vehicles based on the same aluminium hull which form part of the British Army's battle group formation. It is designed to provide the commander with an armoured platform to allow him to keep up with his forward elements. There is a compartment in the back with a desk, map boards and radios. Space is a real problem, although there is a tent which can be extended from the rear to give more room, but at the expense of mobility. Its cramped conditions while on the move (particularly while closed down during a nuclear, biological and chemical [NBC] exercises) make this a difficult vehicle to work in. Like many such armoured fighting vehicles currently in service around the world, its crew is prone to severe motion sickness.

Country of origin:	United Kingdom
Crew:	3
Weight:	8172kg (17,978lb)
Dimensions:	length 5.12m (16ft 9in); width 2.24m (7ft 4in); height 2.6m (8ft 6in)
Range:	483km (301 miles)
Armour:	classified
Armament:	one 7.62mm machine gun
Powerplant:	one 4.2-litre petrol engine developing 190hp (141kW)
Performance:	maximum road speed 80km/h (50mph); fording 1.067m (3ft 6in); vertical obstacle 0.5m (1ft 7in); trench 2.057m (6ft 9in)

Bv 206

The Bv 206 is found in service in the UK, US, Finland, Norway, Canada and Italy, as well as with Swedish armed forces. It has two units. The front unit contains the powerplant, transmission and operating crew. The rear unit is either an 11-soldier transportation vehicle or a cargo-carrying unit (maximum cargo haulage is 600kg/1300lb). The two are linked by a steerable connector and the climate inside the units is kept warm via an air heater. Appropriately for the Scandanavian environment, the Bv 206 is fully amphibious without preparation, propulsion coming from its extremely broad tracks. An anti-tank variant, the Pvbv 2062, has a Bofors 90mm (3.54in) recoilless rifle or Hughes TOW ATGW fitted to the roof.

Country of origin:	Sweden
Crew:	5 + 11
Weight:	Front unit 2740kg (6042lb); rear unit 1730kg (3815lb)
Dimensions:	Length: 6.9m (22.64ft); width: 1.87m (6.14ft); height: 2.4m (7.87ft)
Range:	300km (190 miles)
Armour:	None
Armament:	None
Powerplant:	1 x Mercedes-Benz OM603.950 6-cylinder diesel, developing 136hp (101kW)
Performance:	Maximum road speed: 55km/h (34mph); fording: amphibious; gradient: 60 percent; vertical obstacle: 0.5m (1.6ft)

Type 82

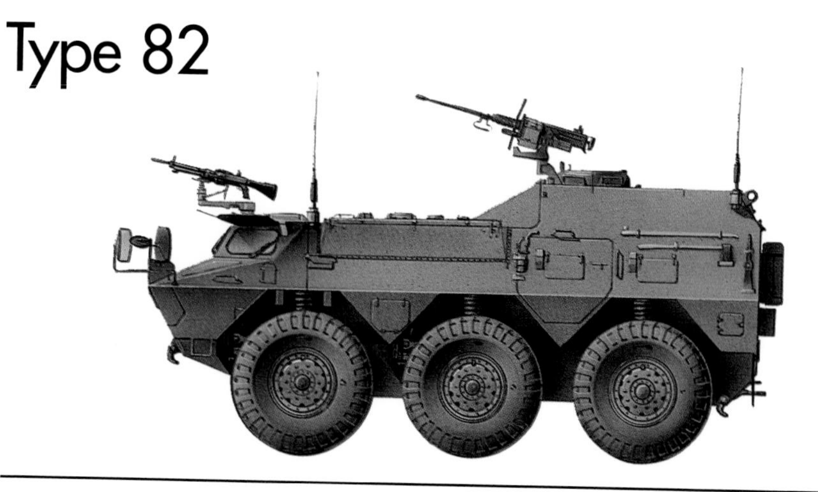

The Type 82 emerged from Japanese Ground Self-Defence Forces trials in the 1970s for a new, wheeled reconnaissance vehicle. Trials of a 4x4 and a 6x6 vehicle resulted in the selection of the latter. This became the Type 82 Command and Communications Vehicle and production began in 1982. The vehicle transports a crew of eight, with two personnel responsible for driving and observation and the rest manning communications equipment in the raised rear of the vehicle. The front and back sections are connected by an inner gangway to the right of the hull. The Type 82 has side and rear doors set into the all-welded hull and armament is provided by roof-mounted machine guns.

Country of origin:	Japan
Crew:	8
Weight:	13,500kg (29,800lb)
Dimensions:	Length: 5.72m (18.77ft); width: 2.48m (8.14ft); height: 2.38m (7.81ft)
Range:	500km (310 miles)
Armour:	Classified
Armament:	1 x 7.62mm (0.3in) MG; 1 x 12.7mm (0.5in) MG
Powerplant:	1 x Isuzu diesel, developing 305hp (227kW) at 2700rpm
Performance:	Maximum road speed: 100km/h (62mph); fording: 1m (3.3ft); gradient: 60 percent; vertical obstacle: 0.6m (2ft); trench: 1.5m (4.9ft)

M4 C2V

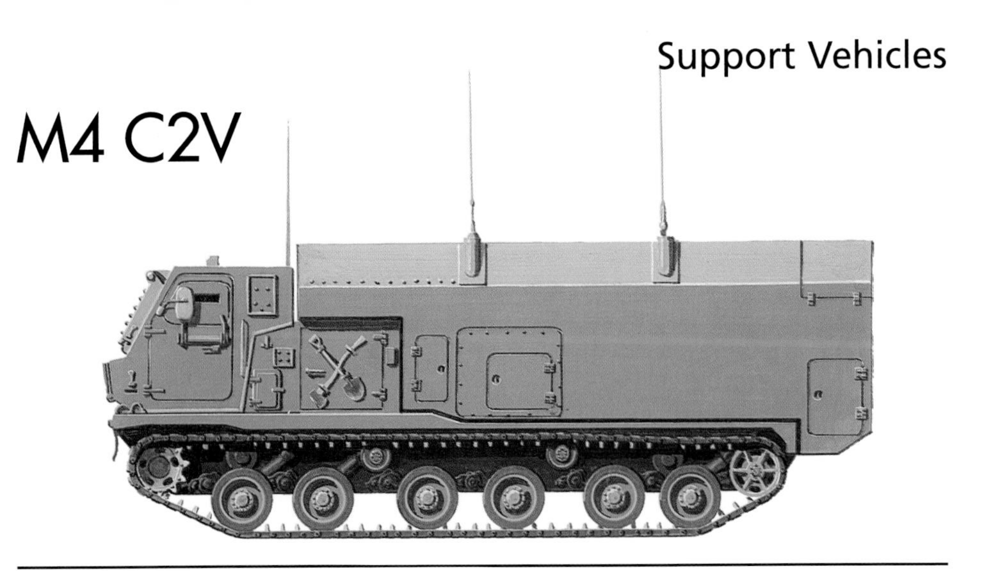

The M4 is a modern Command and Control Vehicle (C2V) manufactured by United Defense. It utilizes the tracked chassis of the M993 Bradley Fighting Vehicle, and consequently has the same performance as any modern main battle tank or infantry fighting vehicle. An armoured module containing advanced C2V electronics is mounted on the chassis, including the Army Battle Command System (ABCS) Common Hardware and Software (CHS) communications suite. The commander of the vehicle depends on a wireless Local Area Network (LAN) system so that communications can be made while mobile. The M4's principal role is to provide operational C2V coordination amongst armoured units. It has full NBC protection at all times.

Country of origin:	United States
Crew:	1 + 8
Weight:	25,000–30,000kg (55,100–66,100lb)
Dimensions:	Length: 7.49m (24.57ft); width: 2.97m (9.74ft); height: 2.7m (8.86ft)
Range:	400km (250 miles)
Armour:	Details classified
Armament:	None
Powerplant:	1 x Cummins VTA-903T 8-cylinder turbo diesel, developing 590hp (440kW)
Performance:	Maximum road speed: 65km/h (40mph)

Bren Gun Carrier

The Bren Carrier was more correctly known as the Universal (Bren Gun) Carrier. Produced between 1934 and 1960, it was used to transport a two-man Bren gun team, though initially it was designed as a gun tractor for a Vickers machine gun and a four-man crew. It was the advent of the Bren gun in 1936 which put an end to its gun tractor days. In effect, the Carrier was little more than an armoured metal box. The engine was placed in the centre of the vehicle next to the driver and gunner – the noise was apparently deafening. Despite their crudity, the Carriers were much used, and around 10 could be found in each infantry battalion. Various experimental models abounded, including versions mounting 25-pounder (87.6mm/3.45in) guns.

Country of origin:	United Kingdom
Crew:	2
Weight:	4000kg (8800lb)
Dimensions:	Length: 3.65m (11.97ft); width: 2.11m (6.92ft); height: 1.57m (5.15ft)
Range:	250km (150 miles)
Armour:	10mm (0.39in) maximum
Armament:	1 x 7.62mm (0.3in) Bren MG
Powerplant:	1 x Ford V8 petrol, developing 85hp (63kW) at 3500rpm
Performance:	Maximum road speed: 48km/h (30mph)

SdKfz 250/10

The SdKfz 250 was developed following a mid-1930s requirement for a one-tonne (0.98 tons) halftrack to provide mobility for infantry and other units operating with panzer divisions. The first example appeared in 1939 and saw action for the first time in May 1940 during the invasion of France. Production continued until 1944, with later models having redesigned hulls to make manufacture easier and cut down on the amount of raw materials required, as the basic design was rather expensive. Variants included a communications vehicle and mobile observation post, as well as a number of specialised weapons carriers, mounting everything from anti-aircraft guns to anti-tank cannons. The vehicle remained in service until the end of the war proving to be a reliable and popular halftrack.

Country of origin:	Germany
Crew:	6
Weight:	5380kg (11,836lb)
Dimensions:	length 4.56m (14ft 11.5in); width 1.945m (6ft 4.6in); height 1.98m (6ft 6in)
Range:	299km (186 miles)
Armour:	6-14.5mm (0.23-0.6in)
Armament:	one 3.7cm Pak 35/36 anti-tank gun
Powerplant:	one six-cylinder petrol engine developing 100hp (74.6kW)
Performance:	maximum road speed 59.5km/h (37mph); fording 0.75m (29.5in); vertical obstacle 2.0m (6ft 6.7in)

SdKfz 251/1

The SdKfz 251 had its origins in the same requirement as the SdKfz 250. However, the 251 series was a heavier vehicle. It entered service in 1939, intended as an armoured personnel carrier. The 250 was a useful vehicle, capable of keeping up with panzer formations. There were 22 special-purpose variants, including rocket-launcher (referred to as the 'infantry Stuka'), flame-thrower, anti-tank, communications vehicle, observation post and ambulance and infrared searchlight carrier. Early reliability problems did not prevent the vehicle being produced by the thousands, and it was a sturdy vehicle used on all fronts, becoming a virtual trademark of German panzer formations. The SdKfz 251/1 was the standard armoured personnel carrier for the panzergrenadier group.

Country of origin:	Germany
Crew:	12
Weight:	7810kg (17,182lb)
Dimensions:	length 5.80m (19ft 0.3in); width 2.10m (6ft 10.7in); height 1.75m (5ft 8.9in)
Range:	300km (186 miles)
Armour:	6-14.5mm (0.23-0.6in)
Armament:	two 7.92mm machine guns
Powerplant:	one Maybach six-cylinder petrol engine developing 100hp (74.6kW)
Performance:	maximum road speed 52.5km/h (32.5mph); fording 0.6m (2ft); vertical obstacle 2.0m (6ft 6.7in)

M3

American half-track production began in earnest in 1941, and by the end of the war over 40,000 of all types had been produced. The M3 was widely used by all Allied forces, mainly as a personnel carrier, although also saw service as an ambulance, communications vehicle and artillery tractor. In fact, it was so prolific that it became something of a trademark of Allied forces, particularly after the D-Day landings of June 1944. After World War II, the M3 was gradually reduced to the role of recovery vehicle. However, vehicles supplied to the Soviet Union before 1945 continued to see service with some Warsaw Pact countries for many years. It also remained a frontline vehicle for the Israeli Defence Force until relatively recently, seeing service in all the Arab–Israeli wars.

Country of origin:	United States
Crew:	13
Weight:	9299kg (20,458lb)
Dimensions:	length 6.18m (20ft 3.5in); width 2.22m (7ft 3.5in); height 2.26m (7ft 5in)
Range:	282km (175 miles)
Armour:	8mm (0.31in)
Armament:	one 12.7mm machine gun; one 7.62mm machine gun
Powerplant:	one White 160AX six-cylinder petrol engine developing 147hp (109.6kW)
Performance:	maximum road speed 64.4km/h (40mph); fording 0.81m (2ft 8in)

Ram/Kangaroo

The Ram/Kangaroo was an expedient vehicle used to transport Canadian soldiers into action in Europe in late 1944. The vehicle was essentially a turretless Canadian Ram tank, which was developed in 1942 and 1943 but was quickly rendered obsolete by the introduction of the US Sherman tank. By mid-1944, 500 Rams were in storage in England, and these were converted into armoured personnel carriers. The turret was removed, benches were fixed in the interior alongside ammunition racks and a standard infantry No.19 wireless set was fitted. Ram/Kangaroos were light and mobile vehicles, and joined the ranks of several similar Allied tank conversions.

Country of origin:	Canada/United Kingdom
Crew:	2 + 8
Weight:	29,000kg (63,900lb)
Dimensions:	Length: 5.79m (19ft); width: 2.78m (9.12ft); height: 2.47m (8.1ft)
Range:	230km (140 miles)
Armour:	88mm (3.46in) maximum
Armament:	1 x 7.62mm (0.3in) MG
Powerplant:	1 x Continental R-975 9-cylinder diesel, developing 399hp (298kW)
Performance:	Maximum road speed: 40km/h (25mph); vertical obstacle: 0.6m (2ft); trench: 2.26m (7.41ft)

OT-810

German half-track designs were so successful that after World War II many countries adopted them their own armed forces. Czechoslovakia took over old stocks of German Sdfz.251 half-tracks (Czechoslovakia was actually one of the manufacturers of the Sdfz.251 chassis) and used them as armoured personnel carriers. In the late 1950s, the vehicles were modified and were designated the OT-810. The German engine was removed and replaced by a Tatra six-cylinder air-cooled diesel. Armoured roof hatches were added to the troop compartment. Later, an anti-tank variant was produced with an M59A 82mm (3.23in) recoilless rifle on board, fired either from the vehicle or carried outside as an independent weapon.

Country of origin:	Czechoslovakia
Crew:	2 + 10
Weight:	9000kg (19,800lb)
Dimensions:	Length: 5.71m (18.73ft); width: 2.1m (6.89ft); height: 1.88m (6.17ft)
Range:	600km (370 miles)
Armour:	(Steel) 12mm (0.47in) maximum
Armament:	1 x 7.62mm (0.3in) MG
Powerplant:	1 x Tatra 928-3 6-cylinder diesel, developing 120hp (89kW)
Performance:	Maximum road speed: 55km/h (34mph); fording: 0.5m (1.6ft); gradient: 24 percent; vertical obstacle: 0.23m (0.77ft); trench: 1.98m (6.34ft)

M75

The International Harvester M75 was an initial US attempt to replace the wartime M3 half-track and produce a modern armoured personnel carrier. Its design was flawed in that it relied on expensive tank components for its production, especially the running gear, engine and transmission. Mainly for reasons of cost, only 1729 were produced between 1951 and 1954. The M75 looked towards the M113 in design concept. It featured a steel armoured box with a sloped glacis front big enough for two crew and 10 soldiers. Twin doors at the rear of the hull provided entry and exit. Armament consisted of one 12.7mm (0.5in) Browning M2 HB machine gun mounted on the roof.

Country of origin:	United States
Crew:	2 + 10
Weight:	18,828kg (41,516lb)
Dimensions:	Length: 5.19m (17.03ft); width: 2.84m (9.32ft); height: 2.77m (9.09ft)
Range:	185km (115 miles)
Armour:	(Steel) 15.9mm (0.63in)
Armament:	1 x 12.7mm (0.5in) Browning M2 HB
Powerplant:	1 x Continental AO-895-4 6-cylinder petrol, developing 295hp (220kW) at 2660rpm
Performance:	Maximum road speed: 71km/h (44mph); fording: 1.22m (4ft); gradient: 60 percent; vertical obstacle: 0.46m (1.5ft); trench: 1.68m (5.51ft)

M59

The M59 was in production between 1954 and 1959, before being phased out in favour of the M113 armoured personnel carrier. It was a basic tracked APC with an all-welded steel hull, a two-man crew, and carrying capacity for 10 soldiers. In theory, it was amphibious, propulsion coming from its tracks when in the water. However, experience showed that even mildly choppy water could destabilize its float characteristics. The commander of an M59 had a dedicated viewing cupola. Initially this had a 360-degree traverse, but later it was replaced with a fixed cupola fitted with four periscopes. The M59 spawned only one production variant, the M84 107mm (4.21in) mortar carrier.

Country of origin:	United States
Crew:	2 + 10
Weight:	19,323kg (38,197lb)
Dimensions:	Length: 5.61m (18.4ft); width: 3.26m (10.7ft); height: 2.27m (7.45ft)
Range:	164km (102 miles)
Armour:	(Steel) 16mm (0.63in)
Armament:	1 x 12.7mm (0.5in) Browning M2 HB MG
Powerplant:	1 x General Motors Model 302 6-cylinder petrol, developing 127hp (95kW) at 3350rpm
Performance:	Maximum road speed: 51km/h (32mph); fording: amphibious; gradient: 60 percent; vertical obstacle: 0.46m (1.5ft); trench: 1.68m (5.51ft)

M113A2

The M113 was the result of a mid-1950s US requirement for a lightweight, amphibious and airportable armoured infantry vehicle. Production began in the early 1960s, since when 70,000 have been built and exported to nearly 50 countries, the vehicle being constantly updated to meet modern requirements. In particular, the early versions afforded the gunner no protection at all, this being addressed as a priority following combat experience, notably in Vietnam, the Middle East, North Africa and the Far East. With many variants, including mortar carrier, command vehicle, anti-aircraft and flame-thrower vehicles, the M113 will stay in service well into the 21st century and will probably be the most widely used armoured vehicle ever built.

Country of origin:	United States
Crew:	2 + 11
Weight:	11,341kg (24,950lb)
Dimensions:	length 2.686m (8ft 9in); width 2.54m (8ft 4in); height 2.52m (8ft 3in)
Range:	483km (300 miles)
Armour:	up to 44mm (1.73in)
Armament:	one 12.7mm machine gun; two 7.62mm machine guns
Powerplant:	one six-cylinder water-cooled diesel, developing 215bhp (160kW)
Performance:	maximum road speed 67.59km/h (42mph); maximum water speed 5.8km/h (3.6mph); fording amphibious; vertical obstacle 0.61m (2ft); trench 1.68m (5ft 6in)

M113 Zelda

The US M113 entered into production in 1954 to fulfil a US Army order for air-transportable armoured vehicles, and used aluminium armour to keep weight low. Since then, over 70,000 have been made and service continues in over 35 countries despite US production ceasing in 1992. The M113 is an armoured hull mounted on a tracked suspension capable of transporting 11 soldiers with the protection of 38mm (1.49in) of armour. It is fully amphibious. Hundreds of variants have been produced, from missile launchers to engineer vehicles. The Israeli Zelda is a standard M113 but with additional side and floor armour to protect against rocket-propelled grenades and mine detonations respectively.

Country of origin:	Israel
Crew:	2 + 11
Weight:	12,500kg (27,600lb)
Dimensions:	Length: 5.23m (17.16ft); width: 3.08m (10.1ft); height: 1.85m (6.07ft
Range:	480km (300 miles)
Armour:	(Aluminium) 38mm (1.49in)
Armament:	Various MG configurations
Powerplant:	1 x Detroit Diesel 6V-53T 6-cylinder diesel, developing 212hp (158kW) at 2800rpm
Performance:	Maximum road speed: 61km/h (38mph); fording: amphibious; gradient: 60 percent; vertical obstacle: 0.6m (2ft); trench: 1.68m (5.51ft)

BTR-50

Between 1957 and the early 1970s, the BTR-50 served as the standard Soviet armoured personnel carrier before it was superseded by the BMP-1. It was a lightly armed (1 x 7.62mm/0.3in machine gun) APC with a large carrying capacity of 20 personnel. The low-profile hull meant that the occupants entered and exited over the vehicle's side rather than through hatches and doors. A later version, the BTR-50K, had an enclosed armoured roof and roof hatches for access. The chassis of the vehicle was basically that of the PT-76 light tank and its engine was a modified version of that used in the T-54 main battle tank. Waterjets powered the vehicle when in amphibious mode.

Country of origin:	USSR
Crew:	2 + 20
Weight:	14,200kg (31,300lb)
Dimensions:	Length: 7.03m (23.06ft); width: 3.14m (10.3ft); height: 2.07m (6.79ft)
Range:	400km (250 miles)
Armour:	(Steel) 10mm (0.39in)
Armament:	1 x 7.62mm (0.3in) MG
Powerplant:	1 x Model V6 6-cylinder diesel, developing 240hp (179kW) at 1800rpm
Performance:	Maximum road speed: 44km/h (27mph); fording: amphibious; gradient: 70 percent; vertical obstacle: 1.1m (3.6ft); trench: 2.8m (9.2ft)

AMX VCI

The AMX VCI (Véhicule de Combat d'Infanterie) went into production in 1957 to meet a French Army requirement to replace the cancelled Hotchkiss TT6 and TT9 armoured personnel carriers. As the name suggests, the vehicle is constructed around the modified chassis of the AMX-13 light tank. It carried three crew and 10 soldiers, the latter sitting back to back in a bisected internal compartment at the rear, accessible by double doors. Standard armament is a 12.7mm (0.5in) M2 HB machine gun pintle-mounted on the roof. Updated AMX VCIs have NBC and night-vision systems. The AMX VCI was developed into a large number of variants, ranging from TOW-armed anti-tank vehicles to the RATAC radar-carrier vehicle.

Country of origin:	France
Crew:	3 + 10
Weight:	15,000kg (33,100lb)
Dimensions:	Length: 5.7m (18.7ft); width: 2.67m (8.76ft); height: 2.41m (7.9ft)
Range:	350km (220 miles)
Armour:	(Steel) 30mm (1.18in) maximum
Armament:	1 x 12.7mm (0.5in) M2 HB MG
Powerplant:	1 x SOFAM 8Gxb 8-cylinder petrol, developing 250hp (186kW) at 3200rpm
Performance:	Maximum road speed: 60km/h (37mph); fording: 1m (3.3ft); gradient: 60 percent; vertical obstacle: 1m (3.3ft); trench: 1.6m (5.3ft)

SU-60

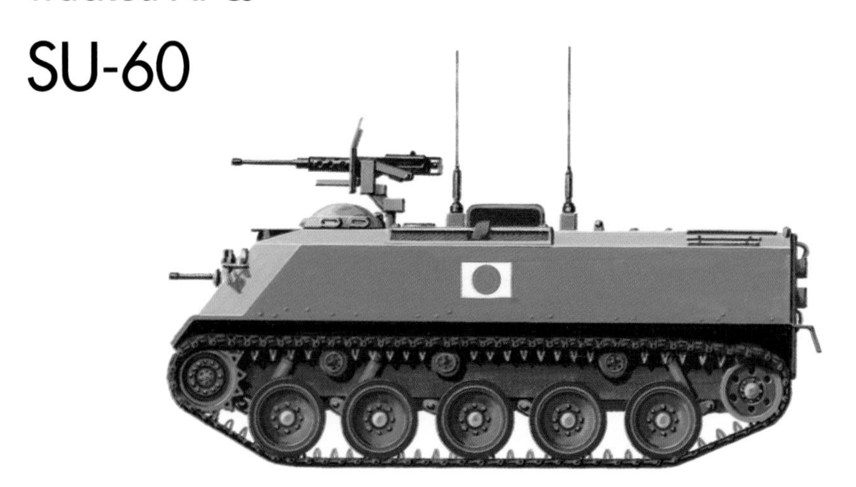

The SU-60 was Japan's first post-war tracked armoured personnel carrier. It entered service with the Japanese Ground Self Defence Force in 1960 and was eventually replaced by the Type 73 in the early 1970s. A general US M113 appearance belies a different crew configuration. The driver and bow machine-gunner sat at the front of the vehicle on the right and left respectively, with the commander between them. The final crew member sat just behind and to the right of the commander, and would operate the 12.7mm (0.5in) roof-mounted machine gun. Variants of the SU-60 include two mortar carriers, an NBC detection vehicle, an anti-tank vehicle and a bulldozer.

Country of origin:	Japan
Crew:	4 + 6
Weight:	11,800kg (26,000lb)
Dimensions:	Length: 4.85m (15.91ft); width: 2.4m (7.87ft); height: 1.7m (5.58ft)
Range:	300km (190 miles)
Armour:	Steel (details classified)
Armament:	1 x 12.7mm (0.5in) Browning M2 HB MG
Powerplant:	1 x Mitsubishi 8 HA 21 WT 8-cylinder diesel, developing 220hp (164kW) at 2400rpm
Performance:	Maximum road speed: 45km/h (28mph); fording: 1m (3.3ft); gradient: 60 percent; vertical obstacle: 0.6m (2ft); trench: 1.82m (5.97ft)

Saurer 4K 4FA-G1

The basic Saurer 4K 4FA armoured personnel carrier entered production in 1961 and began a long line of variants. In its standard form, it was a steel-armoured APC with a two-plus-eight personnel capacity and a single 12.7mm (0.5in) Browning M2 HB machine gun mounted on a forward cupola. Little sophistication was present – the 4K 4FA could not conduct amphibious operations and had no night-vision systems. The variants of the 4K 4FA ranged from the minor to the major. The 4K 3FA-G1 had a 230hp (172kW) engine as opposed to the 250hp (186kW) engine of the 4FA. By contrast, variants existed with Oerlikon 20mm (0.78in) cannon turrets and even 81mm (3.19in) Oerlikon-Bührle multiple rocket launchers.

Country of origin:	Austria
Crew:	2 + 8
Weight:	12,200kg (26,900lb)
Dimensions:	Length: 5.35m (17.55ft); width: 2.5m (8.2ft); height: 1.65m (5.41ft)
Range:	370km (230 miles)
Armour:	(Steel) 20mm (0.78in) maximum
Armament:	1 x 12.7mm (0.5in) MG
Powerplant:	1 Saurer 4FA 6-cylinder turbo diesel, developing 250hp (186kW) at 2400rpm
Performance:	Maximum road speed: 65km/h (40mph); fording: 1m (3.3ft); gradient: 75 percent; vertical obstacle: 0.8m (2.6ft); trench: 2.2m (7.2ft)

FV432

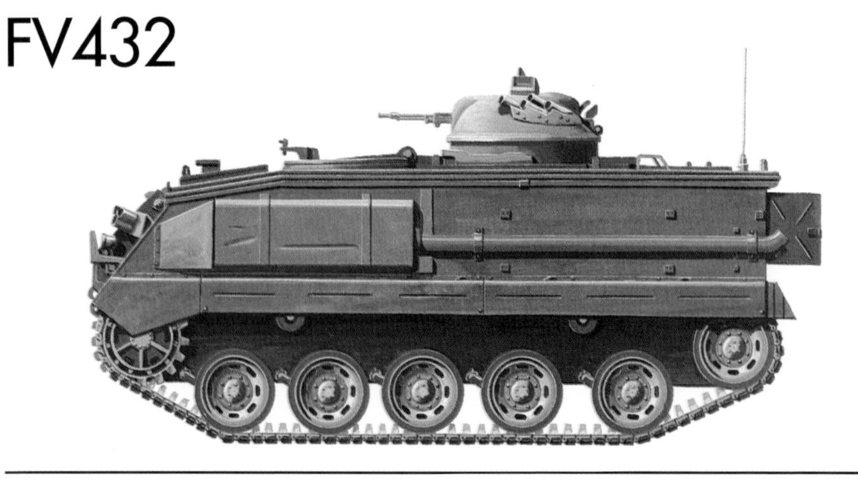

In 1962, the FV432 was the first fully tracked armoured personnel carrier to be accepted into service by the British Army since World War II. Between 1963 and 1971 a total of 3000 were built by GKN Sankey. Few were exported, as the similar American M113 was a much cheaper option. At one time known as the Trojan, the FV432's main purpose was to transport fighting men to the battlefield, carrying 10 troops, the vehicle was one of the first to be fitted with a nuclear, biological and chemical (NBC) defence system. Initially the vehicles were fitted with flotation screens to give an amphibious capability, but these were removed as they were prone to damage. Variants included a command vehicle, ambulance, mortar carrier and mine-layer, as well as an anti-tank version armed with Swingfire missiles.

Country of origin:	United Kingdom
Crew:	2 + 10
Weight:	15,280kg (33,616lb)
Dimensions:	length 5.251m (17ft 7in); width 2.80m (9ft 2in); height (with machine gun) 2.286m (7ft 6in)
Range:	483km (300 miles)
Armour:	12mm (0.47in)
Armament:	one 7.62mm machine gun
Powerplant:	one Rolls-Royce K60 six-cylinder multi-fuel engine developing 240hp (170kW)
Performance:	maximum road speed 52.2km/h (32mph); fording 1.066m (3ft 6in); vertical obstacle 0.609m (2ft); trench 2.05m (6ft 9in)

OT-62

Soviet armoured personnel carriers were widely distributed throughout Europe and the Middle East during the 1960s and 1970s, often through export but also through licensed production or simple copy. The OT-62 was the Czech version of the Russian BTR-50PK. It entered service with the Czech military in 1964 and with the Polish Army in 1966 as a variant called TOPAS. Like the BTR-50PK, the OT-62 has an all-welded armoured hull with slightly less carrying capacity (18 as opposed to 20 passengers) but more powerful engines. Two waterjets at the rear of the vehicle provide propulsion during amphibious use. The Polish TOPAS version was designed for vehicular recovery operations.

Country of origin:	Czechoslovakia
Crew:	3 + 18
Weight:	15,100kg (33,300lb)
Dimensions:	Length: 7m (22.97ft); width: 3.22m (10.56ft); height: 2.72m (8.92ft)
Range:	460km (290 miles)
Armour:	14mm (0.55in) maximum
Armament:	1 x 7.62mm (0.3in) PKY MG and various other configurations
Powerplant:	1 x PV6 6-cylinder turbo diesel, developing 300hp (224kW) at 1200rpm
Performance:	Maximum road speed: 60km/h (37mph); fording: amphibious; gradient: 70 percent; vertical obstacle: 1.1m (3.6ft); trench: 2.8m (9.2ft)

M-60P

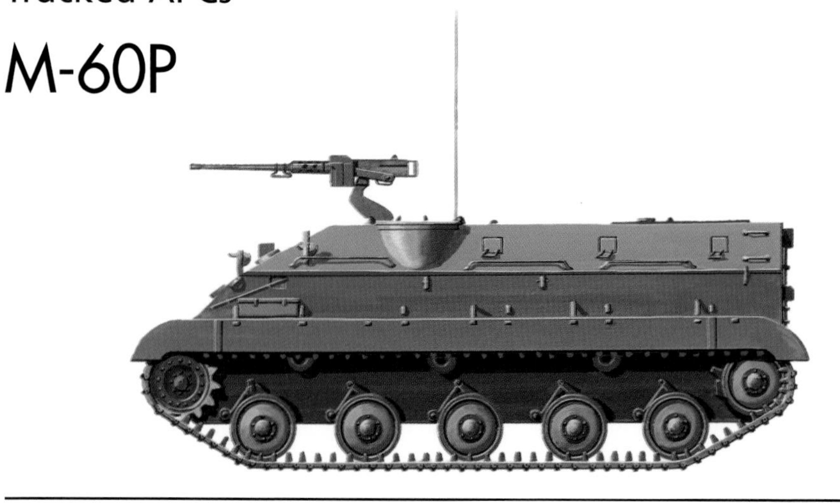

The M60P appears to look to the West and the US M113 for its inspiration rather than to the East and Soviet armoured personnel carriers. Like subsequent Yugoslav APCs, however, it is a medley of various foreign parts and design elements. The Soviet SU-76 self-propelled gun chassis provides the basis for the suspension, an Austrian Steyr-type engine gives the power, and Western APCs, such as the US M59 and British FV432, contribute to overall design. An M60PB anti-tank variant was later produced. This featured two 82mm (3.23in) recoilless rifles, though by the mid-1970s these were ineffective against modern main battle tank armour. The M60P only operated in Yugoslavia, and is still in service today with its successor nations Bosnia, Croatia and Serbia.

Country of origin:	Yugoslavia
Crew:	3 + 10
Weight:	11,000kg (24,300lb)
Dimensions:	Length: 5.02m (16.47ft); width: 2.77m (9.09ft); height: 2.77m (9.09ft)
Range:	400km (250 miles)
Armour:	(Steel) 25mm (0.98in)
Armament:	1 x 12.7mm (0.5in) MG; 1 x 7.62mm (0.3in) MG
Powerplant:	1 x FAMOS 6-cylinder diesel, developing 140hp (104kW)
Performance:	Maximum road speed: 45km/h (28mph); fording: 1.25m (4.1ft); gradient: 60 percent; vertical obstacle: 0.6m (2ft); trench: 2m (6.6ft)

Pbv

Design on the Pbv 302 began in 1961 and full-scale production began in 1966. The Pbv was similar in layout to the American M113 and was one of the first vehicles of its type with a fully enclosed weapon station. The troop compartment is at the rear with room for 10 fully equipped soldiers. There are no firing ports, but soldiers are able to fire through the hatches on the top. The turret is manually operated, and the 20mm cannon can be fed from a belt holding 135 rounds of from 10-round box magazines. Fully amphibious, the Pbv is propelled through the water by its tracks. Variants include a command vehicle, observation vehicle and ambulance. Few were exported, mainly because of the strict controls placed on exports of military equipment by the Swedish government.

Country of origin:	Sweden
Crew:	2 + 10
Weight:	13,500kg (29,700lb)
Dimensions:	length 5.35m (17ft 7in); width 2.86m (9ft 5in); height 2.50m (8ft 2in)
Range:	300km (186 miles)
Armour:	classified
Armament:	one 20mm Hispano cannon
Powerplant:	one Volvo-Penta Model THD 100B 6-cylinder inline diesel engine developing 280hp (209kW)
Performance:	maximum road speed 66km/h (41mph); fording amphibious; vertical obstacle 0.61m (2ft); trench 1.80m (5ft 11in)

BMP-1

The BMP-1 is one of the more heavily armed Russian APCs, and the first of the BMP series designed to replace the BTR-50. Its primary armament is a turret-mounted 73mm (2.87in) short-recoil gun, fed with fin-stabilized rocket-assisted ammunition from a 40-round magazine. This weapon features a low-pressure system which negates excessive backblast into the cabin. In addition, the BMP-1 carries a single Sagger ATGW missile and a 7.62mm (0.3in) coaxial machine gun. Equal attention is paid to armour, the all-welded steel hull capable of stopping 12.7mm (0.5in) machine gun rounds. The BMP-1 is fully amphibious and propelled in water by its tracks.

Country of origin:	USSR
Crew:	3 + 8
Weight:	13,900kg (30,650lb)
Dimensions:	Length: 6.74m (22.11ft); width: 2.94m (9.65ft); height: 1.9m (6.23ft)
Range:	600km (370 miles)
Armour:	(Steel) 33mm (1.29in)
Armament:	1 x 73mm (2.87in) gun; 1 x Sagger ATGW missile; 1 x 7.62mm (0.3in) coaxial MG
Powerplant:	1 x UTD-20 6-cylinder diesel, developing 300hp (223kW)
Performance:	Maximum road speed: 80km/h (50mph); fording: amphibious; gradient: 60 percent; vertical obstacle: 0.8m (2.6ft); trench: 2.2m (7.2ft)

YW 531

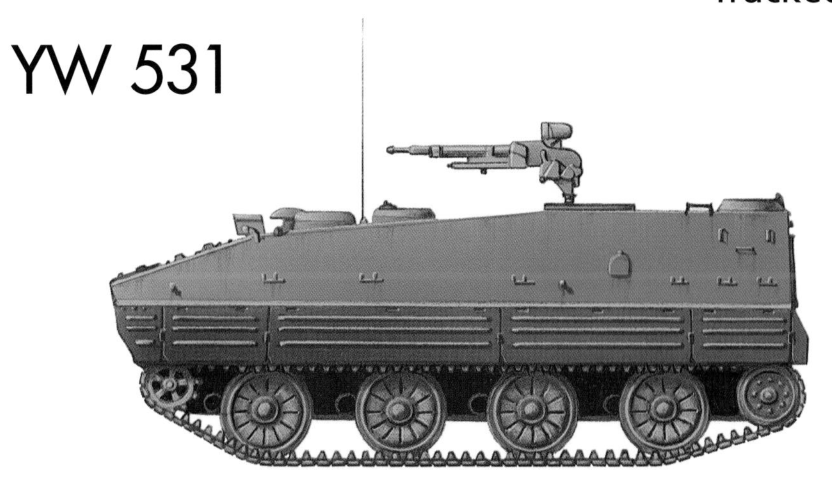

The YW 531 armoured personnel carrier was developed in the late 1960s for the Chinese Army and exported to military forces in Vietnam, Angola, Tanzania and Iraq throughout the 1970s. It was capable of holding 13 troops in the rear of the vehicle, with a two-man crew of driver and commander. The engine was located behind the commander, who sat on the right of the hull at the front and viewed the battlefield through a hatch or a 360-degree rotatable periscope which was integral to the hatch. Driver vision was provided by two periscopes. Like most communist APCs, the YW 531 was fully amphibious, the Chinese vehicle requiring a trim board to be fitted to the front of the hull before entering the water.

Country of origin:	China
Crew:	2 + 13
Weight:	12,500kg (27,600lb)
Dimensions:	Length: 5.74m (18.83ft); width: 2.99m (9.8ft); height: 2.11m (6.92ft)
Range:	425km (260 miles)
Armour:	Not available
Armament:	1 x 12.7mm (0.5in) MG
Powerplant:	1 x Deutz Type 6150L 6-cylinder diesel, developing 257hp (192kW)
Performance:	Maximum road speed: 50km/h (31mph); fording: amphibious; vertical obstacle: 0.6m (2ft); trench: 2m (6.6ft)

YW 703

The YW 703 is actually a version of the Norinco YW 531H armoured personnel carrier, China's main APC type. A 25mm (0.98in) cannon separates the YW 703 from all the other YW 531H derivatives, of which there are many. Other combat versions include the Type 85, armed with a 120mm (4.72in) or 82mm (3.23in) mortar, and a 122mm (4.8in) self-propelled howitzer version. Non-combat variants include the Type 85 command-post vehicle, an armoured recovery vehicle, and an ambulance. The YW 531H can be confused with the YW 534, though the former does not have the bank of four smoke grenade launchers set on either side of the turret.

Country of origin:	China
Crew:	3 + 7
Weight:	15,400kg (31,000lb)
Dimensions:	Length: 6.15m (20.18ft); width: 3.13m (10.27ft); height: 1.88m (6.17ft)
Range:	500km (310 miles)
Armour:	Steel (details classified)
Armament:	1 x 25mm (0.98in) cannon
Powerplant:	1 x Deutz Type BF8L413F 8-cylinder diesel, developing 320hp (239kW)
Performance:	Maximum road speed: 65km/h (40mph); fording: amphibious; vertical obstacle: 0.6m (2ft); trench: 2.2m (7.2ft)

BMD

The BMD was designed specifically for Soviet airborne forces to give increased firepower and mobility for troops behind enemy lines once on the ground. This was particularly important as the Soviets had only sufficient air transport to deliver one airborne division at a time. It entered service in 1970, and 330 were destined for each airborne division. Based on the BMP-1, the vehicle was fitted with an unusual hydraulic suspension-adjustment system to alter the level of ground clearance. Fully amphibious, the vehicle had night vision and a nuclear, chemical and biological (NBC) defence system, plus a smoke generating system. Variants included a mortar carrier and command vehicle. The BMD was used to spearhead the Soviet invasion of Afghanistan in 1979.

Country of origin:	USSR
Crew:	3 + 4
Weight:	6700kg (14,740lb)
Dimensions:	length 5.40m (17ft 9in); width 2.63m (9ft 8in); height 1.97m (6ft 6in)
Range:	320km (200 miles)
Armour:	15-23mm (0.59-0.9in)
Armament:	one 73mm gun; one coaxial 7.62mm machine gun; two front-mounted 7.62mm machine guns; one AT-3 'Sagger' ATGW
Powerplant:	one V-6 liquid-cooled diesel engine developing 240hp (179kW)
Performance:	maximum road speed 70km/h (43mph); fording amphibious; vertical obstacle 0.80m (2ft 8in); trench 1.60m (5ft 3in)

Marder

The Marder Schützenpanzer was the first mechanised infantry combat vehicle to enter service in the West, and was one of a family of vehicles based on the chassis of the Swiss SPX12-3. Production began in 1970, and by 1975 some 3000 had been built. At the time, it was the most advanced of its type in the world. With excellent armour and high cross-country speed, it was able to operate with Leopard main battle tanks in combined operations. The troops inside were able to use their weapons from inside by means of a periscope and firing ports. A remote-controlled machine gun was provided for local defence. Later versions carried the Milan anti-tank guided missile. Variants include a surface-to-air missile (SAM) launcher and a radar carrier. Over 6000 rounds of ammunition are carried in the vehicle.

Country of origin:	West Germany
Crew:	4 + 6
Weight:	28,200kg (62,040lb)
Dimensions:	length 6.79m (22ft 3in); width 3.24m (10ft 8in); height 2.95m (9ft 8in)
Range:	520km (323 miles)
Armour:	classified
Armament:	one 20mm Rh 202 cannon; one coaxial 7.62mm machine gun
Powerplant:	one MTU MB 833 six-cylinder diesel, developing 600hp (447kW)
Performance:	maximum road speed 75km/h (46.6mph); fording 1.50m (4ft 11in); vertical obstacle 1.00m (3ft 3in); trench 2.50m (8ft 2in)

AMX-10P

Designed in the mid-1960s, the first French AMX-10s rolled off the production line in 1973. With an all-aluminium hull, the AMX-10 was fully amphibious, being propelled by two waterjets. It also carried a nuclear, biological and chemical (NBC) defence system and night-vision equipment. Inside, there was capacity for eight troops. The vehicle has spawned a range of variants, including an ambulance, a repair vehicle, an anti-tank vehicle with four guided weapons and a mortar tractor for towing a Brandt 120mm mortar. The AMX-10 has been exported to many countries including Greece, Qatar, Mexico, Saudi Arabia and Indonesia, the vehicles for the latter having improved amphibious capability as they are designed to leave landing craft offshore and float in under their own power.

Country of origin:	France
Crew:	3 + 8
Weight:	14,200kg (31,240lb)
Dimensions:	length 5.778m (18ft 11in); width 2.78m (9ft 1in); height 2.57m (8ft 5in)
Range:	600km (373 miles)
Armour:	classified
Armament:	one 20mm cannon; one 7.62mm coaxial machine gun
Powerplant:	one HS-115 V-8 water-cooled diesel, developing 280hp (209kW)
Performance:	maximum road speed 65km/h (40mph); fording amphibious; vertical obstacle 0.70m (2ft 4in); trench 1.60m (5ft 3in)

Type 73

Like the US M113, the Type 73 has an aluminium-armoured hull, a choice made after Komatsu's steel-armoured prototype was rejected in favour of Mitsubishi's aluminium contribution. Unlike the US vehicle, the Type 73 is not amphibious unless an optional swim-kit is fitted. However, NBC and night-vision equipment is standard. Production and service began in 1973, and 225 of the vehicles have entered use with the Japanese Ground Self Defence Force. To date, the Type 73 has only been produced in one variant, a command post vehicle, although components from the Type 73 are used in the Type 75 ground wind-measuring system and Type 75 130mm (5.12in) rocket launcher.

Country of origin:	Japan
Crew:	3 + 9
Weight:	13,300kg (29,300lb)
Dimensions:	Length: 5.8m (19ft); width: 2.8m (9.2ft); height: 2.2m (7.2ft)
Range:	300km (190 miles)
Armour:	Aluminium (details classified)
Armament:	1 x 12.7mm (0.5in) MG; 1 x 7.62mm (0.3in) MG
Powerplant:	1 x Mitsubishi 4ZF V4 diesel, developing 300hp (202kW) at 2200rpm
Performance:	Maximum road speed: 70km/h (43mph); fording: amphibious with swim-kit; gradient: 60 percent; vertical obstacle: 0.7m (2.3ft); trench: 2m (5.6ft)

AIFV

The shortcomings of the M113 prompted the US Army to order a new vehicle with better protection for the gunner and firing ports for the troops in the rear. The FMC Corporation realised that the resulting M2 would be too heavy and expensive for most countries, and thus developed the AIFV primarily for export. Better armed and armoured (with steel appliqué armour layers) than the M113, the vehicle is fully amphibious. The main gun is enclosed for better protection and the seven troops in the back all have firing ports. Night-vision and nuclear, biological and chemical (NBC) systems are available. The AIFV is a good compromise between the M113 and the M2 and has proved popular with Turkey, Belgium, the Philippines and the Netherlands all ordering significant quantities.

Country of origin:	United States
Crew:	3 + 7
Weight:	13,687kg (30,111lb)
Dimensions:	length 5.258m (17ft 3in); width 2.819m (9ft 3in); height (overall) 2.794m (9ft 2in)
Range:	490km (305 miles)
Armour:	classified
Armament:	one 25mm Oerlikon cannon; one 7.62 coaxial machine gun
Powerplant:	one Detroit-Diesel 6V-53T V-6 diesel engine developing 264hp (197kW)
Performance:	maximum road speed 61.2km/h (38mph); fording amphibious; vertical obstacle 0.635m (2ft 1in); trench 1.625m (5ft 4in)

MT-LB

The MT-LB was a multi-purpose vehicle which entered service in 1974. It was designed to replace the 30-year-old AT-P armoured artillery tractors, but went on to fulfil a multitude of roles. Configurations included: artillery tractor, repair vehicle, engineer vehicle, mobile command and control centre, ambulance, Gopher SAM system and standard armoured personnel carrier. The basic vehicle was fully amphibious and had the option of swapping its 350mm (13.78in) wide tracks for 565mm (22.24in) versions to reduce its ground pressure in snowy or muddy conditions. As an APC it could carry 11 personnel, a rear hatch being the only access for crew and passengers.

Country of origin:	USSR
Crew:	2 + 11
Weight:	14,900kg (32,900lb)
Dimensions:	Length: 7.47m (24.5ft); width: 2.85m (9.35ft); height: 2.42m (7.94ft)
Range:	525km (330 miles)
Armour:	(Steel) 3–10mm (0.11–0.39in)
Armament:	1 x 12.7mm (0.5in) MG; or 1 x 7.62mm (0.3in) MG
Powerplant:	1 x YaMZ-238N 8-cylinder diesel, developing 220hp (164kW) at 2400rpm
Performance:	Maximum road speed: 62km/h (39mph); fording: amphibious; gradient: 60 percent; vertical obstacle: 0.6m (2ft); trench: 2.41m (7.9ft)

M-80 MICV

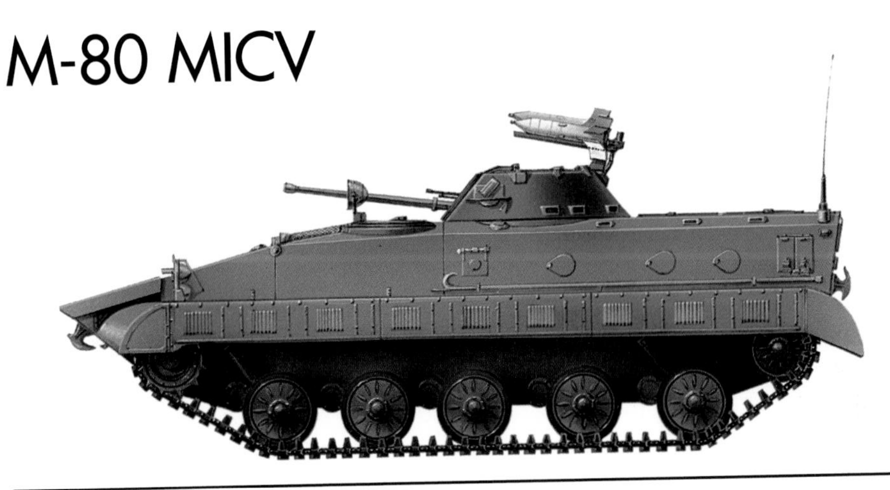

Though indebted to Soviet armoured personnel carrier design, the M-80 Mechanised Infantry Combat Vehicle (MICV) is essentially a Yugoslav design. It is an amphibious APC with an all-welded steel armour hull, with NBC protection and night-vision devices fitted as standard. Its most distinctive feature is the configuration of turret armament. As well as two Yugoslav copies of the Soviet Sagger ATGW, the turret mounts a 30mm (1.18in) cannon and a 7.62mm (0.3in) machine gun. Both these weapons are set in turret slits to allow anti-aircraft engagement at an elevation of 75 degrees. Consequently, the M-80 is able to engage low-flying aircraft at ranges of up to 1500m (4900ft).

Country of origin:	Yugoslavia
Crew:	3 + 7
Weight:	13,700kg (30,200lb)
Dimensions:	Length: 6.4m (20.99ft); width: 2.59m (8.49ft); height: 2.3m (7.55ft)
Range:	500km (310 miles)
Armour:	(Steel) 30mm (1.18in)
Armament:	2 x Yugoslav Sagger ATGWs; 1 x 30mm (1.18in) cannon; 1 x 7.62mm (0.3in) MG
Powerplant:	1 x HS-115-2 8-cylinder turbo diesel, developing 260hp (194kW)
Performance:	Maximum road speed: 60km/h (37mph); fording: amphibious; gradient: 60 percent; vertical obstacle: 0.8m (2.6ft); trench: 2.2m (7.2ft)

BMP-2

First seen in public in 1982, the BMP-2 was designed to supplement rather than replace the BMP-1, having an almost identical chassis. Its low silhouette and long sloping front is useful in that it presents a small target. This is vital because its armour is extremely poor. One remarkable feature is that the rear doors are hollow and serve as fuel tanks, with obvious dangers for the troops inside. There are few concessions to comfort, the crew compartment being very crowded and uncomfortable, although the troops can fire their weapons from within. The two-man turret has the commander on the right and the gunner on the left, the 30mm cannon having a powered elevation for use against helicopters and slow-flying aircraft. The BMP-2 saw action in Afghanistan.

Country of origin:	USSR
Crew:	3 + 7
Weight:	14,600kg (32,120lb)
Dimensions:	length: 6.71m (22ft); width 3.15m (10ft 4in); height: 2m (6ft 7in)
Range:	600km (375 miles)
Armour:	classified
Armament:	one 30mm cannon; one At-5 anti-tank missile launcher; one 7.62mm coaxial machine gun
Powerplant:	one Model UTD-20 six-cylinder diesel engine developing 300hp (223kW)
Performance:	maximum road speed 65km/h (40.6mph); fording amphibious; vertical obstacle 0.7m (2ft 4in); trench 2.4m (8ft 2in)

FV433 Stormer

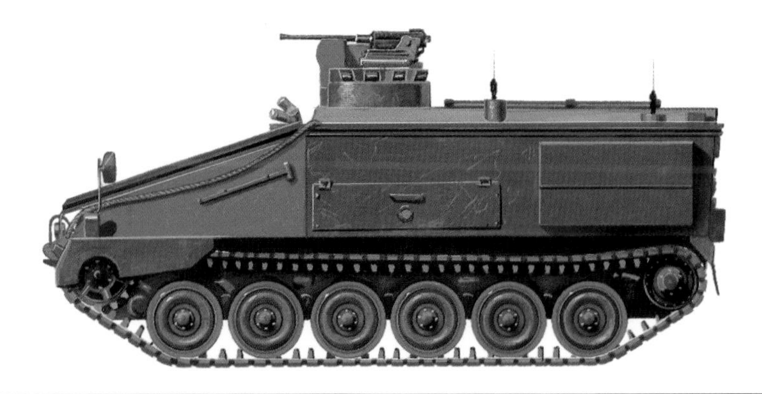

The Stormer is another British vehicle to use the Alvis Scorpion hull as its foundation. Development of the Stormer ran through the 1970s and production itself began in 1981. It is a fairly standard armoured personnel carrier, carrying three crew and eight infantry with a good road speed of 80km/h (50mph). It has sold well in export, particularly to Indonesia, Malaysia and Oman. The Stormer's main credit is its versatility. The basic vehicle can be fitted with lots of optional equipment and weaponry, including NBC systems, a flotation screen, night-vision instruments and guns ranging from 12.7mm (0.5in) machine guns to 90mm (3.54in) cannon and Starstreak missiles.

Country of origin:	United Kingdom
Crew:	3 + 8
Weight:	12,700kg (28,000lb)
Dimensions:	Length: 5.33m (17.49ft); width: 2.4m (7.87ft); height: 2.27m (7.45ft)
Range:	650km (400 miles)
Armour:	Aluminium (details classified)
Armament:	Various
Powerplant:	1 x Perkins T6/3544 6-cylinder turbo diesel, developing 250hp (186kW) at 2600rpm
Performance:	Maximum road speed: 80km/h (50mph); fording: amphibious; gradient: 60 percent; vertical obstacle: 0.6m (2ft); trench: 1.75m (5.74ft)

M2 Bradley

The M2 Bradley was the US Army's first mechanised infantry combat vehicle. The first production models appeared in 1981, and they were soon being produced at the rate of 600 per year. The hull of the M2 is made of aluminium, with a layer of spaced laminate armour for added protection. The 25mm cannon has a stabiliser to allow for firing on the move. The troop compartment in the rear is fitted with firing ports and periscopes to allow the troops to fire from within the vehicle. Night vision and a nuclear, biological and chemical (NBC) defence system are standard. The Bradley plays a key role in the US Army's combined arms concept, but critics say it is too big, too expensive and too difficult to maintain and is insufficiently armoured to operate with main battle tanks on the battlefield.

Country of origin:	United States
Crew:	3 + 7
Weight:	22,666kg (49,865lb)
Dimensions:	length 6.453m (21ft 2in); width 3.20m (10ft 6in); height; 2.972m (9ft 0in)
Range:	483km (300 miles)
Armour:	classified
Armament:	one Hughes Helicopter 25mm Chain Gun; one 7.62mm coaxial machine gun; two anti-tank launchers.
Powerplant:	one Cummins eight-cylinder diesel, developing 500hp (373kW)
Performance:	maximum road speed 66km/h (41mph); fording amphibious; vertical obstacle 0.914m (3ft); trench 2.54m (8ft 4in)

BMS-1 Alacran

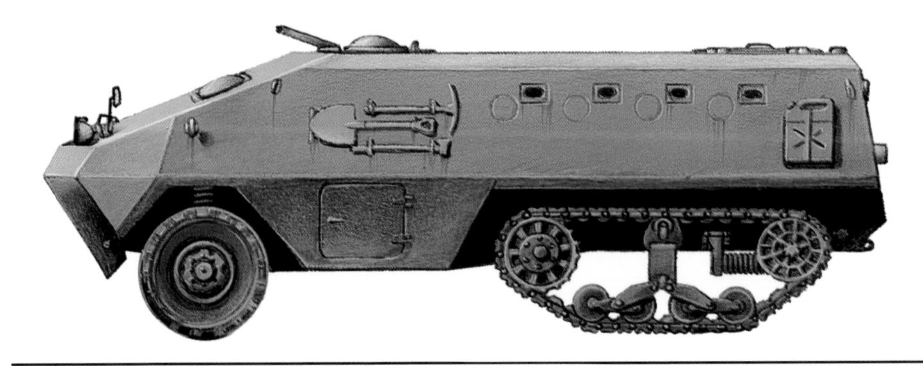

The BMS-1 Alacran is produced by the Chilean Industrias Cardoen company. It is unusual in being a modern armoured personnel carrier in half-track configuration, the product of a cancelled design initiative to update the World War II-era US M-3A1 half-tracks still in service with the Chilean Army. The Alacran can carry 12 fully equipped soldiers. It has an all-welded steel hull with the driver positioned on the front left and the commander just behind. Seven firing ports and eight vision blocks are provided around the troop compartment. Standard armament is a single machine gun, but cannon, ATGW systems and rocket launchers can be fitted.

Country of origin:	Chile
Crew:	2 + 12
Weight:	10,500kg (23,150lb)
Dimensions:	Length: 6.37m (20.9ft); width: 2.38m (7.81ft); height: 2.03m (6.66ft)
Range:	900km (560 miles)
Armour:	Not available
Armament:	1 x 7.62mm (0.3in) or 12.7mm (0.5in) MG
Powerplant:	1 x Cummins V-555 turbo diesel, developing 225hp (167kW) at 3000rpm
Performance:	Maximum road speed: 70km/h (43mph); fording: 1.6m (5.3ft); gradient: 70 percent

Cobra

The Cobra armoured personnel carrier was a Belgian-developed machine. Introduced in the mid-1980s, it was doomed to commercial failure, despite being a sound vehicle in design and operation. It had a nine-man carrying capacity, a steel armoured body, and two main weapons: a 7.62mm (0.3in) GPMG and a roof-mounted Browning M2 HB 12.7mm (0.5in) machine gun. It was fully amphibious without need for modification and had a speed over water of 10km/h (6.2mph), powered by waterjet units located at the rear. Possibly its most distinctive feature was its drive system: a turbo engine powering an electric generator which in turn drove both wheels and waterjets.

Country of origin:	Belgium
Crew:	3 + 9
Weight:	8500kg (18,700lb)
Dimensions:	Length: 4.52m (14.83ft); width: 2.75m (9.02ft); height: 2.32m (7.61ft)
Range:	600km (370 miles)
Armour:	Steel (details classified)
Armament:	1 x 7.62mm (0.3in) GPMG; 1 x Browning M2 HB 12.7mm (0.5in) MG
Powerplant:	1 x Cummins VT-190 6-cylinder turbo diesel, developing 190hp (141kW) at 3300rpm
Performance:	Maximum road speed: 75km/h (46mph); fording: amphibious

Warrior

The Warrior Mechanised Combat Vehicle entered development in 1972 and entered service with the British Army in 1987. The Warrior was part of a movement to change armoured personnel carriers from their role of merely transporting troops to and from the battlefield into a more capable infantry combat vehicle, this concept being inspired by the success of the Soviet BMP. Designed to supplement the FV432, the Warrior is heavier and much more heavily armoured. It is treated as a mobile fire base from which troops can fight, rather than a mere transport vehicle. Variants include a command vehicle, recovery vehicle, engineer and observation vehicle. It has been sold to Kuwait, whose Warriors have anti-tank launchers each side of the turret and air conditioning.

Country of origin:	United Kingdom
Crew:	3 + 7
Weight:	25,700kg (56,540lb)
Dimensions:	length 6.34m (20ft 10in); width 3.034m (10ft); height 2.79m (9ft 2in)
Range:	660km (412 miles)
Armour:	classified
Armament:	one 30mm Rarden cannon; one 7.62mm co-axial machine gun; four smoke dischargers
Powerplant:	one Perkins V-8 diesel engine developing 550hp (410kW)
Performance:	maximum road speed 75km/h (46.8mph); fording 1.3m (4ft 3in); vertical obstacle 0.75m (2ft 5in); trench 2.5m (8ft 2in)

Type 89

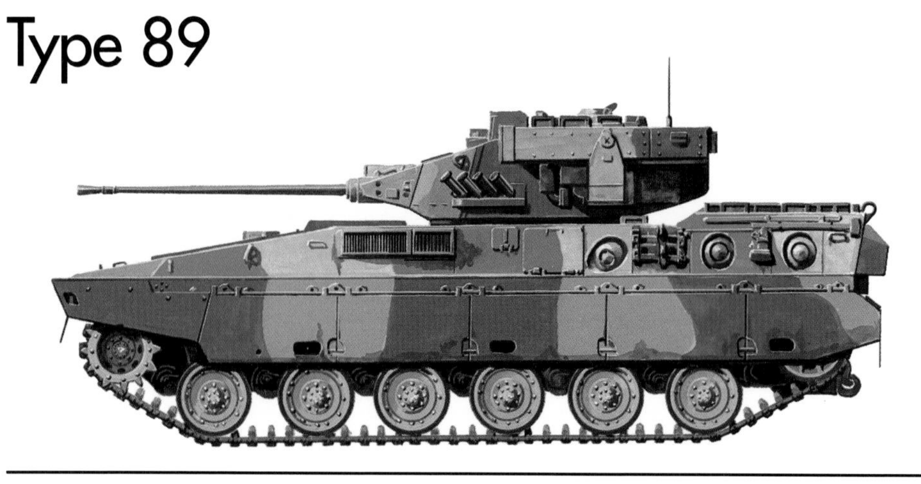

The Mitsubishi Type 89 Mechanised Infantry Combat Vehicle is a true fighting machine. With the dimensions of a small tank, it boasts one 35mm (1.38in) Oerlikon Contraves cannon, a coaxial 7.62mm (0.3in) machine gun, and two preloaded ATGWs (usually Jyu-MAT medium-range missiles). A crew of three man the forward section (which includes the engine) and turret of the vehicle, and seven other combat personnel can be transported in the rear. Six firing ports are provided around the sides and rear of the Type 89 to allow small arms to be deployed against infantry attack. Production of the Type 89 began in 1991, and the vehicle plays a key role in Japanese warfighting strategies.

Country of origin:	Japan
Crew:	3 + 7
Weight:	26,500kg (58,400lb)
Dimensions:	Length: 6.8m (22.3ft); width: 3.2m (10.49ft); height: 2.5m (8.2ft)
Range:	400km (250 miles)
Armour:	Classified
Armament:	1 x 35mm (1.38in) Oerlikon Contraves cannon; 1 x coaxial 7.62mm (0.3in) machine gun; 2 x ATGWs (Jyu-MAT anti-tank missiles)
Powerplant:	1 x 6-cylinder diesel developing 600hp (447kW)
Performance:	Maximum road speed: 70km/h (43mph); fording: 1m (3.3ft); gradient: 60 percent; vertical obstacle: 0.8m (2.6ft); trench: 2.4m (7.9ft)

KIFV K-200

The Korean Infantry Fighting Vehicle K-200 is the first of a series of South Korean fighting vehicles developed by the Dae Woo Industries company. Borrowing from the US AIFV, it has become a powerful and reliable armoured personnel carrier. It can carry nine infantry and its three-man crew into battle at speeds of 74km/h (46mph). In amphibious mode, it achieves 7km/h (4mph) on water, propelled by its tracks. Standard armament is usually two machine guns: a 12.7mm (0.5in) and a 7.62mm (0.3in) weapon. However, optional armament configurations include 20mm (0.78in) Vulcan cannon and two mortar carriers – 81mm (3.19in) and 106mm (4.17in). An NBC reconnaissance variant has recently been developed.

Country of origin:	South Korea
Crew:	3 + 9
Weight:	12,900kg (28,400lb)
Dimensions:	Length: 5.48m (19.15ft); width: 2.84m (9.32ft); height: 2.51m (8.23ft)
Range:	480km (300 miles)
Armour:	Aluminium and steel (details classified)
Armament:	1 x 12.7mm (0.5in) MG; 1 x 7.62mm (0.3in) MG
Powerplant:	1 x MAN D-284T V8 diesel, developing 280hp (208kW) at 2300rpm
Performance:	Maximum road speed: 74km/h (46mph); fording: amphibious; gradient: 60 percent; vertical obstacle: 0.64m (2.1ft); trench: 1.68m (5.51ft)

BMP-3

The BMP-3 entered service in 1990, and is the latest in the BMP range. Classified as an Infantry Combat Vehicle, its extensive armament almost places it in the category of small tank. Its turret boasts a 100mm (3.93in) gun which can fire either conventional shells or AT-10 laser-guided ATGWs. Alongside this weapon is a 30mm (1.18in) cannon, and the turret also bears a 7.62mm (0.3in) PKT coaxial machine gun. Another machine gun is set in the forward hull. Despite the increase in stored ammunition and the consequent extra space this takes up, the BMP-3 takes only one less soldier than the BMP-1 (seven instead of eight), though it is almost a metre (3.3ft) longer.

Country of origin:	USSR
Crew:	3 + 7
Weight:	18,700kg (41,200lb)
Dimensions:	Length: 7.14m (23.42ft); width: 3.23m (10.59ft); height: 2.65m (8.69ft)
Range:	600km (370 miles)
Armour:	Steel (details classified)
Armament:	1 x 100mm (3.93in) gun; 1 x 30mm (1.18in) cannon; 2 x 7.62mm (0.3in) PKT MG
Powerplant:	1 x UTD-29M 10-cylinder diesel, developing 500hp (373kW)
Performance:	Maximum speed: 70km/h (43mph); fording: amphibious; gradient: 60 percent; vertical obstacle: 0.8m (2.6ft); trench: 2.5m (8.2ft)

Bionix 25

The Bionix 25 IFV entered service in 1997 with the Singapore Armoured Forces. It is one of the new generation of armoured combat vehicles – fast, manoeuvrable and with enhanced survivability. The tracked configuration supports six road wheels on each side, and the front-drive system can power the Bionix 25 to a 70km/h (43mph) maximum speed. While the vehicular technology is produced by Singapore Technologies Automotive, the turret-mounted 25mm (0.98in) cannon is from the Boeing Company. This is stabilized for accuracy in rough terrain while a thermal sight enables night firing. Seven infantry can ride in the Bionix 25, access provided by a power-operated ramp in the hull rear.

Country of origin:	Singapore
Crew:	3 + 7
Weight:	23,000kg (50,700lb)
Dimensions:	Length: 5.92m (19.42ft); width: 2.7m (8.86ft); height: 2.53m (8.3ft)
Range:	415km (260 miles)
Armour:	Classified
Armament:	1 x 25mm (0.98in) Boeing M242 cannon; 1 x coaxial 7.62mm (0.3in) MG; 1 x turret-mounted 7.62mm (0.3in) MG; 2 x 3 smoke grenade launchers
Powerplant:	1 x Detroit Diesel Model 6V-92TA diesel, developing 475hp (354kW)
Performance:	Maximum speed: 70km/h (43mph); fording: 1m (3.3ft); gradient: 60 percent; vertical obstacle: 0.6m (2ft); trench: 2m (6.6ft)

VCC-80/Dardo IFV

The Dardo IFV emerged on the world scene in 1998, but is actually derived from an earlier vehicle, the VCC-80 MICV. This entered production 10 years earlier, and is a tracked infantry vehicle armed with a 25mm (0.98in) Oerlikon Contraves KBA cannon. The Dardo is little different. Its main modification lies in the turret, which was adapted to mount TOW anti-tank missiles on either side. Sophisticated technology runs throughout the VCC-80/Dardo, though it has yet to be proven in combat. The armour is of the latest layered aluminium/steel type and laser range-finding and night-vision systems are standard. A highly sloped glacis plate at the front of the vehicle provides maximum deflection against projectiles.

Country of origin:	Italy
Crew:	2 + 7
Weight:	23,000kg (50,700lb)
Dimensions:	Length: 6.7m (21.98ft); width: 3m (9.84ft); height: 2.64m (8.66ft)
Range:	600km (370 miles)
Armour:	Layered aluminium/steel (details classified)
Armament:	1 x 25mm (0.98in) Oerlikon Contraves KBA cannon;1 x 7.62mm (0.3in) coaxial machine gun; 2 x TOW launchers; 2 x 3 smoke grenade launchers
Powerplant:	1 x IVECO 8260 V-6 turbo diesel, developing 520hp (388kW)
Performance:	Maximum speed: 70km/h (43mph); fording: 1.5m (4.9ft); gradient: 60 percent; vertical obstacle: 0.85m (2.79ft); trench: 2.5m (8.2ft)

Morris-Martel

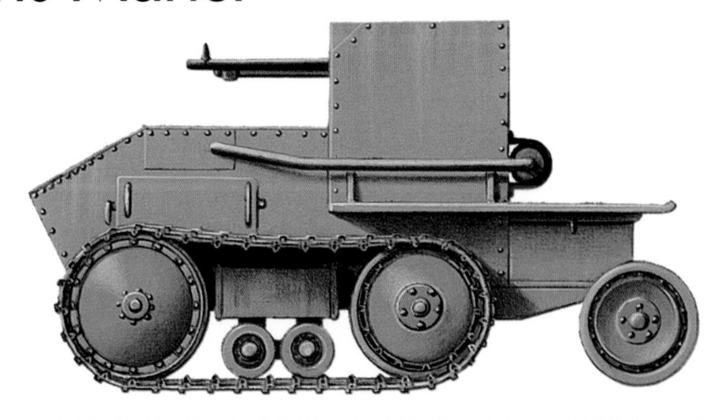

The Morris-Martel emerged from the production facilities of Morris Commercial Motors and the creativity of Sir Gifford le Q. Martel. Martel was impressed by theories of armoured cavalry warfare in the post-WWI period. He subsequently designed a one-man armoured vehicle combining a Maxwell engine and the axle from a Ford truck for use in fast infantry assaults. Steering was done by the rear wheels. The War Office was initially enthused by this idea with the proviso that it became a two-man vehicle (one driver, one machine-gunner). Four prototypes were built by Morris, and eight more in 1927 for an Experimental Armoured Force, but this is as far as Martel's ideas went and the idea was soon dropped.

Country of origin:	United Kingdom
Crew:	2
Weight:	2200kg (4850lb)
Dimensions:	Length: 3m (9.9ft); width: 1.5m (4.9ft); height: 1.6m (5.3ft)
Range:	100km (60 miles)
Armour:	Not applicable
Armament:	1 x 7.92mm (3.1in) MG
Powerplant:	1 x Morris 4-cylinder petrol, developing 16hp (12kW)
Performance:	Maximum road speed: 25km/h (16mph)

Burford-Kegresse

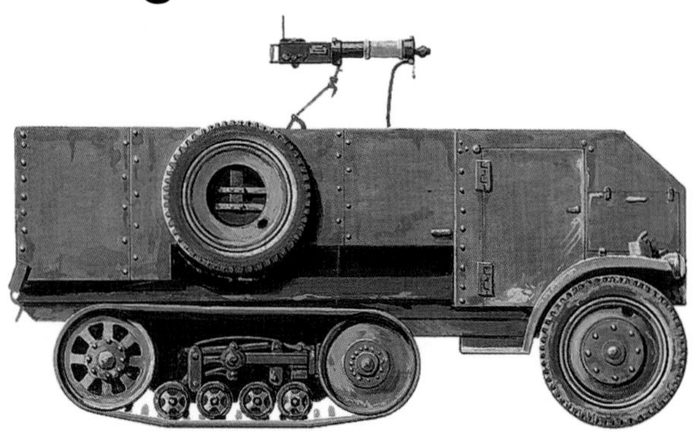

The French Kegresse half-track vehicle impressed many in the British forces with its great strength and sporting achievements. Yet Anglo-French relations dictated that the British would not simply buy French. Instead, Kegresse components were imported into Britain and assembled into similar vehicles at a factory in Slough, England. Three companies were involved in British production: Crossley, Vulcan and Burford. The Burford-Kegresse was directly based on the French M23 model, the tracked section featuring two main drive wheels with four minor wheels in between. The drive track was made of metal-reinforced rubber. The Burford vehicle could hold 12 infantry in addition to the two-man crew.

Country of origin:	United Kingdom
Crew:	2 + 12
Weight:	3500kg (7700lb)
Dimensions:	Length: 4.95m (16.24ft); width: not available; height: 2.1m (6.89ft) approx.
Range:	Not available
Armour:	Not available
Armament:	1 or 2 x Vickers 7.7mm (0.303in) MG
Powerplant:	1 x Burford 6-cylinder petrol
Performance:	Maximum road speed: 35km/h (22mph)

M23

The origins of the M23 lie with Adolphe Kegresse, one of Russia's chief military vehicle engineers, who left to live in France in 1917. There, he began designing a series of half-tracks in cooperation with Citroën, and in 1923 a prototype of the Citroën-Kegresse AMC M23 was unveiled. It used the powerplant of the Citroën B2/10CV, a Kegresse P4 tracked mechanism, and an armoured hull built by Schneider. Kegresse used rubber tracks on the vehicle. The same track system on the Citroën B2/10CV was highly successful in the cross-Sahara desert rally of 1922–23. The M23 was armed with a 37mm (1.46in) SA-18 cannon or a single machine gun. Few were made and they were obsolete by World War II.

Country of origin:	France
Crew:	3
Weight:	2200kg (4850lb)
Dimensions:	Length: 3.4m (11.2ft); width: 1.4m (4.6ft); height: 2.3m (7.6ft)
Range:	200km (125 miles)
Armour:	Not available
Armament:	1 x 37mm (1.46in) SA-18 cannon or 1 x MG
Powerplant:	1 x Citroën 4-cylinder petrol, developing 17hp (13kW)
Performance:	Maximum road speed: 40km/h (25mph)

M28

The M28 was an 'improved' version of Kegresse's earlier M23. In effect, it was simply a larger vehicle, with the length extended out to 4.3m (14ft) and the height reaching 2.4m (8ft). The extended dimensions pushed the weight to 6000kg (13,200lb), and the power plant was upgraded from a four-cylinder engine generating 17hp (13kW) to a six-cylinder version developing 50hp (37kW). Armaments also changed. The M23 alternated between cannon and machine-gun armament, whereas the M28 combined the two. Its turret had a 37mm (1.46in) cannon extending from the rear and a single Hotchkiss machine gun at the front. Though more heavily armed, the M28 remained an impractical combat vehicle.

Country of origin:	France
Crew:	3
Weight:	6000kg (13,200lb)
Dimensions:	Length: 4.3m (14ft); width: 1.7m (5.6ft); height: 2.4m (8ft)
Range:	200km (125 miles)
Armour:	Not available
Armament:	1 x 37mm (1.46in) SA-18 cannon; 1 x 7.7mm (0.31in) MG
Powerplant:	1 x Citroën 6-cylinder petrol, developing 17hp (13kW)
Performance:	Maximum road speed: 45km/h (28mph)

P 107

The P 107 came in two basic variants: an artillery tractor for light field pieces and an engineer tractor. The latter had an open cargo body behind the cab and was used to tow trailers carrying combat engineer equipment. Following the fall of France to the Germans in 1940, the P 107 was pressed into Wehrmacht service, being used to tow field and anti-tank guns. Then the Germans stripped the vehicles of their superstructures and fitted armoured hulls in their place. Most of these conversions remained in France for training purposes and general duties, though they did see combat following the D-Day landings in June 1944. The Germans retained the mounted roller under the nose of the vehicle, which was used to assist the vehicle in and out of ditches.

Country of origin:	France
Crew:	5-7
Weight:	4050kg (8910lb)
Dimensions:	length 4.85m (15ft 10.9in); width 1.80m (5ft 10.9in); height 1.95m (6ft 4.8in)
Range:	400km (248.5 miles)
Armour:	none (original version)
Armament:	none
Powerplant:	one four-cylinder petrol engine developing 55hp (41.0kW)
Performance:	maximum road speed 45km/h (28mph)

SdKfz 2

The SdKfz 2 was developed for use by German infantry and airborne units. It was designed to be an artillery tractor for very light weaponry. Known as the Kettenkrad, the first of these small tractors entered service in 1941. However, by this time German airborne troops were generally being used as regular infantry, so the vehicle's intended role was largely redundant. As a result, the SdKfz 2 was used mainly as a supply vehicle in difficult terrain, where other vehicles could not travel. Their impact was limited by their low cargo capacity and limited production numbers. By 1944, they were seen as an expensive luxury and production ceased. One interesting variant was a high-speed cable-laying vehicle for linking command posts and forward positions.

Country of origin:	Germany
Crew:	3
Weight:	1200kg (2640lb)
Dimensions:	length 2.74m (8ft 11.9in); width 1.00m (3ft 3.4in); height 1.01m (3ft 3.8in)
Range:	100km (62.5 miles)
Armour:	none
Armament:	none
Powerplant:	one Opel Olympia 38 petrol engine developing 36hp (26.8kW)
Performance:	maximum road speed 80km/h (49.7mph)

SdKfz 7

Development of the SdKfz 7 can be traced back to a 1934 requirement for an eight-tonne (7.87 tons) half-track. The vehicle first appeared in 1938 and was destined to be used mainly as the tractor for the 8.8cm flak guns. The vehicle could carry up to 12 men and a considerable quantity of supplies, as well as pulling up to 8000kg (17,600lb). Most were fitted with a winch, and the vehicle was widely admired as a useful vehicle, being also used as a weapons carrier, to particularly good effect with anti-aircraft weapons. They also saw service as observation and command posts for V2 rocket batteries. They were admired even by their enemies, with the British trying to make exact copies of captured vehicles and some vehicles being appropriated for use by the Allies after World War II.

Country of origin:	Germany
Crew:	12
Weight:	11,550kg (25,410lb)
Dimensions:	length 6.85m (20ft 3in); width 2.40m (7ft 10.5in); height 2.62m (8ft 7.1in)
Range:	250km (156 miles)
Armour:	8mm (0.31in)
Armament:	basic version – none.
Powerplant:	one Maybach HL 62 six-cylinder petrol engine developing 140hp (104.4kW)
Performance:	maximum road speed 50km/h (31mph); fording 0.5m (1ft 7in); vertical obstacle 2.0m (6ft 6.7in)

SdKfz 9

The SdKfz 9 was by far the largest of all World War II half-tracks. It originated as a result of a 1936 requirement for a heavy recovery vehicle to operate alongside panzer units. The vehicle was used both for recovery and for towing heavy artillery and bridging units. A weapons-carrying version was produced in 1943 mounting an 8.8cm anti-aircraft gun, where it saw action in Poland and France. The recovery version was fitted with a crane and stabilising legs to allow it to cope with heavy tanks. However, even with an earth spade at the back for extra traction, two SdKfz 9s were generally required to recover tanks such as the massive Tiger, and when the more capable Bergepanther arrived the SdKfz's role was diminished somewhat and therefore production ceased in 1944.

Country of origin:	Germany
Crew:	9
Weight:	18,000kg (39,600lb)
Dimensions:	length 8.25m (27ft 0.8in); width 2.60m (8ft 6in); height 2.76m (9ft 0.7in)
Range:	260km (162 miles)
Armour:	8-14.5mm (0.31-0.57in)
Armament:	none, though sometimes one 8.8cm Flak gun
Powerplant:	one Maybach HL V-12 petrol engine developing 250hp (186.4kW)
Performance:	maximum road speed 50km/h (31mph); fording 0.6m (2ft); vertical obstacle 2.0m (6ft 6.7in)

SdKfz 10/4

The SdKfz 10 was a general light utility vehicle/troop transporter introduced into the German armed forces in 1937. As an artillery tractor, it was used to draw weapons such as the 370mm (14.6in) PaK 35/36 or the 150mm (5.9in) sIG 33 field gun. It could also carry eight fully armed soldiers. Over 17,000 SdKfz 10s were produced between 1938 and the end of World War II, and many variants were designed for combat roles. The SdKfz 10/4, for example, was an anti-aircraft model. It initially mounted a single-barrel 20mm (0.78in) Flak 30 cannon, though many were subsequently upgraded to the Flak 38. The sides and rear of the hull could be folded flat to create an operating platform for the gun crew.

Country of origin:	Germany
Crew:	7
Weight:	4900kg (10,800lb)
Dimensions:	Length: 4.75m (15.58ft); width: 1.93m (6.33ft); height: 1.62m (5.31ft)
Range:	300km (190 miles)
Armour:	(Steel) 14.5mm (0.57in) maximum
Armament:	1 x 20mm (0.78in) Flak 30 or Flak 38 cannon
Powerplant:	1 x Maybach HL 42 TRKM 6-cylinder petrol, developing 100hp (75kW)
Performance:	Maximum road speed: 65km/h (40mph)

SdKfz 11

The first versions of the SdKfz 11 appeared in 1934 and after a series of manufacturing changes, the vehicle entered full production in 1939. Primarily intended as an artillery tractor, it was used initially by 10.5cm howitzer batteries. The vehicle proved so successful that it was later used to tow a wide variety of guns at the expense of heavier purpose-built vehicles, eventually seeing most service with Nebelwerfer batteries to tow the rocket launchers. The vehicle was one of the few to remain in production right through the war, and a number of variants were produced, including two designed specifically for chemical warfare decontamination, but these were not produced in significant numbers as large-scale chemical warfare never occurred during World War II.

Country of origin:	Germany
Crew:	9
Weight:	7100kg (15,620lb)
Dimensions:	length 5.48m (17ft 11.7in); width 1.82m (5ft 11.7in); height 1.62m (5ft 3.8in)
Range:	122km (76 miles)
Armour:	8-14mm (0.31-0.55in)
Armament:	none
Powerplant:	one six-cylinder petrol engine developing 100hp (74.6kW)
Performance:	maximum road speed 53km/h (33mph); fording 0.75m (29.5in); vertical obstacle 2.0m (6ft 6.7in)

SdKfz 250/3

The basic SdKfz 250 was a one-ton half-track with an armoured hull and an open-top crew compartment occupying approximately half of the vehicle. It was one of the first half-tracks used by Germany in World War II, and 6000 were produced during the course of the war. It was conceived as an infantry carrier and support vehicle, and had a crew of six, armed with two 7.92mm (0.31in) MG34 or MG42 machine guns. The first version, the SdKfz 250/1, was only the first among 10 subsequent variants. The SdKfz 250/3 Leichter Funkpanzerwagen was an FuG12-radio vehicle used to control and coordinate motorized units. It was mounted with a large 2m (6.56ft) rod aerial, and later a 2m (6.56ft) star aerial.

Country of origin:	Germany
Crew:	6
Weight:	5340kg (11,775lb)
Dimensions:	Length: 4.56m (14.96ft); width: 1.95m (6.4ft); height: 1.66m (5.45ft)
Range:	350km (220 miles)
Armour:	(Steel) 15mm (0.59in) maximum
Armament:	1 x 7.92mm (0.31in) MG34 MG
Powerplant:	1 x Maybach hL 42 6-cylinder diesel, developing 120hp (89kW) at 3000rpm
Performance:	Maximum road speed: 65km/h (40mph); fording: 0.75m (2.46ft); gradient: 24 percent

SdKfz 251/20

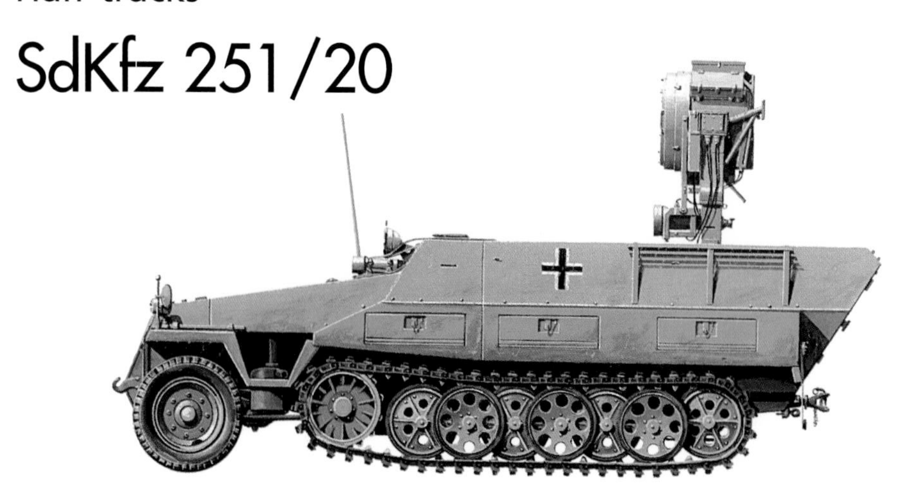

The SdKfz 251/20 was one of the seemingly endless variants of the basic 251 model. Known as the 'Uhu', it was produced towards the end of the World War II and was used mainly on the Eastern Front. Like all the other 251 models, it was designed to operate with, and as part of, the panzer divisions, needing to be speedy, tough and reliable. It carried an infrared searchlight and its primary purpose was to illuminate enemy targets and allow panzer units to attack at night. The fact that the German war machine was still churning out such specialised variants at the end of the war is testament to the durability and excellent qualities of the vehicle. The main searchlight had a 360-degree traverse and could be folded down when not in use. In total around 60 were built before the war ended.

Country of origin:	Germany
Crew:	4
Weight:	7824kg (17,248lb)
Dimensions:	length 5.80m (19ft 0.3in); width 2.10m (6ft 10.7in); height 1.75m (5ft 8.9in)
Range:	300km (186 miles)
Armour:	6-14.5mm (0.23-0.6in)
Armament:	none
Powerplant:	one Maybach six-cylinder petrol engine developing 100hp (74.6kW)
Performance:	maximum road speed 52.5km/h (32.5mph); fording 0.6m (2ft); vertical obstacle 2.0m (6ft 6.7in)

Maultier

German trucks proved totally unable of operating successfully during the first winter of the Russian campaign in 1941-1942. It was thus decided to produce a low-cost half-track to take over many of the trucks' duties. The Wehrmachtsschlepper could not be produced in sufficient numbers to fulfil this need so Opel and Daimler-Benz chassis were fixed to tracked assemblies from PzKpfw II tanks. The new Maultier as it was known was a reasonable success, although lacking the mobility of 'proper' halftracks. By late 1942, the Maultier was being pressed into service as a launch-vehicle for the Nebelwerfer rocket launcher, with over 3000 conversions being ordered by the German Army. In combat Maultiers were organised into Nebelwerfer brigades.

Country of origin:	Germany
Crew:	3
Weight:	7100kg (15,620lb)
Dimensions:	length 6.00m (19ft 8.2in); width 2.20m (7ft 2.6in); height 2.50m (8ft 6in)
Range:	130km (81.25 miles)
Armour:	8-10mm (0.31-0.39in)
Armament:	one 15cm Nebelwerfer (later versions); one 7.92mm machine gun
Powerplant:	one 3.6-litre six-cylinder petrol engine developing 91hp (68kW)
Performance:	maximum road speed 38km/h (30mph); fording 0.6m (2ft); vertical obstacle 2.0m (6ft 6.7in); trench 1m (3ft 3in)

Schwerer Wehrmachtsschlepper

By 1941, the German Army was in need of a medium halftrack, but it had to be economical to produce as the German war machine was already stretched. The Schwerer Wehrmachtsschlepper, or army heavy tractor, was intended for use by infantry units as a general supply vehicle and personnel carrier. To keep costs down, luxuries like a closed cab and rubber-capped tracks were mainly dispensed with. Production was slow, partly due to the lack of priority accorded the vehicle and partly due to the attentions of RAF Bomber Command. However, production continued until the end of the World War II, with a few vehicles seeing service in the post-war Czech Army. Variants included a rocket launcher, anti-aircraft vehicle and a frontline supply vehicle fitted with an armoured cab.

Country of origin:	Germany
Crew:	2
Weight:	13,500kg (29,700lb)
Dimensions:	length 6.68m (21ft 11in); width 2.50m (8ft 2.4in); height 2.83m (9ft 3.4in)
Range:	300km (187 miles)
Armour:	8-15mm (0.31-0.59in)
Armament:	one 3.7cm gun; one 7.92mm machine gun
Powerplant:	one Maybach HL 42 six-cylinder petrol engine developing 100hp (74.6kW)
Performance:	maximum road speed 27km/h (16.8mph); fording 0.6m (2ft); vertical obstacle 2.0m (6ft 6.7in)

Bedford Traclat

The Bedford Tracked Light Artillery Tractor, or 'Traclat', was developed specifically as an artillery tow-vehicle for the 25pdr (87.6mm/3.45in) field gun, the 40mm (1.57in) Bofors anti-aircraft gun, and the 17pdr (76.2mm/3in) anti-tank gun. The Traclat's performance was impressive. Even towing a 25pdr gun weighing 1800kg (4000lb), it could travel at 48km/h (30mph) up a 1 in 30 gradient and even pull the gun up a 1 in 2 gradient. The tracked system enabled the vehicle to cope with muddy or snowy terrain with a ground pressure of only 3.67kg/sq cm (52.9lb/sq in). It was also waterproofed and fitted with air-intake extensions for fording operations. The war ended without the Traclat being tested in action.

Country of origin:	United Kingdom
Crew:	10
Weight:	6812kg (15,020lb)
Dimensions:	Length: 6.4m (20.9ft); width: 2.29m (7.51ft); height: 2.75m (9.02ft)
Range:	322km (200 miles)
Armour:	Not applicable
Armament:	None
Powerplant:	2 x Bedford 3500cc engines, developing 136hp (101kW)
Performance:	Maximum road speed: 48km/h (30mph)

BTR-40

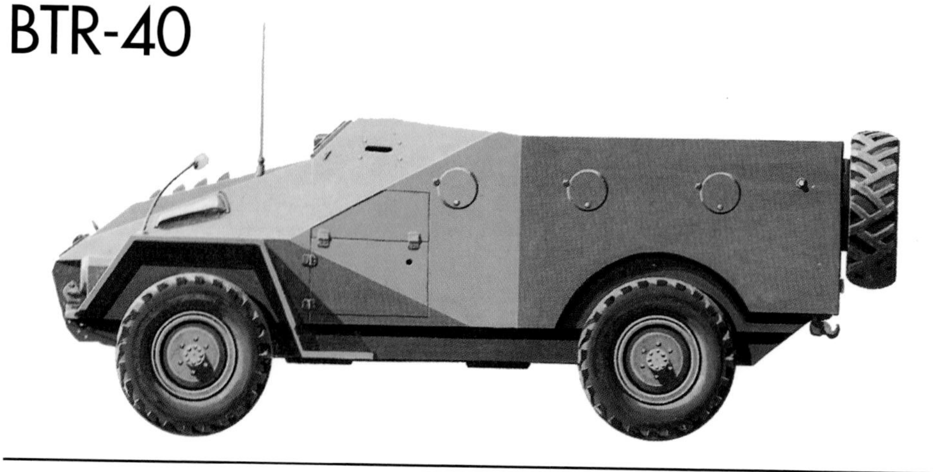

The BTR-40 entered service in 1951. Based on a GAZ-43 4 x 4 truck chassis, it was able to carry eight troops as part of the Soviet doctrine of armoured spearheads supported by mechanised infantry. The vehicle filled a variety of roles such as ambulance, reconnaissance and command vehicle, in addition to being an armoured personnel carrier. The BTR-40 lacked the tyre-pressure regulation system common to many post-World War II Soviet vehicles, nor did it have a nuclear, biological and chemical (NBC) defence system. There was a specialised chemical warfare variant, though, the BTR-40kh, which was used to mark clear lanes through contaminated areas. The BTR-40 was phased out of frontline Red Army service from the late 1950s onwards. It was exported extensively to Soviet client states.

Country of origin:	USSR
Crew:	2 + 8
Weight:	5300kg (11,660lb)
Dimensions:	length 5m (16ft 5in); width 1.9m (6ft 3in); height 1.75m (5ft 9in)
Range:	285km (178 miles)
Armour:	8mm (0.31in)
Armament:	one 7.62mm machine gun
Powerplant:	one GAZ-40 six-cylinder water-cooled petrol engine developing 80hp (60kW)
Performance:	maximum road speed 80km/h (50mph); fording 0.8m (2ft 8in); vertical obstacle 0.47m (1ft 6in); trench 0.7m (2ft 4in)

BTR-152V1

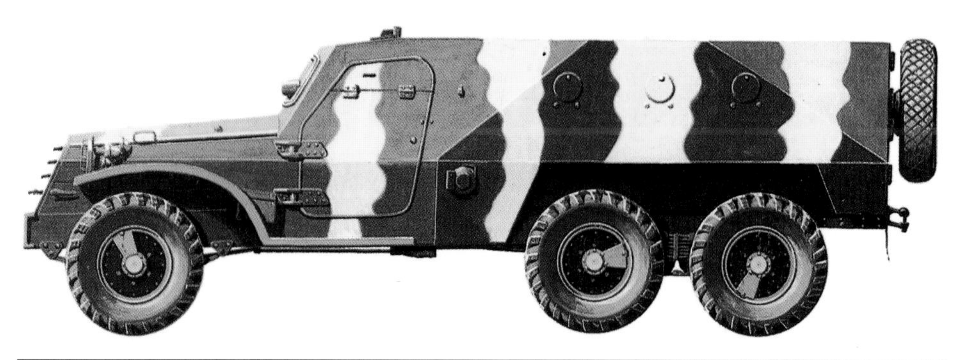

The BTR-152 was one of the first Soviet armoured personnel carriers, as Soviet forces had not used the type during World War II. First seen in public in 1951, the vehicle consisted of a ZIL-157 truck chassis with an armoured body. The main drawback of the early vehicle was the open-topped compartment, which left troops vulnerable to overhead shell bursts. In addition, its cross-country mobility was poor and it had no amphibious capability. Late vehicles have the central tyre pressure regulation system that allows the driver to adjust tyre pressure to suit the terrain being driven on. It was replaced in frontline service in the early 1960s by the BTR-60, but was exported widely to around 30 countries, seeing combat in the Middle East (with Syria, Egypt and Iraq in the Arab-Israeli wars), Africa and the Far East.

Country of origin:	USSR
Crew:	2 + 17
Weight:	8950kg (19,690lb)
Dimensions:	length 6.83m (22ft 4.9in); width 2.32m (7ft 7.3in); height 2.05m (6ft 8.7in)
Range:	780km (485 miles)
Armour:	4-13.5mm (0.15-0.53in)
Armament:	one 7.62mm machine gun
Powerplant:	one ZIL-123 six-cylinder petrol engine developing 110hp (82kW)
Performance:	maximum road speed 75km/h (47mph); fording 0.8m (2ft 7.5in); vertical obstacle 0.6m (1ft 11.6in); trench 0.69m (2ft 3.2in)

Alvis Saracen

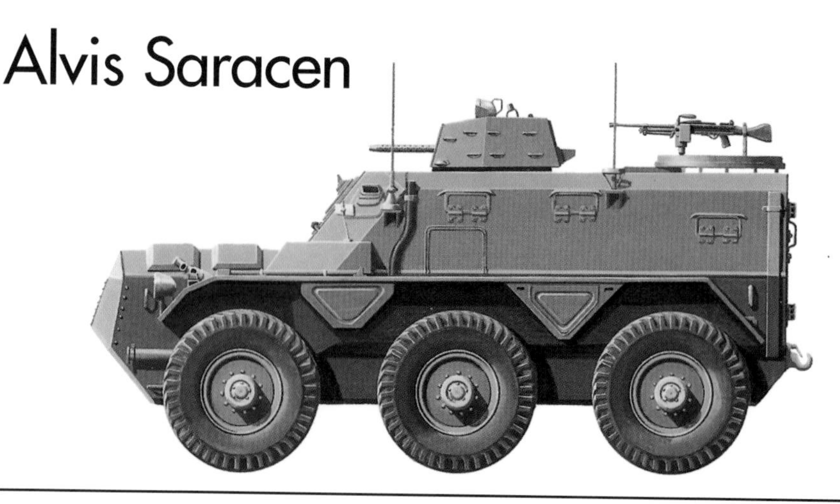

The Saracen was part of the FV600 family of armoured vehicles developed for the British Army after World War II. The Saracen, first produced in 1952, was given priority because of its suitability for use in the guerrilla situation then occurring in Malaya. The vehicle was the only real British armoured personnel carrier in service during the 1950s, but began to be phased out in the 1960s in favour of the FV432 tracked vehicle, with its better armour range and mobility. It remained in service in Northern Ireland, however, into the 1980s, as well as in parts of Africa and the Middle East. It shares many components with the Alvis 6 x 6 Saladin. Variants included an ambulance and command vehicle, but radar-carrying, self-propelled gun and mine-clearing versions never entered service.

Country of origin:	United Kingdom
Crew:	2 + 10
Weight:	8640kg (19,008lb)
Dimensions:	length 5.233m (17ft 2in); width 2.539 (8ft 4in); height 2.463m (8ft 1in)
Range:	400km (248 miles)
Armour:	16mm (0.62in)
Armament:	two 7.62mm machine guns
Powerplant:	one Rolls-Royce B80 Mk 6A eight-cylinder petrol engine developing 160hp (119kW)
Performance:	maximum road speed 72km/h (44.7mph); fording 1.07m (3ft 6in); vertical obstacle 0.46m (1ft 6in); trench 1.52m (5ft 0in)

MOWAG

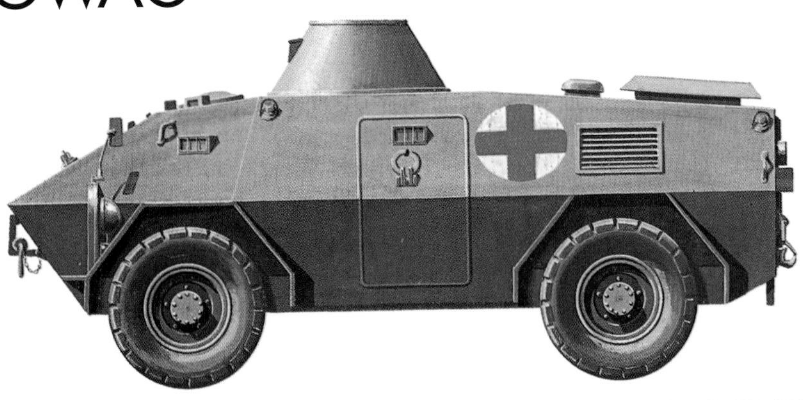

The MOWAG was designed by Kreuzlingen for easy conversion to a number of diverse roles, such as ambulance, command vehicle or armoured personnel carrier. The MOWAG entered production in 1964, and its small size (there was only room for three troops in the rear, plus the commander, machine gunner and driver) proved ideal for internal security duties, particularly when fitted with a blade for clearing obstacles, a public address system and wire mesh protection for the vision blocks and headlamps. The vehicle was also available with bullet-proof tyres (with metal disks attached to the outside of the tyre). Export customers included Greece, Argentina, Bolivia, Chile and Iraq, all of which no doubt saw the vehicle's value in internal suppression.

Country of origin:	Switzerland
Crew:	3 + 3
Weight:	8200kg (18,040lb)
Dimensions:	length 5.31m (17ft 5in); width 2.2m (7ft 3in); height 1.88m (6ft 2in)
Range:	400km (248 miles)
Armour:	8mm (0.31in)
Armament:	one 12.7mm or 7.62mm machine gun
Powerplant:	one V-8 four-stroke water-cooled petrol engine developing 202hp (151kW)
Performance:	maximum road speed 80km/h (50mph); fording 1.1m (3ft 7in); vertical obstacle 0.4m (1ft 4in); trench not applicable

OT-64C(1)

The OT-64 was Czechoslovakia and Poland's answer to the Soviet BTR-60. The OT-64 entered service in 1964, with the advantage over its Soviet counterpart of having a fully enclosed compartment for troops and being diesel, rather than petrol-powered, which extended range and reduced the risk of fire. It was heavier, though, with a lower power-to-weight ratio. Fully amphibious with two propellers, entry was through the rear, and a winch, nuclear, biological and chemical (NBC) defence system and night vision capability were fitted as standard. There were command and recovery variants and some OT-64s were adapted for anti-aircraft and anti-tank capability, the latter being fitted with 'Sagger' anti-tank guided weapons. North African and Middle East countries were the main export customers.

Country of origin:	Czechoslovakia/Poland
Crew:	2 + 15
Weight:	14,500kg (31,900lb)
Dimensions:	length 7.44m (24ft 5in); width 2.55m (8ft 4.4in); height 2.06m (6ft 9in)
Range:	710km (441 miles)
Armour:	10mm (0.39in)
Armament:	one 7.62mm machine gun
Powerplant:	one Tatra V-8 diesel engine developing 180hp (134kW)
Performance:	maximum road speed 94.4km/h (59mph); fording amphibious; vertical obstacle 0.5m (1ft 7.7in); trench 2m (6ft 7in)

UR-416

The UR-416 was developed from the chassis of the civilian Unimog 4 x 4 which appeared in the 1950s. Work on the military version began in the early 1960s and production began in 1966. The UR-416 was a relatively inexpensive vehicle, easy to maintain and operate. Room was provided for eight troops in the rear compartment and there were firing ports to allow them to use their weapons from inside. Variants included a command vehicle, repair vehicle and an ambulance. The UR-416 has been widely exported, particularly to Africa and South America and is used by several European countries for such duties as airport security and riot control, the vehicles being fitted with public address systems, fire extinguishers and blades for removing obstacles when on anti-riot duties.

Country of origin:	West Germany
Crew:	2 + 8
Weight:	7600kg (16,720lb)
Dimensions:	length 5.21m (17ft 1in); width 2.30m (7ft 6.5in); height 2.225m (7ft 3.6in)
Range:	700km (435 miles)
Armour:	9mm (0.35in)
Armament:	one 7.62mm machine gun
Powerplant:	one Daimler-Benz OM 352 six-cylinder diesel engine developing 120hp (89kW)
Performance:	maximum road speed 85km/h (53mph); fording 1.4m (4ft 7in); vertical obstacle 0.55m (1ft 9.7in); trench not applicable

PSZH-IV

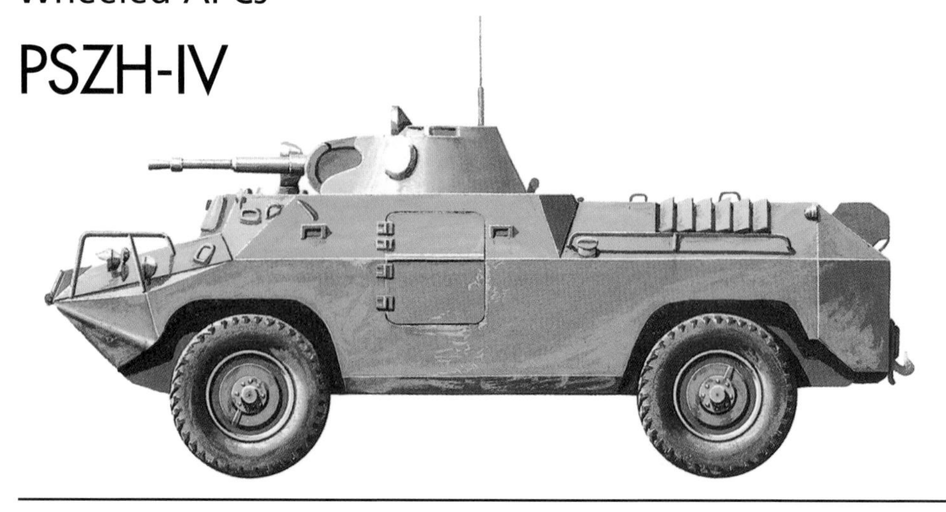

The PSZH-IV was a development of the FUG 4 x 4 amphibious scout car designed for the Hungarian Army in the early 1960s. Appearing in the mid-1960s (when it was thought by the West to be a reconnaissance vehicle), the vehicle was of all-welded steel construction and was a fully amphibious armoured personnel carrier, being propelled in water by two water jets and able to carry six troops (though their only means of exit and entry are via the small two-part door in each side of the hull). It was equipped with a tyre-pressure regulation system, nuclear, biological and chemical (NBC) defence system and infrared night-vision equipment. Variants included a command vehicle, ambulance and a NBC reconnaissance vehicle. It is in service with the armies of Bulgaria, Hungary, the Czech Republic and Iraq.

Country of origin:	Hungary
Crew:	3 + 6
Weight:	7500kg (16,500lb)
Dimensions:	length 5.70m (18ft 8.4in); width 2.50m (8ft 2.4in); height 2.30m (7ft 7in)
Range:	500km (311 miles)
Armour:	14mm (0.55in)
Armament:	one 14.5mm machine gun; one coaxial 7.62mm machine gun
Powerplant:	one Caspel four-cylinder diesel engine developing 100hp (74.57kW)
Performance:	maximum road speed 80km/h (50mph); fording amphibious; vertical obstacle 0.4m (1ft 3.7in); trench 0.6m (1ft 11.6in)

Panhard M3

The Panhard M3 remains one of the world's most successful armoured personnel carriers, if only for its massive export sales to over 35 countries with particular concentrations in Africa and the Middle East. There is little exceptional about the M3, and consequently it is ideal for transforming into local variants. It is a 4x4 armoured vehicle which can carry 10 men as well as a two-man crew, and negotiate rough terrain with confidence. Access and exit are through two side and two rear doors. It is fully amphibious, and can maintain 4km/h (2.5mph) in water, propelled by its wheels. The many M3 variants include engineer vehicles, anti-aircraft vehicles, an ambulance and radar versions.

Country of origin:	France
Crew:	2 + 10
Weight:	6100kg (13,450lb)
Dimensions:	Length: 4.45m (14.59ft); width: 2.55m (8.37ft); height: 2m (6.56ft)
Range:	600km (370 miles)
Armour:	12mm (0.47in) maximum
Armament:	Various
Powerplant:	1 x Panhard M4 HD 4-cylinder petrol, developing 90hp (67kW)
Performance:	Maximum road speed: 90km/h (56mph); fording: amphibious; gradient: 60 percent; vertical obstacle: 0.3m (1ft); trench: 0.8m (2.6ft)

Grenadier

The MOWAG Grenadier was an armoured car/armoured personnel carrier from the late 1960s and early 1970s which demonstrated multi-tasking in military vehicles. As an APC, it could carry eight personnel plus the driver, protecting them from small-arms fire. Even bullet-proof tyres could be fitted. It was fully amphibious, powered by a three-blade propeller. Extensive weapons fittings made it a purposeful combat vehicle. Options included a turret-mounted 20mm (0.78in) cannon, 80mm (3.15in) multiple rocket launchers, various anti-tank weapons and remote-control 7.62mm (0.3in) machine guns. The Grenadier series was effectively replaced by MOWAG's Piranha series of armoured cars in the 1980s.

Country of origin:	Switzerland
Crew:	1 + 8
Weight:	6100kg (13,450lb)
Dimensions:	Length: 4.84m (15.88ft); width: 2.3m (7.54ft); height: 2.12m (6.96ft)
Range:	550km (340 miles)
Armour:	Not disclosed
Armament:	Various (see text)
Powerplant:	1 x MOWAG 8-cylinder petrol, developing 202hp (150kW) at 3900rpm
Performance:	Maximum road speed: 100km/h (62mph)

BTR-60PB

The BTR-60 was introduced into Red Army service in the late 1960s to replace the BTR-152. The early BTR-60s still had an open-topped compartment, but this was soon remedied. The vehicle was fully amphibious and was propelled in water by a single water jet. It carried 14 troops, who were able to fight from inside the vehicle by means of firing ports, but who had to enter and exit the vehicle through roof hatches, with the obvious exposure to danger that this carried. Exported to over 30 countries, the BTR-60 has seen action in many parts of the world, having an integral role in protecting Soviet convoys in Afghanistan during the Russian occupation of the country, and even taking on the Americans during the invasion of Grenada in 1983, although they were quickly knocked out.

Country of origin:	USSR
Crew:	2 + 14
Weight:	10,300kg (22,660lb)
Dimensions:	length 7.56m (24ft 9.6in); width 2.825m (9ft 3.2in); height 2.31m (7ft 6.9in)
Range:	500km (311 miles)
Armour:	7-9mm (0.27-0.35in)
Armament:	one 12.7mm machine gun; two 7.62mm machine guns
Powerplant:	two GAZ-49B six-cylinder petrol engines, each developing 90hp (67kW)
Performance:	maximum road speed 80km/h (50mph); fording amphibious; vertical obstacle 0.4m (1ft 3.7in); trench 2m (6ft 7in)

TAB-72

The TAB-72 made its first appearance in 1972 and still forms an antiquated part of the Romanian and Serbian military. It is a reasonably straightforward copy of the 8x8 Soviet BTR-60PB. The main difference is that the TAB-72's two engines are capable of generating 140hp (104kW) instead of the Soviet vehicle's 90hp (67kW), an extra output which dramatically improves the TAB-72's cross-country mobility. Like the BTR-60PB, the TAB-72 features a frontal turret mounting two machine guns – a 14.5mm (0.57in) KPV and a 7.62mm (0.3in) PKT. These are used to engage both aerial and ground targets. The only variant of the TAB-72 is a mortar carrier, which carries an 82mm (3.23in) mortar.

Country of origin:	Romania
Crew:	3 + 8
Weight:	11,000kg (24,300lb)
Dimensions:	Length: 7.22m (23.69ft); width: 2.83m (9.28ft); height: 2.7m (8.8ft)
Range:	500km (310 miles)
Armour:	9mm (0.35in)
Armament:	1 x 14.5mm (0.57in) KPV MG; 1 x 7.62mm (0.3in) PKT MG
Powerplant:	2 x 6-cylinder petrol, developing 140hp (104kW) each
Performance:	Maximum road speed: 95km/h (60mph); fording: amphibious; gradient: 60 percent; vertical obstacle: 0.4m (1.3ft); trench: 2m (6.6ft)

VXB-170

The VXB-170 was a 4x4 armoured personnel carrier developed by the French military truck manufacturer Berliet in the mid-1960s. It went into production in 1973. It mainly went into service with the French gendarmerie, who found it a useful multi-purpose armoured vehicle ideally suited for security use. The VXB-170 is a 4x4 fully amphibious APC with a carrying capacity of 12 or 13 soldiers. Windows are bullet-proofed and can be opened to provide firing-ports if necessary. Four roof hatches and three side doors provide multiple entry and exit routes. An optional feature was a 4500kg (9900lb) capacity winch which could be installed in the front of the hull.

Country of origin:	France
Crew:	12
Weight:	12,700kg (28,000lb)
Dimensions:	Length: 5.99m (19.65ft); width: 2.5m (8.2ft); height: 2.05m (6.73ft)
Range:	750km (470 miles)
Armour:	7mm (0.28in)
Armament:	1 x 7.62mm (0.3in) MG
Powerplant:	1 x Berliet V800M 8-cylinder diesel, developing 170hp (127kW)
Performance:	Maximum road speed: 85km/h (53mph); fording: amphibious; gradient: 60 percent

EE-11

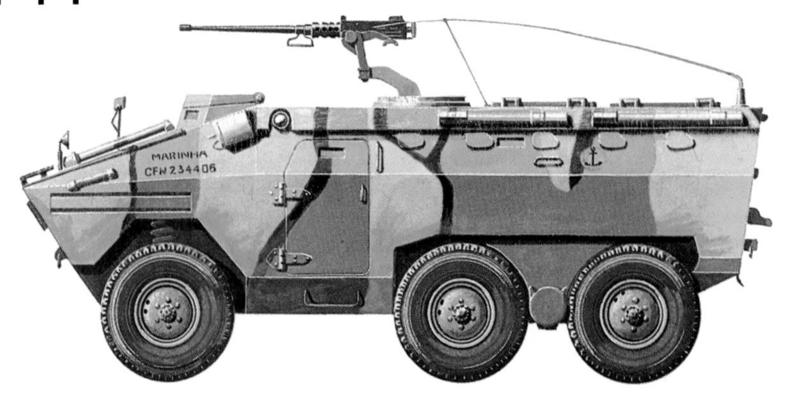

In 1970, ENGESA began work on an armoured 6 x 6 wheeled vehicle in response to a Brazilian armed forces requirement. Production of the Urutu armoured personnel vehicle began in 1974. The vehicle was fully amphibious, being fitted with a trim vane, bilge pumps and two propellers. The Urutu was fitted with tyre-pressure regulation system, night vision and nuclear, biological and chemical (NBC) defence system and could carry up to 12 troops in the rear (who exit via doors in each side and one in the rear). Firing ports were available to allow these troops to fight from within the vehicle. Variants included an ambulance, cargo-transport, command vehicle, anti-aircraft and anti-tank versions, the latter being fitted with Milan or HOT anti-tank guided weapons.

Country of origin:	Brazil
Crew:	1 + 12
Weight:	13,000kg (28,600lb)
Dimensions:	length 6.15m (20ft 2in); width 2.59 (8ft 6in); height 2.09m (6ft 10.3in)
Range:	850km (528 miles)
Armour:	classified
Armament:	one 12.7mm machine gun; one 7.62mm machine gun
Powerplant:	one Detroit Diesel 6V-53N six-cylinder diesel engine developing 212hp (158kW)
Performance:	maximum road speed 90km/h (56mph); fording amphibious; vertical obstacle 0.6m (1ft 11.6in); trench not applicable

TM 125

In spite of its small appearance, the TM 125 can carry 12 personnel, the passengers sitting five abreast down each side of the hull. The hull features a total of six firing ports, while vision for driver and commander is provided by two windows. Armoured shutters can be closed over the windows if necessary. Operational durability is enhanced by using run-flat tyres – even with all tyres totally deflated the TM 125 can maintain 40km/h (25mph) for distances up to 80km (50 miles). TM 125s come with a variety of armament options, including Rheinmetall 20mm (0.78in) cannon and TOW ATGWs. The vehicle is also fully amphibious, powered by two propellers mounted at the rear of the hull and steered by the front wheels.

Country of origin:	West Germany
Crew:	2 + 10
Weight:	7600kg (16,800lb)
Dimensions:	Length: 5.54m (18.18ft); width: 2.46m (8.07ft); height: 2.01m (6.59ft)
Range:	700km (430 miles)
Armour:	Not available
Armament:	Optional
Powerplant:	1 x Daimler-Benz OM 352 4-cylinder turbo diesel, developing 125hp (93kW)
Performance:	Maximum road speed: 85km/h (53mph); fording: amphibious; gradient: 80 percent; vertical obstacle: 0.55m (1.8ft)

VAB

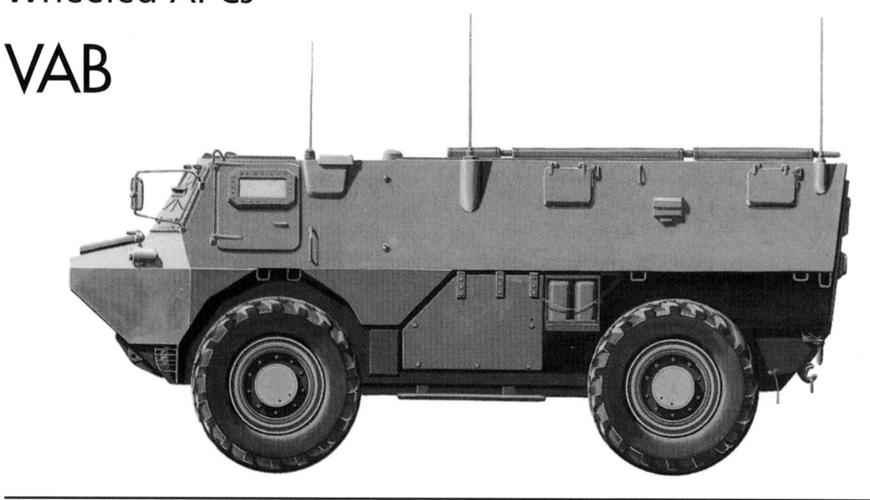

In 1974 Renault was selected to build a wheeled armoured personnel carrier to complement the AMX-10 tracked vehicle being issued to infantry battalions. Produced in 4 x 4 and 6 x 6 versions, the vehicle is fully amphibious being propelled in water either by its wheels or by twin water jets. A nuclear, biological and chemical (NBC) defence system and night-vision capability are fitted as standard. Variants include an ambulance, internal security vehicle, command vehicle, anti-tank and mortar carrier. The vehicle has sold well abroad, in North Africa and the Middle East, in countries where France has a major influence, and in particular in Morocco, where it has been used in a counter-insurgency role against Polisario guerrillas. The VAB is a very rugged vehicle.

Country of origin:	France
Crew:	2 + 10
Weight:	13,000kg (28,660lb)
Dimensions:	length 5.98m (19ft 7.4in); width 2.49m (8ft 2in); height 2.063m (6ft 9in)
Range:	1000km (621 miles)
Armour:	classified
Armament:	one 7.62mm machine gun
Powerplant:	one MAN six-cylinder inline diesel engine developing 235hp (175kW)
Performance:	maximum road speed 92km/h (57mph); fording amphibious; vertical obstacle 0.6m (2ft); trench not applicable

Casspir

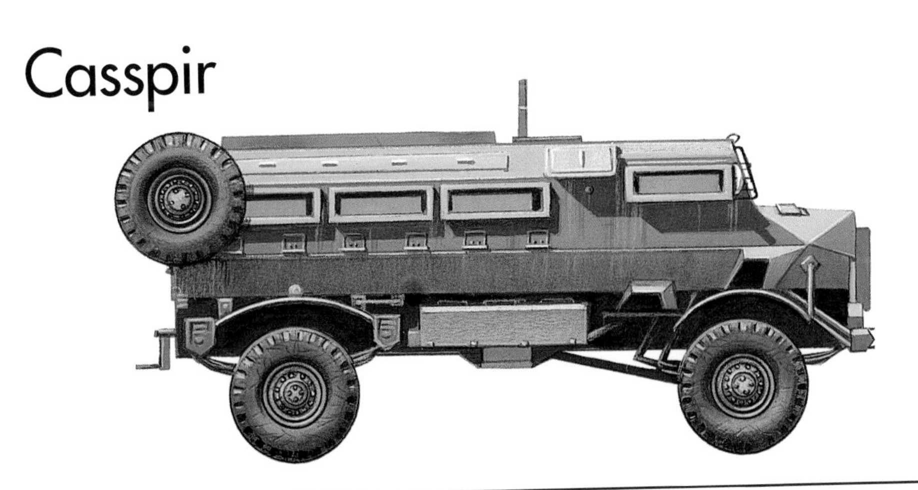

After more than 20 years of service, the Casspir remains one of South Africa's most dependable armoured personnel carriers. It is instantly recognizable by its high ground clearance of 0.41m (1.35ft) at the axles. This is part of the Casspir's defence against anti-tank mines. Also, the belly of the hull is V-shaped to deflect any explosive forces away from the troop compartment. To suit the rough South African terrain the Casspir has a long-range fuel tank for an 850km (530 mile) maximum range. It also contains a drinking water tank. Since its introduction, the Casspir has been heavily used for security and riot control work. Consequently all windows have protective shutters and rubber bullet and CS gas launchers can be fitted.

Country of origin:	South Africa
Crew:	2 + 10
Weight:	12,580kg (27,700lb)
Dimensions:	Length: 6.87m (22.54ft); width: 2.5m (8.2ft); height: 2.85m (9.35ft)
Range:	850km (530 miles)
Armour:	Steel (details classified)
Armament:	1–3 x 7.62mm (0.3in) MGs
Powerplant:	1 x ADE-325T 6-cylinder diesel, developing 170hp (127kW) at 2800rpm
Performance:	Maximum road speed: 90km/h (56mph); fording: 1m (3.3ft); gradient: 65 percent; vertical obstacle: 0.5m (1.6ft); trench: 1.06m (3.48ft)

Panhard VCR

The VCR is another fine addition to Panhard's range of military vehicles. It comes in 6x6 or 4x4 configurations. The 6x6 version can raise its centre tyres when on roads or hard surfaces to reduce tyre wear and improve fuel efficiency. When off-road, the central tyres are then lowered to improve traction and mobility. All VCRs are fully amphibious. They are propelled by their wheels in the water, though the VCR/TT version has two waterjets, one either side of the hull. Like all Panhard vehicles, the VCR has numerous variants. As well as SAM, ATGW, command post, ambulance and repair vehicle variants, the VCR can be fitted with NBC protection and night-vision devices.

Country of origin:	France
Crew:	3 + 9
Weight:	7000kg (15,400lb)
Dimensions:	Length: 4.57m (14.99ft); width: 2.49m (8.17ft); height: 2.03m (6.66ft)
Range:	800km (500 miles)
Armour:	(Steel) 12mm (0.47in)
Armament:	1 x 7.62mm (0.3in) MG
Powerplant:	1 x Peugeot PRV 6-cylinder petrol, developing 145hp (108kW) at 5500rpm
Performance:	Maximum road speed: 100km/h (62mph); fording: amphibious; gradient: 60 percent; vertical obstacle: 0.8m (2.6ft); trench: 1.1m (3.6ft)

Ratel 20

The Ratel was designed by the South Africans to replace the British Saracen, when it became clear that political considerations might place future supplies in jeopardy. The prototype appeared in 1976, with the first production vehicles arriving just a year later. Designed specifically for South African needs, the vehicle has an exceptional range (needed for large-scale anti-guerrilla operations in the vast expanses of Africa) with excellent mobility, armour and firepower. It has seen combat extensive service, being used for counter-insurgency raids in Namibia and Angola, and has been exported to Morocco for similar duties. Variants include the Ratel 60, which is equipped with a 60mm mortar, the Ratel 90, which mounts the 90mm gun, and the Ratel repair, which is optimised for field repairs.

Country of origin:	South Africa
Crew:	4 + 7
Weight:	19,000kg (41,800lb)
Dimensions:	length 7.212m (23ft 8.4in); width 2.516m (8ft 3in); height 2.915m (9ft 6.8in)
Range:	1000km (621 miles)
Armour:	20mm (0.78in)
Armament:	one 20mm cannon; two 7.62mm machine guns
Powerplant:	one D 3256 BTXF six-cylinder diesel engine developing 282hp (210kW)
Performance:	maximum road speed 105km/h (65mph); fording 1.2m (3ft 11.2in); vertical obstacle 0.35m (1ft 1.7in); trench 1.15m (3ft 9.3in)

BMR-600

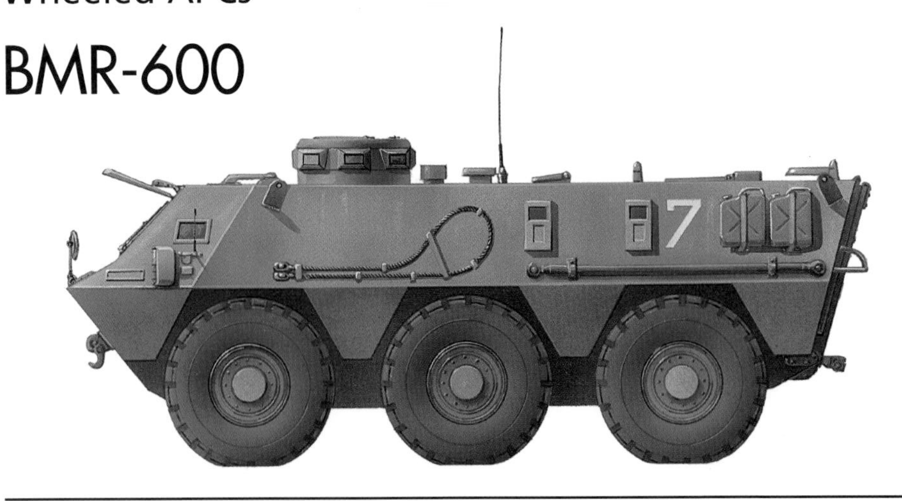

The BMR-600 infantry fighting vehicle was developed for the Spanish Army during the 1970s, and has gone on to see export service in Egypt, Saudi Arabia and Peru. In many ways it is a conventional armoured personnel carrier. It is fully amphibious with two waterjets providing propulsion from the rear of the hull. Lightweight aluminium armour provides protection from small-arms fire and shell splinters for the two crew members and 11 other occupants. A cupola on the roof provides a weapon mount. In the Spanish Army, a 12.7mm (0.5in) Browning M2 HB is fitted as standard, though a 20mm (0.78in) cannon is optional. Other combat versions of the BMR-600 include ATGW launcher and 81mm (3.19in) mortar carrier.

Country of origin:	Spain
Crew:	2 + 11
Weight:	14,000kg (30,900lb)
Dimensions:	Length: 6.15m (20.18ft); width: 2.5m (8.2ft); height: 2m (6.6ft)
Range:	1000km (620 miles)
Armour:	(Aluminium) 38mm (1.49in) estimated
Armament:	1 x 12.7mm (0.5in) Browning M2 HB
Powerplant:	1 x Pegaso 9157/8 6-cylinder diesel, developing 310hp (231kW) at 2200rpm
Performance:	Maximum road speed: 103km/h (64mph); fording: amphibious; gradient: 60 percent; vertical obstacle: 0.6m (2ft); trench: 1.35m (4.43ft)

Tatrapan

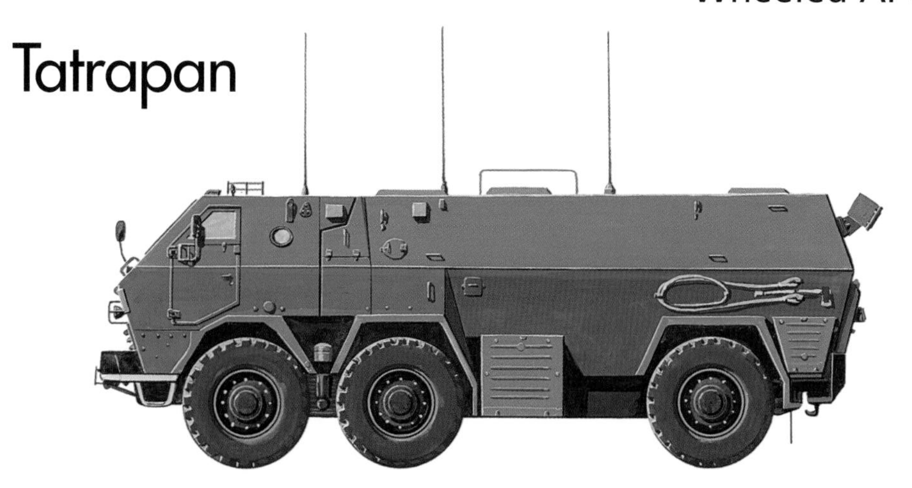

The Tatrapan is a 6x6 armoured personnel vehicle designed around the chassis of the TATRA T-815 VP 21 265 truck. It is one of the larger vehicles on the APC market, 8.46m (27.76ft) long and able to carry 11 fully equipped soldiers as well as the two-man crew. The armoured body is of all-welded steel construction. For entry and exit to and from the troop compartment there is one hatch each side between the second and third wheels, two hatches in the roof, and a hatch at the hull rear. The side and rear hatches are all fitted with firing ports. An NBC system is fitted as standard to the Tatrapan. Apart from use with the Czech and Slovakian armed forces, the Tatrapan is used by several Middle Eastern countries.

Country of origin:	Czechoslovakia
Crew:	2 + 11
Weight:	20,600kg (45,400lb)
Dimensions:	Length: 8.46m (27.76ft); width: 2.5m (8.2ft); height: 2.75m (9.02ft)
Range:	850km (530 miles)
Armour:	Steel (details classified)
Armament:	1 x 12.7mm (0.5in) MG; 1 x 7.62mm (0.3in) MG
Powerplant:	1 x Tatra T3-930-51 12-cylinder diesel, developing 355hp (265kW)
Performance:	Maximum road speed: 70km/h (43mph); gradient: 60 percent

BTR-70

The BTR-70 is essentially an improved BTR-60. Its hull is slightly longer than that of the BTR-60, and it features triangular access doors to the troop compartment on both sides, set between the second and third axles. Two roof hatches provide additional access. The troop compartment holds nine infantrymen sitting back to back along a central bench. Three firing ports and a vision block are on each side of the compartment. The two-man crew sit towards the front of the vehicle, and each has three forward and one side-facing periscope. Armament is confined to the small forward turret, and consists of one 14.5mm (0.57in) KPVT machine gun with a coaxial 7.62mm (0.3in) machine gun.

Country of origin:	USSR
Crew:	2 + 9
Weight:	11,500kg (25,400lb)
Dimensions:	Length: 7.53m (24.7ft); width: 2.8m (9.19ft); height: 2.23m (7.32ft)
Range:	600km (370 miles)
Armour:	Steel (details classified)
Armament:	1 x 14.5mm (0.57in) KPVT MG; 1 x coaxial PKT 7.62mm (0.3in) MG
Powerplant:	1 x ZMZ-4905 8-cylinder petrol, developing 240hp (179kW) at 2100rpm
Performance:	Maximum road speed: 80km/h (50mph); fording: amphibious; gradient: 60 percent; vertical obstacle: 0.7m (2.3ft); trench: 2.7m (8.9ft)

Chaimite V-200

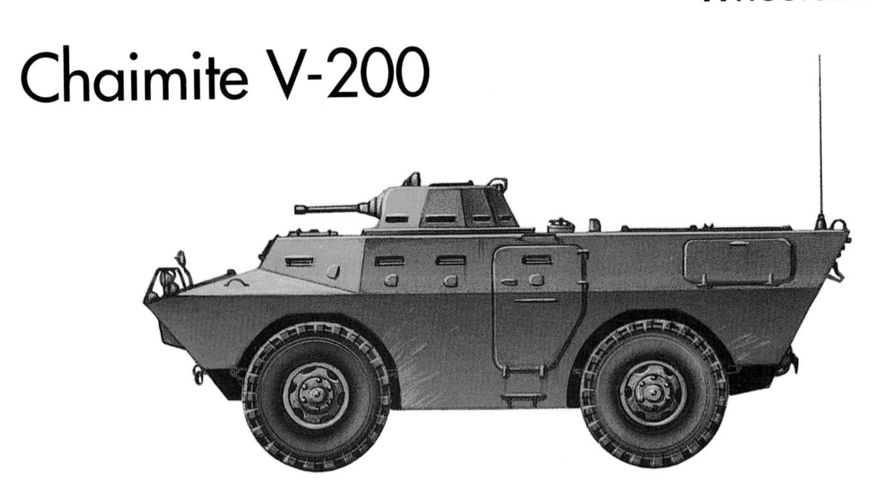

The BRAVIA Chaimite armoured personnel carrier was a Portuguese-licensed version of the US Cadillac Gage Commando V-150 armoured car. It is a 4x4 vehicle with the usual amphibious capabilities and a steel armoured hull. Carrying capacity is nine soldiers. The V-200 is one of nine versions of the Chaimite available, each distinguished usually by its armament. The V-200 is armed simply with twin turret-mounted 7.62mm (0.3in) machine guns. Subsequent versions go up in denominations of 100. The V-400, for example, is fitted with a 90mm (3.54in) cannon, whereas the V-700 is armed with ATGW systems. Recently, 6x6 and 8x8 prototype versions of the Chaimite have been produced.

Country of origin:	Portugal
Crew:	2 + 9
Weight:	7300kg (16,100lb)
Dimensions:	Length: 5.6m (18.37ft); width: 2.26m (7.41ft); height: 2.26m (7.41ft)
Range:	950km (590 miles)
Armour:	(Steel) 7.94mm (0.31in) maximum
Armament:	2 x 7.62mm (0.3in) MGs
Powerplant:	1 x M75 V8 petrol, developing 210hp (157kW)
Performance:	Maximum road speed: 110km/h (68mph); fording: amphibious; gradient: 65 percent; vertical obstacle: 0.9m (2.9ft)

Fiat OTO Melara Type 6614

The Type 6614 is a typical modern armoured personnel carrier. It entered production in 1979 with Fiat and Otobreda, and is still used today in countries as divergent as South Korea, Argentina and Tunisia. It has an armoured hull 6–8mm (0.24–0.31in) thick, enough to protect it from small-arms fire and shell splinters. Firing ports are located in the doors and along the hull, and each has its own vision block situated just above. These allow the 10 soldiers and one crew member to put out heavy fire from inside the vehicle if necessary. Outside there is a roof hatch-mounted 12.7mm (0.5in) machine gun. Specialist equipment includes wheel-arch fire extinguishers and night-vision equipment.

Country of origin:	Italy
Crew:	1 + 10
Weight:	8500kg (18,700lb)
Dimensions:	Length: 5.86m (19.23ft); width: 2.5m (8.2ft); height: 1.78m (5.84ft)
Range:	700km (430 miles)
Armour:	(Steel) 6–8mm (0.24–0.31in)
Armament:	1 x 12.7mm (0.5in) MG
Powerplant:	1 x Fiat 8062.24 6-cylinder turbo diesel, developing 160hp (119kW)
Performance:	Maximum road speed: 100km/h (62mph); fording: amphibious; gradient: 60 percent; vertical obstacle: 0.4m (1.3ft)

TPz-1 Fuchs

Nearly 1000 Transportpanzer 1 Fuchs have been delivered to the German Army alone. Export versions are used in the UK, the US (both of whom bought the specialist NBC reconnaissance variant for the first Gulf War), Israel, the Netherlands, Venezuela and several other countries. Built by Henschel Wehrtechnik, this vehicle was selected from a long series of prototype German armoured personnel carriers developed throughout the 1960s and 1970s. It is a fully amphibious 6x6 vehicle with space for carrying 10 soldiers in a rear troop compartment. In water, it can attain speeds of 10.5km/h (6.5mph) using twin propellers set beneath the rear of the hull. Numerous variants exist, such as an EOD vehicle and a RASIT radar carrier.

Country of origin:	West Germany
Crew:	2 + 10
Weight:	18,300kg (40,350lb)
Dimensions:	Length: 6.76m (22.18ft); width: 2.98m (9.78ft); height: 2.3m (7.55ft)
Range:	800km (500 miles)
Armour:	Steel (details classified)
Armament:	1 x 7.62mm (0.3in) MG
Powerplant:	1 x Mercedes-Benz OM402A 8-cylinder diesel, developing 320hp (239kW) at 2500rpm
Performance:	Maximum road speed: 105km/h (65mph); fording: amphibious; gradient: 70 percent; trench: 1.6m (5.3ft)

Condor

The Condor armoured personnel carrier was developed as a replacement for the UR-416 APC. Since it entered production in 1981, it has achieved good export sales, particularly in Malaysia. Two crew pilot the vehicle, the driver sitting at the front of the vehicle behind bullet-proof windows (shuttered in action), and the commander sitting behind him under a forward hatch cover in the roof. Twelve infantry occupy seats in the rear compartment. The hull is of all-welded steel armour. Armament fittings vary. They include 7.62mm (0.3in) and 12.7mm (0.5in) machine guns, 20mm (0.78in) cannon and ATGW systems. The Condor is fully amphibious, though a trim vane needs to be fitted before entering the water.

Country of origin:	West Germany
Crew:	2 + 12
Weight:	12,400kg (27,300lb)
Dimensions:	Length: 6.13m (20.11ft); width: 2.47m (8.1ft); height: 2.18m (7.15ft)
Range:	900km (560 miles)
Armour:	Steel (details classified)
Armament:	Varied (see text)
Powerplant:	1 x Daimler-Benz OM 352A 6-cylinder supercharged diesel, developing 168hp (125kW)
Performance:	Maximum road speed: 100km/h (62mph); fording: amphibious; gradient: 60 percent; vertical obstacle: 0.55m (1.8ft)

LAV-25

The Light Armoured Vehicle 25 (LAV-25) is in most ways a copy of the Swiss MOWAG Piranha, one of the world's most successful armoured personnel carriers. Built by General Motors of Canada, it is an 8x8 armoured vehicle with capacity for three crew and six passengers, the latter sitting back to back in the hull rear. Like the Piranha, the LAV-25 has evolved into a large number of variants, including maintenance and recovery vehicles, ATGW carriers, Mobile Electronic Warfare Support System and even an Assault Gun Vehicle armed with a 105mm (4.13in) cannon. The standard turret is usually fitted with a 25mm (0.98in) M242 chain gun and a 7.62mm (0.3in) coaxial machine gun.

Country of origin:	Canada
Crew:	3 + 6
Weight:	12,882kg (28,405lb)
Dimensions:	Length: 6.39m (20.96ft); width: 2.5m (8.2ft); height: 2.56m (8.39ft)
Range:	668km (414 miles)
Armour:	Classified
Armament:	1 x 25mm (0.98in) M242 chain gun; 1 x 7.62mm (0.3in) coaxial MG; various other options available (see text)
Powerplant:	1 x Detroit Diesel 6-cylinder diesel, developing 275hp (205kW)
Performance:	Maximum road speed: 100km/h (60mph); fording: amphibious; gradient: 60 percent; vertical obstacle: 0.5m (1.6ft); trench: 2.06m (6.76ft)

VTP-1 Orca

The VTP-1 Orca ('Killer Whale') was developed by Industrias Cardoen SA in the early 1980s to fulfil its own brief for a multi-purpose armoured vehicle. With a carrying capacity of 16 fully armed men and a total length of 7.84m (25.72ft), the Orca stands as possibly the largest 6x6 armoured personnel carrier in the world. It has an all-welded steel hull with armour of 6 to 12mm (0.24–0.47in). Multiple mounts for machine guns are set around the top of the hull over the troop compartment. Even with its great size, the Orca can maintain a high road speed of 120km/h (75mph), and its 6x6 configuration also gives good cross-country mobility and performance.

Country of origin:	Chile
Crew:	2 + 16
Weight:	18,000kg (39,700lb)
Dimensions:	Length: 7.84m (25.72ft); width: 2.5m (8.2ft); height: 2.5m (8.2ft)
Range:	1000km (620 miles)
Armour:	6–12mm (0.24–0.47in)
Armament:	Multiple MGs
Powerplant:	1 x General Motors 6V-53T 6-cylinder diesel, developing 260hp (194kW) at 2400rpm
Performance:	Maximum road speed: 120km/h (75mph); gradient: 60 percent

Saxon

The Saxon was developed in the early 1970s in response to a British Army requirement for a wheeled armoured personnel carrier for the 1980s and 1990s. Based on the Bedford Mk4 4 x 4, the standard truck of the British Army, production began in 1976 and the first models were delivered to British battalions in 1984. The Saxon was one of the best armoured vehicles of its type when it was introduced. One unusual feature was that the mudguards were designed to blow off in the event that the vehicle hit a mine, thus allowing the blast to escape sideways rather than up into the vehicle. The Saxon could be fitted with a range of armaments and variants included a command vehicle, an anti-riot vehicle and an ambulance. Some Saxons have a one-man 7.62mm machine-gun turret fitted.

Country of origin:	United Kingdom
Crew:	2 + 8
Weight:	10,670kg (23,474lb)
Dimensions:	length 5.169m (16ft 11.5in); width 2.489 (8ft 2in); height 2.86m (9ft 4.6in)
Range:	510km (317 miles)
Armour:	classified
Armament:	one 7.62mm machine gun
Powerplant:	one Bedford 500 six-cylinder diesel engine developing 164hp (122kW)
Performance:	maximum road speed 96km/h (60mph); fording 1.12m (3ft 8in); vertical obstacle 0.41m (1ft 4in); trench not applicable

BTR-80

The BTR-80 was part of the steady development of the BTR family which entered production in 1984. Its key contribution to the series was to switch from the two petrol engines of the BTR-60 and BTR-70 to a single powerful V8 diesel. Seven fully laden soldiers can travel in the BTR-80 as well as the three-man crew, and the troop compartment has a total of six firing ports. The main weaponry is a turret-mounted 14.5m (0.57in) KPVT machine gun and a coaxial 7.62mm (0.3in) PKT machine gun. Sophisticated features of the BTR-80 include central tyre-pressure regulation, NBC fittings, and front four wheels steering. It is also fully amphibious, powered by a single waterjet.

Country of origin:	USSR
Crew:	3 + 7
Weight:	13,600kg (23,000lb)
Dimensions:	Length: 7.65m (25.09ft); width: 2.9m (9.51ft); height: 2.46m (8.07ft)
Range:	600km (370 miles)
Armour:	(Steel) 9mm (0.35in)
Armament:	1 x 14.5m (0.57in) KPVT MG; 1 x coaxial 7.62mm (0.3in) PKT MG
Powerplant:	1 x V8 diesel, developing 260hp (193kW)
Performance:	Maximum road speed: 90km/h (56mph); fording: amphibious; gradient: 60 percent; vertical obstacle: 0.5m (1.6ft); trench: 2m (6.6ft)

FS100 Simba

Alvis, the company responsible for the production of the Simba, defines the vehicle as 'a 4x4 wheeled armoured personnel carrier, primarily used in internal security and counter-insurgency roles'. The Simba is characteristic of a climate in which peacekeeping and anti-terrorism duties occupy much of the military timetable. It comes in several variants. An armoured personnel version can transport eight fully armed soldiers, and is armed with a single turret-mounted machine gun. The armoured infantry fighting vehicle version has a 20 or 25mm (0.78 or 0.98in) cannon. Other variants include ATGW vehicles and 81mm (3.19in) mortar carriers. Only the Philippines have bought the Simba, choosing the APC.

Country of origin:	United Kingdom
Crew:	2 + 8
Weight:	10,000kg (22,100lb)
Dimensions:	Length: 5.35m (17.55ft); width: 2.5m (8.2ft); height: 2.59m (8.49ft)
Range:	660km (410 miles)
Armour:	(Steel) 8mm (0.31in) estimated maximum
Armament:	Various (see text)
Powerplant:	1 x Perkins 210Ti 8-cylinder diesel, developing 210hp (157kW) at 2500rpm
Performance:	Maximum road speed: 100km/h (62mph); fording: 1m (3.3ft); gradient: 60 percent; vertical obstacle: 0.45m (1.48ft)

Al-Faris AF-40-8-1

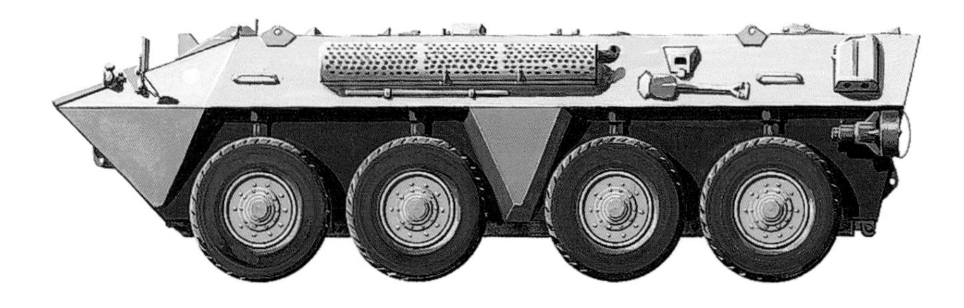

The Al-Faris AF-40-8-1 is a conventionally designed 8x8 armoured personnel carrier. There are actually two versions of the vehicle on the market: the AF-40-8-1, the APC version, and the AF-40-8-2, an armoured reconnaissance vehicle. Both have the same steel hull and basic features, but the latter is usually more heavily armed. The Al-Faris has many armament options ranging from TOW ATGWs and 106mm (4.17in) recoilless rifles to turrets fitted with 120mm (4.72in) heavy mortars and 25mm (0.98in) cannon. An ingenious feature of the Al Faris is its adjustable suspension, which can be used to alter ground clearance from 150mm (5.91in) to 600mm (23.62in).

Country of origin:	Saudi Arabia
Crew:	1 + 11
Weight:	19,500kg (43,000lb)
Dimensions:	Length: 7.9m (25.92ft); width: 2.94m (9.65ft); height: 2.36m (7.74ft)
Range:	800km (500 miles)
Armour:	Steel (details classified)
Armament:	Various (see text)
Powerplant:	1 x Deutz BF 10L513 10-cylinder diesel, developing 400hp (298kW)
Performance:	Maximum road speed: 90km/h (55mph); fording: amphibious; gradient: 80 percent; vertical obstacle: 1.52m (4.99ft); trench: 2.5m (8.2ft)

RAM V-2L

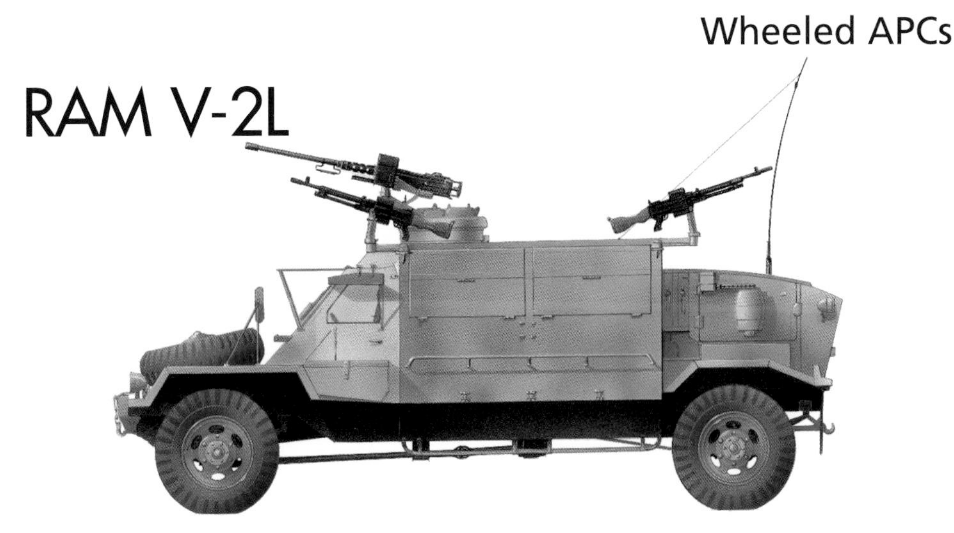

The RAM V-2L is one variant amongst many in a series of light vehicles built by RAMTA Structures and Systems, a subsidiary of Israel Aircraft Industries. The first of the RAM family was the V-1, a 4x4 light armoured fighting vehicle which held two crew, seven passengers, and was armed with 7.62mm (0.3in) machine guns and 106mm (4.17in) recoilless rifles. The key distinction between the RAM V-1 and the subsequent V-2 is that the former has an open-top hull, whereas the latter is fully enclosed. Both the V-2 and V-1 split into many sub-variants, including versions fitted with TOW ATGW launchers and 20mm (0.78in) cannon anti-aircraft turrets.

Country of origin:	Israel
Crew:	2 + 7 or 8
Weight:	5750kg (12,700lb)
Dimensions:	Length: 5.52m (18.11ft); width: 2.03m (6.66ft); height: 1.72m (5.64ft)
Range:	800km (500 miles)
Armour:	(Steel) 8mm (0.31in)
Armament:	1 x 12.7mm (0.5in) MG; 2 x 7.62mm (0.3in) MG
Powerplant:	1 x Deutz 6-cylinder diesel, developing 132hp (98kW)
Performance:	Maximum road speed: 96km/h (60mph); fording: 1m (3.3ft); gradient: 64 percent; vertical obstacle: 0.8m (2.6ft)

Fahd

The Fahd is a large armoured personnel carrier able to carry 10 fully armed soldiers as well as the two-man crew. Though an Egyptian vehicle, it was designed in Germany and actually uses a Mercedes-Benz truck chassis. The armoured hull provides the usual APC protection against small-arms fire and shell splinters, and steel shutters close over the windows when in combat. A standard Fahd is completely unarmed but there are many options for roof-mounted machine guns, cannons and ATGW launchers. A variant has even been produced fitted with the 30mm (1.18in) cannon turret from the Russian BMP-2. Firing ports are provided on both sides of the troop compartment.

Country of origin:	Egypt
Crew:	2 + 10
Weight:	10,900kg (24,000lb)
Dimensions:	Length: 6m (19.68ft); width: 2.45m (8.04ft); height: 2.1m (6.89ft)
Range:	800km (500 miles)
Armour:	Steel (details classified)
Armament:	None as standard (see text)
Powerplant:	1 x Mercedes-Benz OM-352 A 6-cylinder turbo diesel, developing 168hp (125kW) at 2800rpm
Performance:	Maximum road speed: 90km/h (56mph); fording: 0.7m (2.29ft); gradient: 70 percent; vertical obstacle: 0.5m (1.6ft); trench: 0.9m (2.9ft)

SIBMAS

The SIBMAS 6 x 6 armoured personnel carrier started as a private venture in the mid-1970s by the Belgian company BN Constructions Ferroviaires et Métalliques, with the first vehicles being delivered in 1983 to the Royal Malaysian Army, who eventually bought nearly 200 as fire-support vehicles, armed with the 90mm Cockerill Mk III gun. As expected, the basic model is fully amphibious without preparation and is propelled in the water by its wheels or by two propellers. Night vision and nuclear, biological and chemical (NBC) systems can be fitted as well as a range of different armaments. There are three entry doors: one in each side and one at the rear. The troop compartment has firing ports. Variants include an ambulance, a command vehicle and a cargo vehicle.

Country of origin:	Belgium
Crew:	3 + 11
Weight:	16,500kg (36,300lb)
Dimensions:	length 7.32m (24ft 0in); width 2.50 (8ft 2.4in); height (hull) 2.24m (7ft 4.2in)
Range:	1000km (621 miles)
Armour:	classified
Armament:	one 90mm Cockerill Mk III gun; one coaxial 7.62mm machine gun; one anti-aircraft 7.62mm machine gun
Powerplant:	one six-cylinder turbocharged diesel developing 320hp (239kW)
Performance:	maximum road speed 100km/h (62mph); fording amphibious; vertical obstacle 0.6m (1ft 11.6in); trench 1.5m (4ft 11in)

V-300 Commando

The V-300 was a 6 x 6 version of the Commando range. Built by Cadillac as a private venture to complement its 4 x 4 vehicles, the first production models were delivered in 1983 for export to Panama. The layout of the vehicle was different from that of the earlier V-150. Troops entered and exited the vehicle through rear doors only (the V-150 having side and rear doors), with additional hatches in the roof. A wide variety of armament could be fitted. Standard equipment includes a front-mounted winch with a capacity to lift 9072kg (19,958lb). Variants include a command post vehicle, ambulance (with a higher roof), a mortar carrier, anti-aircraft model and an anti-tank vehicle. Fully amphibious, the vehicle is propelled through the water by its wheels.

Country of origin:	United States
Crew:	3 + 9
Weight:	13,137kg (28,900lb)
Dimensions:	length 6.40m (21ft 0in); width 2.54m (8ft 4in); height 1.981m (6ft 6in)
Range:	700km (435 miles)
Armour:	classified
Armament:	one 25mm Hughes Helicopter Chain Gun; one 7.62mm coaxial machine gun
Powerplant:	one turbocharged diesel engine developing 235hp (175kW)
Performance:	maximum road speed 93km/h (58mph); fording amphibious; vertical obstacle 0.609m (2ft); trench not applicable

Patria XA-180

The Patria XA-180 is a 6x6 armoured personnel carrier used mainly by Scandinavian military forces and the Republic of Ireland. It was developed in the early 1980s and entered service in 1983 with the Finnish Army. Its bow-like front testifies to a fully amphibious capability, something essential in the wet climes of northern Europe, though a trim vane has to be fitted prior to amphibious operations. The hull is all-welded steel armour with double doors in the hull rear providing entry and exit for up to 10 soldiers. Standard armament on the XA-180 is a roof-mounted machine gun, but variants include an ATGW carrier and an air-defence version fitted with the Crotale New Generation SAM system.

Country of origin:	Finland
Crew:	2 + 10
Weight:	15,000kg (33,100lb)
Dimensions:	Length: 7.35m (24.11ft); width: 2.89m (9.48ft); height: 2.47m (8.1ft)
Range:	800km (500 miles)
Armour:	Steel (details classified)
Armament:	1 x 7.62mm (0.3in) or 12.7mm (0.5in) MG
Powerplant:	1 x Valmet 6-cylinder turbo diesel, developing 236hp (175kW)
Performance:	Maximum road speed: 105km/h (65mph); fording: amphibious; gradient: 70 percent; vertical obstacle: 0.6m (2ft); trench: 1m (3.3ft)

Valkyr

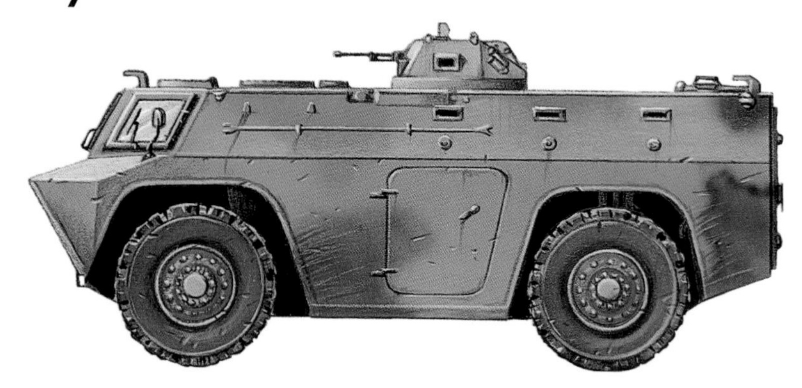

The Valkyr was originally a licensed-built Belgian vehicle, the BDX,which was based on an Irish armoured personnel carrier prototype called the Timoney. In the late 1980s, the British Vickers firm collaborated with the BDX manufacturers, Beherman-Demoen, and produced a UK version called the Valkyr. The Valkyr transports two crew and 10 fully armed infantry. It is amphibious, with propulsion usually provided by its wheels, though two rear-mounted waterjets are optional. The basic Valkyr is armed with a single machine gun, but the armoured fighting vehicle has a large turret featuring a 90mm (3.54in) cannon or a 60mm (2.36in) gun-mortar. A MILAN ATGW system can also be fitted.

Country of origin:	United Kingdom
Crew:	2 + 10
Weight:	11,500kg (25,400lb)
Dimensions:	Length: 5.6m (18.37ft); width: 2.5m (8.2ft); height: 2.27m (7.45ft)
Range:	700km (430 miles)
Armour:	Not available
Armament:	1 x 7.62mm (0.3in) MG
Powerplant:	1 x Detroit Diesel 4-53T V8 diesel, developing 300hp (224kW) at 2800rpm
Performance:	Maximum road speed: 100km/h (62mph); fording: amphibious; gradient: 60 percent; vertical obstacle: 0.45m (1.48ft)

BTR-90

The BTR-90 is Russia's next generation of Infantry Combat Vehicles, and its service status is only just being defined. It is similar to the BTR-80 in general appearance, and can carry 10 fully armed soldiers within its armoured and amphibious hull. What makes it distinctive is its armament. All its weaponry is mounted in a single turret located towards the front of the vehicle, and it consists of one 30mm (1.18in) 2A42 automatic cannon, a coaxial 7.62mm (0.3in) PKT machine gun, an automatic grenade launcher, and four AT-5 Spandrel anti-tank missiles. The spectrum of weaponry allows it to engage the enemy infantry, armour and aircraft equally.

Country of origin:	Russia
Crew:	3 + 10
Weight:	17,000kg (37,500lb)
Dimensions:	Length: 7.64m (25ft); width: 3.2m (10.49ft); height: 2.97m (9.74ft)
Range:	600km (370 miles)
Armour:	Not disclosed
Armament:	1 x 30mm (1.18in) 2A42 automatic cannon; 1 x coaxial 7.62mm (0.3in) PKT MG; 1 x automatic grenade launcher; 4 x AT-5 Spandrel ATGWs
Powerplant:	1 x V8 diesel, developing 210hp (157kW))
Performance:	Maximum road speed: 80km/h (50mph); fording: amphibious

GTK/MRAV

The Gepanzerten Transportkraftfahrzeug/Multi-Role Armoured Vehicle (GTK/MRAV) was a joint German/United Kingdom/Netherlands project to develop a versatile next-generation armoured personnel carrier. The 6x6 base vehicle is the operator compartment and chassis. Onto this permanent base fit different interchangeable mission modules – such as a command-and-control module and a field-ambulance module – to form the rear compartment. The modules can be changed in less than one hour. Consequently, the GTK/MRAV can be many different vehicles within the remit of a single operation. The base vehicle is made of steel armour. In 2003 the UK decided to withdraw from the programme, but Germany and the Netherlands will continue the vehicle's development.

Country of origin:	Germany/United Kingdom/Netherlands
Crew:	Up to 10 men, depending on module
Weight:	26,500kg (58,400lb)
Dimensions:	Length: 7.23m (23.72ft); width: 2.99m (9.8ft); height: 2.37m (7.78ft)
Range:	1050km (625 miles)
Armour:	Classified
Armament:	Various depending on module
Powerplant:	1 x MTU 8-cylinder diesel, developing 710hp (530kW)
Performance:	Maximum road speed: 103km/h (64mph)

Austro-Daimler

Developed in 1904, the Austro-Daimler armoured car was the first military application of four-wheel drive. Typical of the period, it combines a standard car chassis with crude bolt-on armour, in the Austro-Daimler's case 4mm (0.16in) thick. The engine was situated in the front of the vehicle with the driver sitting just behind using a viewing slit in the frontal armour for visibility. Combat potential was provided by a Maxim machine gun or, in later models, two Schwarzlose machine guns mounted in the turret over the rear section of the vehicle. Although the Austro-Daimler gave a respectable on- and off-road performance (by turn-of-the-century standards) the vehicle never entered into military service.

Country of origin:	Austria
Crew:	4
Weight:	2500kg (5500lb)
Dimensions:	Length (hull): 4.86m (15.94ft); width: 1.76m (5.77ft); height: 2.74m (8.99ft)
Range:	250km (150 miles)
Armour:	4mm (0.16in)
Armament:	1 x 7.92mm (0.31in) Maxim MG or 2 x 7.92mm (0.30in) Schwarzlose MGs
Powerplant:	Daimler 4-cylinder petrol, developing 40hp (30kW)
Performance:	Maximum road speed: 45km/h (28mph)

CGV 1906

The French automobile company of Charron, Giradot & Voigt (CGV) was, at the turn of the 20th century, a producer of racing cars. With the growth in demand for military vehicles, however, CGV took a touring-car chassis and fitted it with an armoured barbette mounting an 8mm (0.31in) rear-facing machine gun. This vehicle was presented at the Paris Car Exhibition in 1902. Tests conducted on a new model in Russia in 1905 brought it up to production standard. Only about 12 CGV cars were produced between 1905 and 1908. Russia was a significant export market; indeed, in 1905, one of the vehicles was used to put down rioting in St Petersburg.

Country of origin:	France
Crew:	4
Weight:	3500kg (7700lb)
Dimensions:	Length: 4.46m (14.96ft); width: 1.85m (6ft); height: 2.47m (8.1ft)
Range:	600km (370 miles)
Armour:	6mm (0.23in)
Armament:	1 x 8mm (0.31in) MG
Powerplant:	1 x GCV 4-cylinder petrol, developing 30hp (22kW)
Performance:	Maximum road speed: 45km/h (28mph)

Autoblindé Peugeot

Based on a commercial model, the first Peugeot armoured car was a rather hasty improvisation which appeared in 1914. Improvements followed quickly in terms of armament and firepower. With the development of trench warfare following the first year of World War I, there was a limited role for the Peugeot, since being confined to roads they could do little more than patrol rear areas. They were used to contain the German breakthrough of March 1918, being more suited to this type of fluid warfare, but their role was mainly overshadowed by the newly emerging tanks. The few Peugeots still in service at the end of World War I were handed over to the Polish Army, where they remained in service for some years, seeing action against the Russians.

Country of origin:	France
Crew:	4 or 5
Weight:	4900kg (10,780lb)
Dimensions:	length 4.8m (15ft 9in); width 1.80m (5ft 11in); height 2.80m (9ft 2.25in)
Range:	140km (87 miles)
Armour:	unknown
Armament:	one 37mm gun
Powerplant:	one 40hp (30kW) Peugeot petrol engine
Performance:	maximum speed 40km/h (25mph)

Garford-Putilow

The monstrous Garford-Putilow armoured car hailed from the Putilow factory in St Petersburg in 1914, and 70 such vehicles fought in World War I, the Russian Civil War and the Polish–Soviet campaign of 1939. Chassis were provided by the US Garford Motor Truck Company, and a huge armoured structure was built on the foundation of this standard truck chassis. Total weight was 11,000kg (24,300lb). Consequently the Garford-Putilow had no off-road capability and on-road was slow. Its main armament was a 76.2mm (3in) gun mounted on a 270-degree traversable turret, and three machine guns. During World War II, many Garford-Putilow armoured bodies were subsequently used on armoured trains.

Country of origin:	Russia
Crew:	8
Weight:	11,000kg (24,300lb)
Dimensions:	Length: 5.7m (18.7ft); width: 2.3m (7.55ft); height: 2.8m (9.19ft)
Range:	120km (75 miles)
Armour:	5mm (0.19in) approx.
Armament:	1 x 76.2mm (3in) gun; 3 x Maxim 7.92mm (0.31in) MGs
Powerplant:	1 x Garford 4-cylinder petrol, developing 35hp (26kW)
Performance:	Maximum road speed: 20km/h (13mph)

Rolls-Royce

In 1914, the Royal Naval Air Service noted how the Belgians were using armoured cars to carry out raids on the advancing German Army. They decided to convert some of the Rolls-Royce Silver Ghost cars in their possession. The conversion was a success, and the Admiralty gave permission for an official armoured car based on the Silver Ghost chassis. With strengthened suspension and added armour, the Rolls-Royce saw service all over the world from March 1915, notably in Africa and the Arabian peninsula, where they proved to have excellent cross-country mobility. They were most at home in terrain where they could roam far and wide. They continued in service until being replaced in British Army service in 1922, although some were used in India well into World War II.

Country of origin:	United Kingdom
Crew:	3 or 4
Weight:	3400kg (7480lb)
Dimensions:	length 5.03m (16ft 6in); width 1.91m (6ft 3in); height 2.55m (8ft 4.5in)
Range:	240km (150 miles)
Armour:	9mm (0.35in)
Armament:	Vickers 0.303in machine gun
Powerplant:	one 40/50hp (30/37.3kW) Rolls-Royce petrol engine
Performance:	maximum road speed 95km/h (60mph)

Lanchester

Originally designed to support air bases and retrieve downed pilots, the Lanchester was the most numerous armoured car in service after the Rolls-Royce by the end of 1914. A year later they were formed into armoured car squadrons. The engine of the original car was retained, but the hull was much modified. The army took control of operations at the end of 1915 and decided to use the Rolls-Royce as the standard armoured car, Lanchesters being phased out of service. However, many were sent with navy crews to the Russians, with whom they served with some distinction in terrain as varied as Persia, Romania and Galicia. Reliable and fast, they spearheaded armoured columns and were used for reconnaissance before being shipped back to the UK.

Country of origin:	United Kingdom
Crew:	4
Weight:	4700kg (10,340lb)
Dimensions:	length 4.88m (16ft); width 1.93m (6ft 4in); height 2.286m (7ft 6in)
Range:	290km (180 miles)
Armour:	unknown
Armament:	one Vickers 0.303in machine gun
Powerplant:	one 60hp (45kW) Lanchester petrol engine
Performance:	maximum speed 80km/h (50mph)

Daimler/15

In late 1914, the companies Daimler, Büssing and Ehrhardt were commissioned to develop a prototype armoured car for Germany. Because of other production commitments, Daimler was not able to field its prototype until December 1915, but following testing, prototype models of the Daimler/15 went on to serve on all fronts with reasonable success. The Daimler/15 consisted of an all-wheel-drive car chassis with an armoured structure of Krupp riveted chromium-nickel stainless steel plates. Dual tyres at the rear and sand rims on the front wheels prevented the vehicle sinking into soft ground. Armament was provided by three machine guns. In many ways the Daimler/15's carrying capacity of 10 men made it an incipient APC.

Country of origin:	Germany
Crew:	10
Weight:	9800kg (21,600lb)
Dimensions:	Length: 5.61m (18.4ft); width: 2.03m (6.66ft); height: 3.85m (12.63ft)
Range:	250km (150 miles)
Armour:	Not known
Armament:	3 x 7.92mm (0.31in) MG
Powerplant:	1 x Daimler Model 4-cylinder petrol, developing 80hp (60kW)
Performance:	Maximum road speed: 38km/h (24mph)

Büssing A5P

The Büssing company originally specialized in heavy farm vehicles, which then became models for several German military machines. The firm received its first orders for military vehicles in 1910, producing artillery tractors and supply trailers. In November 1914, Büssing, Daimler and Ehrhardt were requested to develop an armoured car with all-wheel drive. Two years later, Büssing's A5P was began production. It was powered by one of Büssing's legendary 6-cylinder truck engines, and featured a large steel armoured body. Inside the vehicle were 10 crew, six of them working three machine guns. Some A5Ps received two 20mm (0.78in) cannon. The A5P served in Romania and Russia until the end of 1917.

Country of origin:	Germany
Crew:	10
Weight:	10,250kg (22,600lb)
Dimensions:	Length: 9.5m (31.17ft); width: 2.1m (6.89ft); height: not available
Range:	250km (150 miles)
Armour:	Not available
Armament:	3 x 7.92mm (0.31in) MG
Powerplant:	1 x Büssing petrol, developing 90hp (67kW)
Performance:	Maximum road speed: 35km/h (21mph)

Autoblindo Mitragliatrice Lancia Ansaldo IZ

Based on the Lancia IZ truck, the IZ armoured car was quite an advanced design for its day. With a turret-mounted machine gun and later a further small turret on top with an additional machine gun, the vehicle had considerable firepower. Steel rails protruded over the bonnet for cutting wire (a feature that reflected the experience of World War I for European armies). Little used by the Italians in the mountainous fighting against the Austro-Hungarian Army, many were sent to North Africa for policing duties. Total production by 1918 was around 120, and after World War I some were sent to Albania where they formed the sole armoured force of that country for many years. Some were even used by the Italians in the Spanish Civil War, though by this time they were very outdated.

Country of origin:	Italy
Crew:	6
Weight:	3700kg (8140lb)
Dimensions:	length 5.40m (17ft 8.66in); width 1.824m (6ft 0in); height with single turret 2.40m (7ft 10.5in)
Range:	300km (186 miles)
Armour:	9mm (0.35in)
Armament:	two machine guns
Powerplant:	one 35/40hp (26/30kW) petrol engine
Performance:	maximum speed 60km/h (37mph)

Austin-Putilov

The Austin-Putilov was a British design, though mostly produced and used in Russia. The Russians took the basic chassis (all that could be supplied by the over-stretched British production lines) and modified it considerably to cope with the harsh Russian conditions, including later replacing the rear wheels with tracks and adding additional armour and rear steering. Both in terms of numbers and performance, the Austin-Putilov was the most important armoured car the Russians possessed during World War I. Many also saw action in the internal fighting surrounding the October revolution and afterwards in the Russian Civil War. After 1918 some saw service with the Polish Army, with a number being sold to Japan. It was an extremely rugged vehicle.

Country of origin:	United Kingdom/Russia
Crew:	5
Weight:	5200kg (11,440lb)
Dimensions:	length 4.88m (16ft 0in); width 1.95m (6ft 4.75in); height 2.40m (7ft 10.5in)
Range:	200km (125 miles)
Armour:	8mm (0.315in)
Armament:	two Maxim machine guns
Powerplant:	one 50hp (37.3kW) Austin petrol engine
Performance:	maximum speed 50km/h (31mph)

Laffly-White Auto-Mitrailleuse

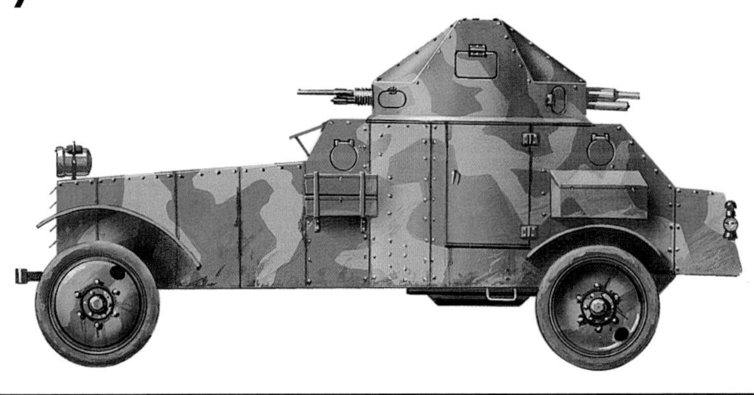

The Laffly-White Auto-Mitrailleuse ('machine-gun car') was created by combining an armoured body designed by the French company Laffly with the truck chassis from the US company White. White trucks were imported into France from 1915, and in 1918, Laffly began production of its armoured car. In spite of cumbersome dimensions, the Laffly-White served into WWII after active use in the Levant and North Africa in colonial police roles. By 1939, its reliability and durability had made it popular, but its slow speed, largely ineffective 37mm (1.46in) gun and high profile rendered it obsolete against German vehicle technology. By 1940, most were replaced by new Panhard vehicles.

Country of origin:	France
Crew:	4
Weight:	6000kg (13,200lb)
Dimensions:	Length: 5.6m (18.4ft); width: 2.1m (6.9ft); height: 2.75m (9ft)
Range:	250km (150 miles)
Armour:	8mm (0.31in)
Armament:	1 x 37mm (1.46in) cannon; 2 x 8mm (0.31in) MGs
Powerplant:	1 x White 4-cylinder petrol, developing 35hp (26kW)
Performance:	Maximum road speed: 45km/h (28mph)

Schupo-Sonderwagen 21

Though the Treaty of Versailles (1919) did not permit the Weimar Republic to equip itself with armoured units, the Allied victors did permit the construction of 150 armoured cars for German police service. Consequently between 1921 and 1925 three companies – Daimler, Ehrhardt and Benz – were engaged in the production of the Schupo-Sonderwagen 21. The Schupo was a huge vehicle weighing in at 11,000kg (24,300lb). Its extreme weight was caused by large amounts of chromium-nickel plated armour, steel-shod wheels, three Maxim 08 machine guns, and nine crew. The front end of the vehicle was designed to batter its way through street barricades. Around 100 Schupo vehicles were produced.

Country of origin:	Germany
Crew:	9
Weight:	11,000kg (24,300lb)
Dimensions:	Length: 6.5m (21.33ft); width: 2.41m (7.9ft); height: 3.45m (11.32ft)
Range:	350km (220 miles)
Armour:	Chromium-nickel plated
Armament:	3 x 7.92mm (0.31in) Maxim 08 MGs
Powerplant:	1 x Ehrhardt 4-cylinder petrol, developing 80hp (60kW)
Performance:	Maximum road speed: 56km/h (35mph)

Daimler DZVR 1919

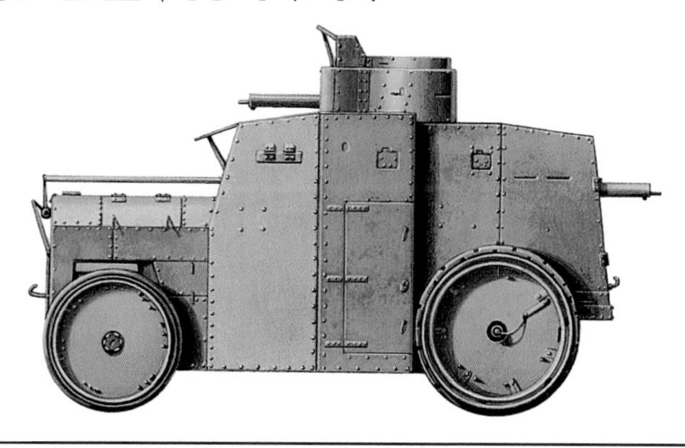

The Daimler DZVR was one of several German vehicles created after the end of World War I under the terms of the Treaty of Versailles. Inter-war Germany required security vehicles to police internal civil unrest and problems on its eastern borders, and 38 DZVR vehicles were ordered for this purpose. The DZVR was based on the chassis of the KD1 artillery tractor, and 1000 of these vehicles were left over from the war. Armour plate, 12mm (0.47in) thick, encased the six-man crew compartment, and a revolving turret at the top held a searchlight. During the 1920s, the searchlight was replaced by a Maxim machine gun. The DZVR remained in police use until the early 1940s.

Country of origin:	Germany
Crew:	6
Weight:	10,500kg (23,200lb)
Dimensions:	Length: 5.9m (19.36ft); width: 2.1m (6.89ft); height: 3.1m (10.17ft)
Range:	150km (100 miles)
Armour:	(Steel) 12mm (0.47in)
Armament:	2 x 7.92mm (0.31in) Maxim MGs
Powerplant:	1 x Daimler M1574 4-cylinder petrol, developing 100hp (75kW)
Performance:	Maximum road speed: 43km/h (27mph)

Pavesi 35 PS

The Pavesi 35 PS emerged from Italian inter-war experiments as an alternative to tracked armoured vehicles. It was developed by the agricultural vehicle company Pavesi-Tolotti of Milan, and consisted of a small armoured car driven by four outsize spoked wheels. Each wheel had a 1.55m (5.09ft) diameter with broad metal rims for powerful cross-country movement. The clearance provided by the wheels was 0.75m (2.46ft) and trenches of 1.4m (4.6ft) width could be crossed. Armament was provided by a single machine gun mounted in the central rotating turret, and later experiments incorporated a 57mm (2.24in) cannon. In use until the late 1920s, it was manufactured in later years by the Fiat company.

Country of origin:	Italy
Crew:	2
Weight:	5000kg (11,000lb)
Dimensions:	Length: 4m (13.12ft); width: 2.18m (7.15ft); height: 2.2m (7.22ft)
Range:	Not available
Armour:	Not available
Armament:	1 x 8mm (0.31in) MG
Powerplant:	1 x Pavesi 4-cylinder petrol, developing 35hp (26kW)
Performance:	Maximum road speed: 30km/h (19mph)

PA-II

The PA-II was the second in a series of armoured vehicles made by Skoda in the inter-war years. The first, the PA-I, was a prototype weighing 7.3 tons and armed with two 7.92mm (0.31in) Maxim 08 machine guns. Though only two PA-Is were produced, they laid the foundations for the 12 PA-IIs produced between 1924 and 1925 and nicknamed the 'Zelva' (turtle) after their carapace shape. Ten of the units were armoured, the remaining two being unarmoured and used for driver training. Three of the armoured vehicles were used by the Austrian police from 1927. PA-IIs were undoubtedly heavily armed – four Maxim MGs – but they were totally obsolete by the beginning of World War II.

Country of origin:	Czechoslovakia
Crew:	5
Weight:	7360kg (16,229lb)
Dimensions:	Length (hull): 6m (19.68ft); width: 2.16m (7.08ft); height: 2.44m (8ft)
Range:	250km (150 miles)
Armour:	3–5.5mm (0.12–0.21in)
Armament:	4 x 7.92mm (0.31in) Maxim 08 MGs
Powerplant:	1 x Skoda 4-cylinder, petrol, developing 70hp (52kW)
Performance:	Maximum road speed: 70km/h (43mph)

Berliet VUDB

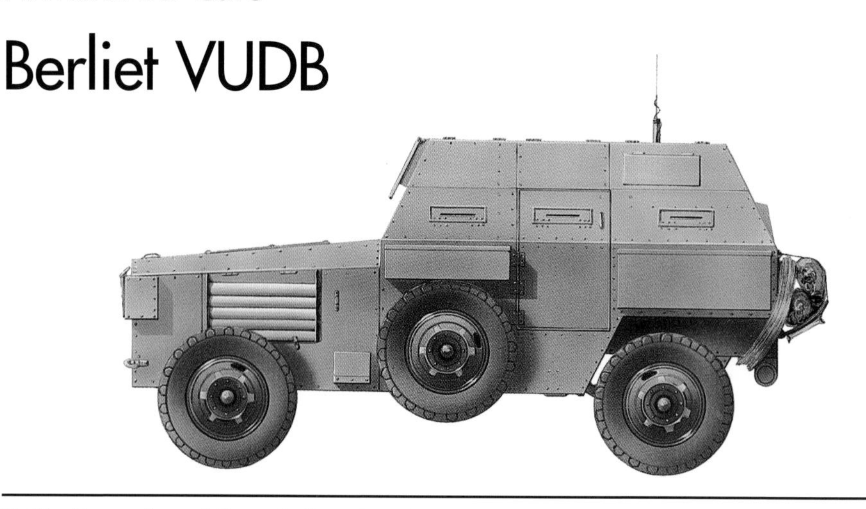

The Lyons based French firm Berliet began producing armoured cars between the wars. Its initial output included the Berliet VUDB, a 4x4 vehicle which saw extensive use in France's North African colonies. The VUDB was produced as a prototype in 1929. In tests, French military officers were impressed with its range of over 350km (220 miles) and speed of 75km/h (47mph), both ideally suited to operations in the North African terrain. In 1930, it entered into service with the French Army. Another 12 vehicles were also built for the Belgian Army. The VUDB featured windows which could be shuttered with armoured plates when under fire, and was armed with three machine guns.

Country of origin:	France
Crew:	3
Weight:	4000kg (8800lb)
Dimensions:	Length: 4.3m (14.11ft); width: 1.96m (6.43ft); height: 2.15m (7ft)
Range:	350km (220 miles)
Armour:	Not available
Armament:	3 x MGs
Powerplant:	1 x Berliet 6-cylinder petrol, developing 49hp (37kW)
Performance:	Maximum road speed: 75km/h (47mph)

BA-10

The BA-10 was built on the chassis of the GAZ-AAA commercial truck (which was modified and reinforced to cope with the extra weight) and first appeared in 1932. It was a bulky, functional piece of equipment whose World War I ancestry was evident from its outmoded appearance. Despite its weight, the BA-10 proved well-suited to the terrain and distances of the Soviet Union, and its main armament was as good as many tanks. The Germans captured large numbers of the vehicle after the invasion of the Soviet Union in June 1941 and used them for anti-partisan duties both in the USSR and in the Balkans, a role in which it excelled. Those that remained in Soviet hands were replaced in frontline service after 1942 and stripped down, to be used as armoured personnel carriers.

Country of origin:	USSR
Crew:	4
Weight:	7500kg (16,500lb)
Dimensions:	length 4.70m (15ft 5in); width 2.09m (6ft 10.5in); height 2.42m (7ft 11.25in)
Range:	320km (199 miles)
Armour:	up to 25mm (0.98in)
Armament:	one 37mm/45mm gun; one 7.62mm machine gun
Powerplant:	one GAZ-M 14-cylinder water-cooled petrol engine developing 85hp (63kW)
Performance:	maximum speed 87km/h (54mph); fording 0.6m (1ft 11in); vertical obstacle 0.38m (1ft 3in); 0.5m (1ft 7in)

SdKfz 231

Although the SdKfz 231 was originally developed at the Kazan test centre in the Soviet Union, the vehicle was a German design intended for German use. A 6 x 4 Daimler-Benz truck chassis was used as the basis, and an armoured hull and turret added. Production ran from 1932-35, by which time around 1000 had been built. The hull was too heavy for the chassis, though, which resulted in poor cross-country performance. However, they were used on roads to good effect during the occupation of Czechoslovakia and the campaigns in Poland and France in 1939-40, their appearance alone having a good propaganda value. Their greatest achievement was to provide an invaluable training vehicle for the German Army's development during the 1930s.

Country of origin:	Germany
Crew:	4
Weight:	5700kg (12,540lb)
Dimensions:	length overall 5.57m (18ft 6.75in); width 1.82m (5ft 11.5in); height 2.25m (7ft 4.5in)
Range:	250km (150 miles)
Armour:	8mm (0.31in)
Armament:	one 20mm KwK 38 cannon; one coaxial 7.62mm machine gun
Powerplant:	one Daimler-Benz, Bussing-NAG or Magirus water-cooled petrol engine developing between 60 and 80hp (45 and 60kW)
Performance:	maximum road speed 65km/h (40mph); fording 0.6m (2ft)

Panzerspähwagen SdKfz 232 (8 Rad)

The SdKfz 232 (8 Rad) was essentially the same as the SdKfz 231 (8 Rad), except that it was fitted with a long-range aerial antenna over the top of the turret. A 6x4 SdKfz 231 was produced between 1932 and 1935, but this had limited off-road performance. The SdKfz 231 (8 Rad) solved this problem admirably with its 8x8 configuration – they could even travel through the infamous autumnal muds of the eastern front and the sands of North Africa without impediment. Yet they were very expensive and complicated to produce, and fewer than 1500 were manufactured. Both the SdKfz 231 and 232 have the suffix 8 Rad (8-wheel) to distinguish them from their six-wheel counterparts.

Country of origin:	Germany
Crew:	4
Weight:	9100kg (20,100lb)
Dimensions:	Length: 5.58m (18.3ft); width: 2.2m (7.22ft); height: 2.9m (9.51ft)
Range:	300km (190 miles)
Armour:	15–30mm (0.59–1.18in)
Armament:	1 x 20mm (0.78in) cannon; 1 x 7.92mm (0.31in) MG
Powerplant:	1 x Büssing-NAG L8V-Gs petrol, developing 160hp (119kW) at 3000rpm
Performance:	Maximum road speed: 85km/h (53mph); fording: 1m (3.3ft); gradient: 30 percent; vertical obstacle: 0.5m (1.6ft); trench: 1.25m (4.1ft)

BA-20

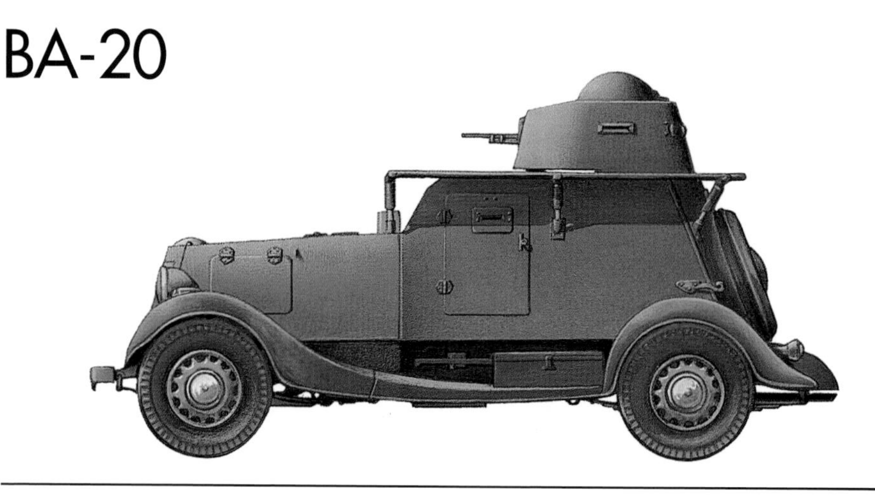

The BA-20 was a Soviet scout/command vehicle which replaced the FAI-M light armoured car. Its truck ancestry is visually clear, and it used the chassis of the GAZ-M1 truck with a superstructure of armoured steel plate. This plate had a thickness of 4–6mm (0.16–0.24in), enough to protect against small-arms fire. The BA-20 had a small turret with a 7.62mm (0.3in) DT machine gun and slightly sloping armoured plates to enhance missile deflection. Two basic versions were produced: the BA-20 with a clothes-line aerial, and the later BA-20M which had a whip aerial. A major upgrade in 1939 using the 6x4 GAZ-21 truck chassis was abandoned before production began.

Country of origin:	USSR
Crew:	2
Weight:	2340kg (5160lb)
Dimensions:	Length: 4.1m (13.5ft); width: 1.8m (5.9ft); height: 2.3m (7.6ft)
Range:	350km (220 miles)
Armour:	(Steel) 4–6mm (0.16–0.24in)
Armament:	1 x 7.62mm (0.3in) MG
Powerplant:	1 x GAZ-M1 4-cylinder petrol, developing 50hp (37kW)
Performance:	Maximum road speed: 90km/h (56mph)

Sumida M.2593

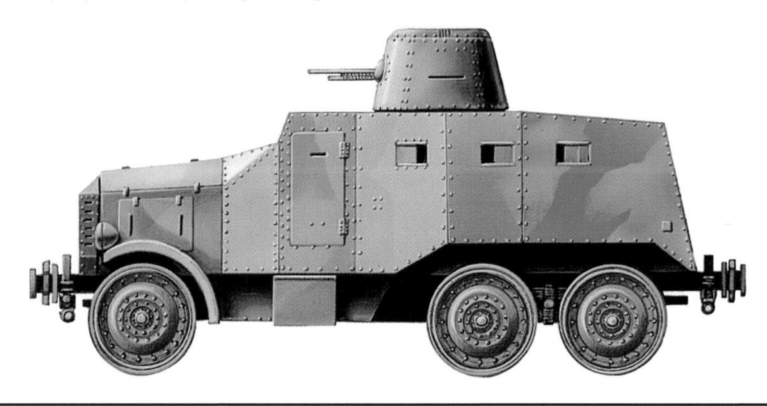

One of the most ingenious armoured vehicles of the inter-war period was the Japanese Sumida M.2593. Produced from 1933 by the Ishikawajima Motor Works, it had the option of travelling by either road or rail. Solid road wheels could be exchanged for railway wheels carried on the side of the vehicle, the front and rear wheels adaptable to different rail gauges. After the swap it could drive at 60km/h (37mph) on rails, powered by its four-cylinder petrol engine. The Sumida proved useful in covering the great distances of mainland China during the Japanese invasion of the late 1930s, but its solid wheels made it unsuitable for off-road manoeuvre.

Country of origin:	Japan
Crew:	6
Weight:	7000kg (15,400lb)
Dimensions:	Length: 6.57m (21.55ft); width: 1.9m (6.23ft); height: 2.95m (9.68ft)
Range:	240km (150 miles)
Armour:	10mm (0.39in)
Armament:	1 x MG
Powerplant:	1 x 4-cylinder petrol, developing 45hp (34kW)
Performance:	Maximum road speed: 40km/h (25mph); maximum rail speed: 60km/h (37mph)

M39 Armoured Car

The M39 was produced by the DAF company in the build-up to World War II, resisting Dutch Army requests to license-build British armoured cars. It was a well-made 6x4 armoured car with an all-welded hull, a rear-mounted Ford Mercury V8 engine and a well-sloped glacis plate. A useful set of driving controls at the rear of the vehicle allowed the rear machine-gunner to control the vehicle in reverse in an emergency. At the front of the hull, two small wheels prevented the forward edge of the glacis plate digging into the ground on rough terrain. After the fall of the Netherlands in 1940, M39s were pressed into German service as Pz. SpWg L202h.

Country of origin:	Netherlands
Crew:	5
Weight:	6000kg (13,200lb)
Dimensions:	Length: 4.75m (15.58ft); width: 2.03m (6.66ft); height: 2.16m (7.09ft)
Range:	320km (200 miles)
Armour:	12mm (0.47in)
Armament:	1 x 37mm (1.46in) cannon; 3 x 8mm (0.31in) MGs
Powerplant:	1 x Ford Mercury V8 petrol, developing 95hp (71kW)
Performance:	Maximum road speed: 60km/h (37mph)

ADGZ

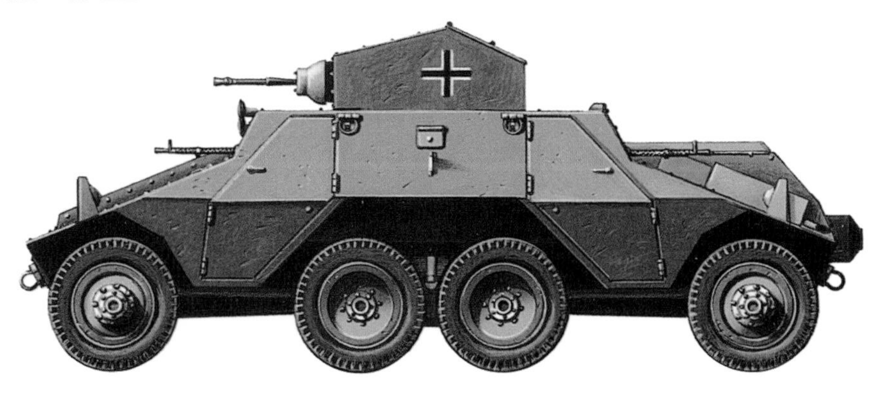

The Daimler ADGZ was in production in Austria between 1935 and 1937, though only very small numbers were ultimately delivered for service – 26 in total. Twelve were delivered to the Austrian Army and 14 were issued to the police and gendarmerie. As an 8x8 vehicle, it had excellent off-road mobility, a fact recognized by the German forces that occupied Austria in 1938. Austrian ADGZs were soon pressed into German Army service and redesignated PzKpfw Steyr ADGZ. Most of these vehicles were deployed by the SS and special police detachments, and they were used heavily on the Eastern front. Production continued under German auspices until the end of 1941.

Country of origin:	Austria
Crew:	6 or 7
Weight:	12,000kg (26,500lb)
Dimensions:	Length: 6.26m (20.54ft); width: 2.16m (7.09ft); height: 2.56m (8.39ft)
Range:	70km (43 miles)
Armour:	Not available
Armament:	1 x 20mm (0.78in) automatic cannon; 3 x 7.92mm (0.30in) MG
Powerplant:	Austro-Daimler M612 6-cylinder petrol, developing 150hp (112kW)
Performance:	Maximum road speed: 70km/h (43mph)

Panhard et Levassor Type 178

The Panhard 178 was designed in the mid-1930s as a 4x4 armoured reconnaissance vehicle for the French Army. Its most common armament was a single 25mm (0.98in) cannon or two 7.5mm (0.29in) machine guns. French production of the Panhard 178 ended with the German occupation in 1940. The Germans, however, were impressed with the design and used large numbers under the designation Panzerspähwagen P 204(f). Some of these were turned into anti-aircraft platforms by fitting them with 37mm (1.46in) anti-aircraft guns. French production of the 178 recommenced in August 1944 after the liberation of Paris, though with a larger turret and 47mm (1.85in) gun. These endured in French Army service until 1960.

Country of origin:	France
Crew:	4
Weight:	8300kg (18,300lb)
Dimensions:	Length: 4.8m (15.74ft); width: 2.01m (6.59ft); height: 2.33m (7.64ft)
Range:	300km (190 miles)
Armour:	18mm (0.7in)
Armament:	1 x 25mm (0.98in) cannon; 1 x 7.5mm (0.29in) MG
Powerplant:	1 x Renault 4-cylinder petrol, developing 180hp (134kW)
Performance:	Maximum road speed: 72km/h (45mph); fording: 0.6m (2ft); gradient: 40 percent; vertical obstacle: 0.3m (1ft); trench: 0.6m (2ft)

SdKfz 222

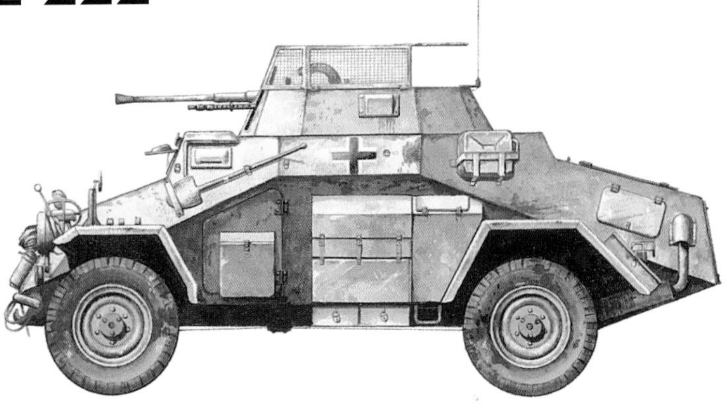

When the Nazis began to rearm the German Army in the mid-1930s, a request was made for a series of light armoured cars based on a standard chassis. The demanding requirements could not be met by adapting commercial models, so a new design was produced. The first production SdKfz 222 appeared in 1938, and thereafter became the standard armoured reconnaissance car of the Wehrmacht. A reliable and popular vehicle, the SdKfz 222 served the army well during the Blitzkrieg against Poland and France in 1939-40, and later in North Africa. However, its restricted range, made evident in the latter theatre, proved problematic during the invasion of the Soviet Union in 1941. That said, it remained in German service in western Europe until the end of World War II.

Country of origin:	Germany
Crew:	3
Weight:	4800kg (10,560lb)
Dimensions:	length 4.80m (14ft 8.5in); width 1.95m (6ft 4.75in); height 2.00m (6ft 6.75in) with grenade screen
Range:	300km (187 miles)
Armour:	14.5-30mm (0.6-1.2in)
Armament:	one 20mm KwK 30 cannon; one 7.92 MG34 machine gun
Powerplant:	one Horch/Auto-Union V8-108 water-cooled petrol engine developing 81hp (60kW)
Performance:	maximum road speed 80km/h (50mph); fording 0.6m (24in)

Daimler Scout Car

When the British Army was forming its first armoured divisions in the late 1930s, a requirement was issued for a 4 x 4 scout car for reconnaissance purposes. The Daimler Scout Car was the result. Entering production just prior to the start of World War II, it was still being made at the end of the war and was to prove one of the most successful reconnaissance vehicles in use by any army in the war. Its inconspicuous nature and excellent mobility compensated for lack of armour and armament, deficiencies that are not necessarily fatal to vehicles that move fast on the battlefield and do not stand and engage in firefights with enemy armour. The folding roof was removed on later models, as experience showed it was rarely used operationally and gave minimal cover in any case.

Country of origin:	United Kingdom
Crew:	2
Weight:	3000kg (6600lb)
Dimensions:	length 3.226m (10ft 5in); width 1.715m (5ft 7.5in); height 1.50m (4ft 11in)
Range:	322km (200 miles)
Armour:	14.5-30mm (0.6-1.2in)
Armament:	one 0.303in Bren machine gun
Powerplant:	one Daimler six-cylinder petrol engine developing 55hp (41kW)
Performance:	maximum speed 88.5km/h (55mph); fording 0.6m (2ft); vertical obstacle 0.533m (1ft 9in); trench 1.22m (4ft)

Autoblinda 41

The Autoblinda had its origins in a dual requirement by the Italians for an armoured car for the cavalry divisions and a high-performance car for use in policing Italy's numerous African colonies. The Autoblinda 40 was produced to meet both these needs. The Autoblinda 41 was fitted with the turret of the L 6/40 light tank, complete with its 20mm cannon. This was a more effective combination, and thus production centred on this version. The vehicle could be adapted for desert use, with special sand tyres, and could also be adapted to run on railway tracks, being extensively used in this capacity for anti-partisan duties in the Balkans. One of the most numerous Italian armoured cars of World War II, the vehicle also saw action in the Western Desert and Tunisia.

Country of origin:	Italy
Crew:	4
Weight:	7500kg (16,500lb)
Dimensions:	length 5.20m (17ft 1.5in); width 1.92m (6ft 4.5in); height 2.48m (7ft 11.5in)
Range:	400km (248 miles)
Armour:	6-40mm (0.23-1.57in)
Armament:	one 20mm Breda cannon; two 8mm machine guns
Powerplant:	one SAP Abm 1 six-cylinder water-cooled inline petrol engine developing 80hp (60kW)
Performance:	maximum road speed 78km/h (49mph); fording 0.7m (28in); vertical obstacle 0.3m (12in); trench 0.4m (1ft 4in)

WZ/34

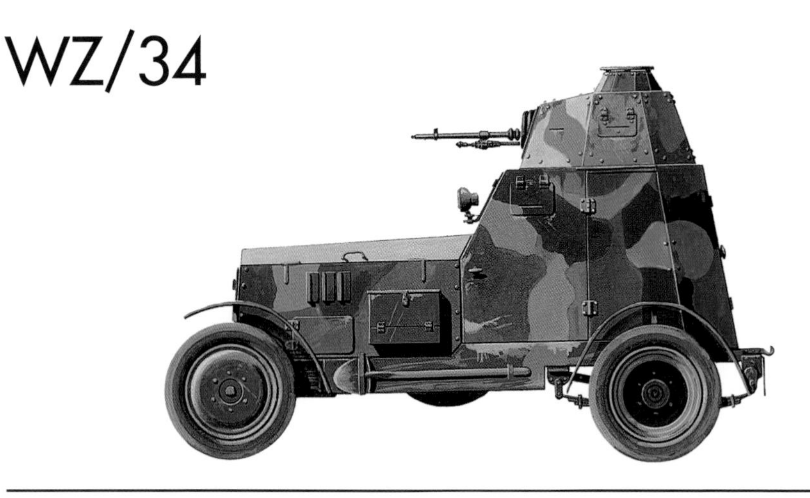

Prior to 1933, Poland's armoured car was the WZ/28, an unsatisfactory halftrack design using the chassis of the French Citroën-Kegresse B2 10CV. Ninety such vehicles were made, but by 1938, 87 of them had been converted into a wheeled 4x2 configuration and renamed the WZ/34. The WZ/34 shape had a recognizable car heritage, though the rear of the vehicle was built up into a high turret mounting either a 37mm (1.46in) SA-18 Puteaux L/21 gun or a 7.92mm (0.31in) Hotchkiss wz.25 machine gun. Neither the armament nor the meagre 6mm (0.23in) riveted armour plate provided any realistic defence against German panzers during the Polish invasion in September 1939.

Country of origin:	Poland
Crew:	2
Weight:	2200kg (4900lb)
Dimensions:	Length: 3.62m (11.87ft); width: 1.91m (6.27ft); height: 2.21m (7.25ft)
Range:	250km (150 miles)
Armour:	6mm (0.23in)
Armament:	1 x 37mm (1.46in) SA-18 Puteaux L/21 gun; or 1 x 7.92mm (0.31in) Hotchkiss wz.25 machine gun
Powerplant:	1 x Citroën B-T4 6-cylinder petrol, developing 20hp (15kW); or 1 x Fiat 6-cylinder petrol developing 25hp (19kW)
Performance:	Maximum road speed: 40km/h (25mph)

Landsverk 180

The Landsverk 180 armoured car was produced from 1938. Its foundation was the chassis of a Scania-Vabis truck with 6x4-wheel drive, though the Landsverk 180 had twin wheels on the rear axles, 10 wheels in total. Armour plate was riveted to the chassis, creating a boxy car-like shape capped by a small turret mounting a Madsen 20mm (0.78in) cannon and coaxial 7.92mm (0.31in) machine gun. Other machine guns were located just beneath the turret and facing backwards out of the rear of the hull. A powerful Scania-Vabis engine gave the Landsverk 180 a respectable top road speed of 80km/h (50mph), but the vehicle was soon obsolete in the context of modern World War II armour.

Country of origin:	Sweden
Crew:	5
Weight:	7000kg (15,400lb)
Dimensions:	Length: 5.87m (19.26ft); width: 2.5m (8.2ft); height: 2.33m (7.64ft)
Range:	290km (180 miles)
Armour:	8.5mm (0.33in)
Armament:	1 x 37mm (1.46in) cannon; 3 x 7.92mm (0.31in) MG
Powerplant:	1 x Scania-Vabis 6-cylinder diesel, developing 80hp (60kW)
Performance:	Maximum road speed: 80km/h (50mph)

Marmon Herrington

In 1938, the South African government ordered the development of an armoured car, based on foreign components but to be assembled in South Africa. The chassis and engine were made by Ford, the transmission by Marmon Herrington in the USA and the armament was imported from the UK. At the time it was first produced, the Marmon Herrington was the only armoured car available to British and South African forces in any numbers, and it saw extensive service in the Western Desert in the campaign against Rommel's *Afrika Korps*. Well-liked and sturdy, the vehicle was surprisingly effective despite light armour and armament, being relatively easy to maintain under operational conditions. The vehicles were much modified to suit local conditions, and were fitted in the field with many different weapons.

Country of origin:	South Africa
Crew:	4
Weight:	6000kg (13,200lb)
Dimensions:	length 4.88m (16ft); width 1.93m (6ft 4in); height 2.286m (7ft 6in)
Range:	322kg (200 miles)
Armour:	12mm (0.47in)
Armament:	one Vickers 7.7mm machine gun; one Boys 0.55in anti-tank rifle; one Bren Gun
Powerplant:	one Ford V-8 petrol engine
Performance:	maximum speed 80.5km/h (50mph)

Humber Mk I

Numerically, the Humber was the most important British armoured car of World War II, a total of 5400 being produced. Based on a pre-war wheeled light tank design by Guy, the Humber was initially fitted only with machine guns, which meant it was outgunned by the opposition. It was later upgunned and was used in North Africa from 1941 onwards, and wherever British troops were in action thereafter. Variants included a special radio carrier, known as Rear Link vehicle, which was fitted with a dummy gun, and an anti-aircraft version fitted with a special machine gun mounting. The vehicle gave excellent service, and was still being used by some armies in the Far East in the early 1960s. Like most British-produced armoured vehicles, the Humber was rugged, reliable and operationally sound.

Country of origin:	United Kingdom
Crew:	3 (4 in Mk III)
Weight:	6850kg (15,070lb)
Dimensions:	length 4.572m (15ft); width 2.184m (7ft 2in); height 2.34m (7ft 10in)
Range:	402km (250 miles)
Armour:	14.5-30mm (0.6-1.2in)
Armament:	one 15mm gun; one 7.92mm Besa machine gun
Powerplant:	one Rootes six-cylinder water-cooled petrol engine developing 90hp (77kW)
Performance:	maximum speed 72km/h (45mph); fording 0.6m (2ft); vertical obstacle 0.533m (1ft 9in); trench 1.22m (4ft)

Daimler Mk I

The Daimler armoured car was based on the same design as the Daimler scout car. Outwardly similar, it weighed almost twice as much and had a two-man turret. Work began in August 1939, but initial problems meant that the first production vehicles did not appear until April 1941. A total of 2694 were built. The turret was the same as that designed for the Tetrarch light airborne tank. The vehicle was equipped with hydraulic disc brakes, one of the earliest vehicles to be fitted with the system. First employed in North Africa, the vehicle established itself as an excellent addition to reconnaissance units, despite its limited combat capability, giving good all-round performance and reliability. The Daimler continued to serve for many years after the end of World War II.

Country of origin:	United Kingdom
Crew:	3
Weight:	7500kg (16,500lb)
Dimentions:	length 3.96m (13ft); width 2.44m (8ft); height 2.235m (7ft 4in)
Range:	330km (205 miles)
Armour:	14.5-30mm (0.6-1.2in)
Armament:	one 2-pounder gun; one Besa 7.92mm coaxial machine gun
Powerplant:	one Daimler six-cylinder petrol engine developing 95hp (71kW)
Performance:	maximum speed 80.5km/h (50mph); fording 0.6m (2ft); vertical obstacle 0.533m (1ft 9in); trench 1.22m (4ft)

BA-64

With the onset of the German–Soviet war in 1941, the Red Army discovered that most of its armoured cars were inadequately armoured and outclassed by German vehicles. The BA-64 was an attempt to remedy these problems. Its armoured plates were angled steeply to increase bullet and missile deflection, the suspension was strengthened over previous vehicles to improve off-road durability and it had bullet-proof tyres and bullet-proof glass in the driver's observation visor. Most significantly, it had four-wheel drive which enabled it to climb 30-degree slopes. Armament remained light – a single 7.62mm (0.3in) Degtyarev machine gun mounted in the turret.

Country of origin:	USSR
Crew:	2
Weight:	2360kg (5200lb)
Dimensions:	Length: 3.67m (12.04ft); width: 1.52m (4.99ft); height: 1.88m (6.17ft)
Range:	560km (350 miles)
Armour:	(Steel) 4–15mm (0.16–0.59in)
Armament:	1 x 7.62mm (0.3in) MG
Powerplant:	1 x GAZ-MM 4-cylinder petrol, developing 54hp (40kW)
Performance:	Maximum road speed: 80km/h (50mph)

T17E1 Staghound

The Staghound was developed in response to a US Army requirement for a Light Armoured Car in the early years of World War II. However, by the time the vehicle was ready for production, the American requirement had changed and so all production models were shipped to British and Commonwealth forces. The vehicle was fast, manoeuvrable and easy to operate and maintain, faring well in its initial combat in Italy in 1943, where small and nimble vehicles were at a premium. The Mk II was fitted with a tank howitzer and the Mk III with the turret from a Crusader tank. Other variants included a mine-clearer and command car. A well-liked vehicle, the Staghound continued in service with the British for several years after the end of World War II.

Country of origin:	United States
Crew:	5
Weight:	13,920kg (30,624lb)
Dimensions:	length 5.486m (18ft 0in); width 2.69m (8ft 10in); height 2.36m (7ft 9in)
Range:	724km (450 miles)
Armour:	8mm (0.31in)
Armament:	one 37mm gun; three 7.62mm machine guns
Powerplant:	two GMC six-cylinder petrol engines each developing 97hp (72kW)
Performance:	maximum speed 89km/h (55mph); fording 0.8m (2ft 8in); vertical obstacle 0.533m (1ft 9in)

SdKfz 234

The SdKfz 234 was produced by Büssing-NAG in response to a 1940 German Army requirement for an 8 x 8 armoured car suitable for operations in hot climates. More streamlined than the earlier 231 series and with thicker armour, the 234's excellent performance ensured its place as probably the best vehicle of its type to see service in World War II with any army. The most famous model was the 234/2 Puma, which used the turret intended for the Leopard light tank. This gave sufficient firepower to deal with most enemy reconnaissance armour encountered. The quality of the vehicle may be judged by the fact that, despite its high cost of manufacture, the vehicle was the only reconnaissance vehicle kept in production by the starved German war industry in 1945.

Country of origin:	Germany
Crew:	4
Weight:	11,740kg (25,828lb)
Dimensions:	length 6.80m (22ft 3.66in); width 2.33m (7ft 6.5in); height 2.38m (7ft 9.5in)
Range:	1000km (625 miles)
Armour:	5-15mm (0.19-0.59in)
Armament:	one 20mm KwK 30/50mm KwK 39/1 cannon; one coaxial 7.92mm machine gun
Powerplant:	one Tatra Model 103 diesel engine developing 210hp (157kW)
Performance:	maximum road speed 85km/h (53mph); fording 1.2m (3ft 10.75in); vertical obstacle 0.5m (1ft 7.75in); trench 1.35m (4ft 5in)

Light Armoured Car M8

The M8 was developed following American observation of operational trends in Europe in 1940-41. A design by Ford was accepted for service, and production of the M8 began in March 1943, continuing until the last month of World War II, by which time over 11,000 had been built. Despite British worries over its thin armour (it was known to British forces rather unkindly as the Greyhound), the M8 was a superb vehicle and widely used. A low silhouette made concealment easy and the vehicle had excellent cross-country mobility, plus the firepower to deal with any similar enemy vehicle (the 37mm gun was a tank armament at the beginning of the war). The M8 became the most important American armoured car, not just because of its excellent qualities, but because it was produced in enormous quantities.

Country of origin:	United States
Crew:	4
Weight:	7940kg (17,468lb)
Dimensions:	length 5.00m (16ft 5in); width 2.54m (8ft 4in); height 2.248m (7ft 4.5in)
Range:	563km (350 miles)
Armour:	8mm (0.31in)
Armament:	one 37mm gun; one 7.62 coaxial machine gun; one 12.7mm anti-aircraft machine gun
Powerplant:	one Hercules JDX six-cylinder petrol engine developing 110hp (82kW)
Performance:	maximum road speed 89km/h (55mph); fording 0.61m (24in); vertical obstacle 0.3m (12in)

Daimler Ferret Mk 2/3

Following a 1946 British requirement for a scout car, the first prototype of the Ferret was built by Daimler in 1949. Thereafter the Ferret remained in production until 1971, by which time nearly 4500 vehicles had been built for over 30 countries. The Mk I version was armed simply with a machine gun mounted on its open top. By the time the vehicle had reached the Mk V stage, the vehicle had acquired a turret and the ability to mount the Swingfire anti-tank missile. It also carried smoke dischargers. Metal channels were often carried on the front of the hull to facilitate movement across ditches or sandy terrain. The Ferret was still in use with the British Army in the 1980s, and had been widely used around the world for internal security roles.

Country of origin:	United Kingdom
Crew:	2
Weight:	4400kg (9680lb)
Dimensions:	length 3.835m (12ft 10in); width 1.905m (6ft 3in); height 1.879m (6ft 2in)
Range:	306km (191 miles)
Armour:	8-16mm (0.31-0.63in)
Armament:	one 7.62mm machine gun
Powerplant:	one Rolls-Royce six-cylinder petrol engine developing 129hp (96kW)
Performance:	maximum road speed 93km/h (58mph); fording 0.914m (3ft); vertical obstacle 0.406m (1ft 4in); trench 1.22m (4ft)

Panhard EBR/FL-10

Panhard and Levassor of Paris began producing armoured car designs in 1937. The first successful prototype was revealed in 1939. It was distinguished by its unusual wheel configuration. It had eight wheels, the four centre ones being fitted with steel rims for improved off-road traction. When on-road, these four wheels were raised and the vehicle driven on the usual four corner wheels. After WWII, Panhard reused the idea, and won a French Army competition for a new heavy armoured car with the EBR. EBRs were armed with a 75mm (2.95in) cannon as standard, and the FL-10 received the turret of the AMX-13 light tank which had a 12-round auto-feed mechanism. Production of EBRs ceased in 1960.

Country of origin:	France
Crew:	4
Weight:	15,200kg (33,500lb)
Dimensions:	Length (gun forwards): 7.33m (24ft); width: 2.42m (7.94ft); height: 2.58m (8.46ft)
Range:	600km (370 miles)
Armour:	40mm (1.57in)
Armament:	1 x 75mm (2.95in) cannon; 1 x 7.62mm (0.3in) coaxial MG
Powerplant:	1 x Panhard 12-cylinder petrol, developing 200hp (149kW)
Performance:	Maximum road speed: 105km/h (65mph); fording: 1.2m (3.9ft); gradient: 60 percent; vertical obstacle: 0.4m (1.3ft)

YP-104

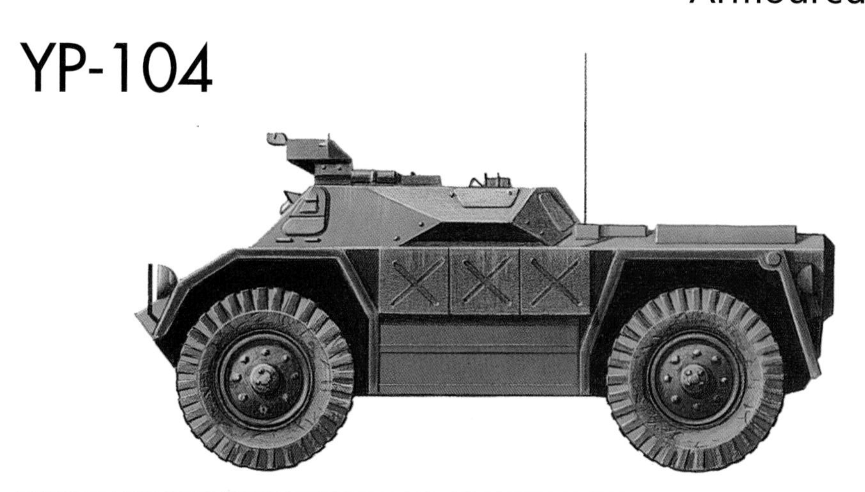

The YP-104 was a Dutch scout car developed in the early 1960s and it served until decommissioned in the late 1970s. Whereas most modern reconnaissance vehicles are armed, the YP-104 relied mainly on its top speed of 98km/h (61mph) for defence, though a single 7.62mm (0.3in) machine gun was an optional fitting. The design of the YP-104 was based closely on the British Daimler Ferret armoured scout car used in the British Army from 1952. Like the Ferret, the YP-104 had an all-welded steel construction with three windows set in a raised crew compartment. The armour was sufficient to protect against light small-arms fire, but not against heavy or persistent machine-gun bursts.

Country of origin:	Netherlands
Crew:	2
Weight:	5400kg (11,900lb)
Dimensions:	Length: 4.33m (14.21ft); width: 2.08m (6.82ft); height: 2.03m (6.66ft)
Range:	500km (310 miles)
Armour:	(Steel) 16mm (0.63in) maximum
Armament:	1 x 7.62mm (0.3in) MG (optional)
Powerplant:	1 x Herkules JXLD 6-cylinder petrol, developing 131hp (98kW)
Performance:	Maximum road speed: 98km/h (61mph); fording: 0.91m (2.99ft); gradient: 46 percent; vertical obstacle: 0.41m (1.35ft); trench: 1.22m (4ft)

FUG

The FUG is an amphibious scout car based upon the Soviet BRDM-1. Amphibious power is provided by two waterjets set in the rear of the hull, and the only preparation required for entering the water is to erect a trim vane at the front of the vehicle. The FUG is in most ways a simple vehicle. Its hull is made of all-welded steel armour plate and its only armament is a single 7.62mm (0.3in) SGMB machine gun. Three more modern features are central tyre-pressure regulation, infrared headlights and NBC options. The FUG is mainly in service today with former Eastern Bloc nations such as Hungary, the Czech Republic, Poland and Romania.

Country of origin:	Hungary
Crew:	2 + 4
Weight:	7000kg (15,400lb)
Dimensions:	Length: 5.79m (18.99ft); width: 2.5m (8.2ft); height: 1.91m (6.23ft)
Range:	600km (370 miles)
Armour:	(Steel) 10mm (0.39in)
Armament:	1 x 7.62mm (0.3in) SGMB MG
Powerplant:	1 x Csepel D.414.44 4-cylinder diesel, developing 100hp (75kW)
Performance:	Maximum road speed: 87km/h (54mph); fording: amphibious; gradient: 32 percent; vertical obstacle: 0.4m (1.3ft)

M706

Cadillac Gage began design on a multi-purpose armoured vehicle at the beginning on the 1960s which, following successful trials, was put into production in 1964 as the V-100 Commando, powered by a Chrysler engine. The US Army later designated the vehicle as M706. The vehicle was primarily destined for export but the conflict in Vietnam in the 1960s soon required a vehicle to fill the dual patrol and escort roles. Significant numbers of M706s saw service with both South Vietnamese and US troops. In Vietnam it proved a versatile and effective counter-insurgency weapon, being ideal for rapid counterattack when attached to ambushed convoys. A scaled-up version, the V-200, was sold to Singapore, and 1971 the V-100 was replaced by the V-150.

Country of origin:	United States
Crew:	3 + 2
Weight:	9888kg (21,753lb)
Dimensions:	length 5.689m (18ft 8in); width 2.26m (7ft 5in); height 1.981m (6ft 6in)
Range:	643km (400 miles)
Armour:	classified
Armament:	two 7.62mm machine guns
Powerplant:	one V-8 diesel engine developing 202bhp (151kW)
Performance:	maximum road speed 88.5km/h (55mph); fording amphibious; vertical obstacle 0.609m (2ft 0in); trench not applicable

BRDM-2

The BRDM-2, also called the BTR-40-P2, was introducted into service in the mid 1960s. Like its predecessor the BRDM-1, the BRDM-2 was an amphibious reconnaissance vehicle but with several significant modifications. Chief amongst these was a new engine, the GAZ-41 V8, which could develop 140hp (104kW) of power instead of the BRDM-1's 90hp (67kW). The greater power was combined with an increased range of 750km (465 miles) as opposed to 500km (310 miles). Armament was also increased on the BRDM-2. One 14.5mm (0.57in) KPVT machine gun was mounted on the turret along with a coaxial 7.62mm (0.3in) machine gun, and a Sagger ATGW launcher could be fitted as an option.

Country of origin:	USSR
Crew:	5
Weight:	7000kg (15,435lb)
Dimensions:	Length: 5.7m (18.7ft); width: 2.35m (7.71ft); height: 2.3m (7.6ft)
Range:	750km (465 miles)
Armour:	(Steel) 10mm (0.39in) maximum
Armament:	1 x 14.5mm (0.5in) or 7.62mm (0.3in) MG
Powerplant:	1 x GAZ-41 V8 petrol, developing 140hp (104kW)
Performance:	Maximum road speed: 100km/h (62mph); fording: amphibious; gradient: 60 percent; vertical obstacle: 0.4m (1.31ft); trench: 1.25m (4.1ft)

V-150 Commando

The V-150 Commando was the successor to the V-100 developed in the early 1960s. It first appeared in the early 1970s, containing a number of improvements on the V-100, its most significant being the installation of a diesel engine to provide a greater range and less risk of fire than with a petrol engine. The V-150 was easily adapted for a number of roles, ranging from armoured personnel carrier to riot control and recovery vehicle. A wide range of armaments could be fitted to give extra flexibility, from anti-aircraft cannon to mortars and anti-tank guided weapons. All versions are fully amphibious, propelled in the water by their wheels. In addition, a wide variety of armaments can be fitted. A popular export model, the V-150 has been sold to around 25 countries.

Country of origin:	United States
Crew:	3 + 2
Weight:	9888kg (21,753lb)
Dimensions:	length 5.689m (18ft 8in); width 2.26m (7ft 5in); height 1.981m (6ft 6in)
Range:	643km (400 miles)
Armour:	classified
Armament:	various, including one 25mm cannon; one 7.62mm machine gun
Powerplant:	one V-540 V-8 diesel engine developing 202hp (151kW)
Performance:	maximum road speed 88.5km/h (55mph); fording amphibious; vertical obstacle 0.609m (2ft 0in); trench not applicable

Fiat-OTOBREDA Type 6616 Armoured Car

The Type 6616 began its production life in 1972 as a joint venture between Fiat and OTO-Melara. Despite the end of production in the late 1980s, it is still in service today with the Italian Carabinieri and several Latin American and African countries. The three-man crew are seated in an amphibious all-welded steel armoured hull with a maximum thickness of 8mm (0.31in). Vision is provided in a 200-degree arc by five vision blocks, while the driver has a dedicated hatch and a roof aperture for a night-vision periscope. Standard main armament is a Rheinmetall 20mm (0.78in) Mk 20 Rh 202 cannon. A further option is a 90mm (3.54in) gun mounted in an OTOBREDA OTO T 90 CKL turret.

Country of origin:	Italy
Crew:	3
Weight:	8000kg (17,600lb)
Dimensions:	Length: 5.37m (17.62ft); width: 2.5m (8.2ft); height: 2.03m (6.66ft)
Range:	700km (450 miles)
Armour:	(Steel) 6–8mm (0.24–0.31in)
Armament:	1 x Rheinmetall 20mm (0.78in) Mk 20 Rh 202 cannon;1 x 7.62mm (0.3in) coaxial machine gun
Powerplant:	1 x Fiat Model 8062.24 supercharged diesel, developing 160hp (119kW) at 3200rpm
Performance:	Maximum road speed: 100km/h (75mph); fording: amphibious; gradient: 60 percent; vertical obstacle: 0.45m (1.47ft)

EGESA EE-9 Cascavel

The EE-9 was produced by the Brazilian armaments company ENGESA in the early 1970s as an attempt to replace obsolete US 6x6 M8 Greyhound armoured cars. It is itself a 6x6 vehicle, and originally utilized the M8 turret on the Mk I Cascavel. Subsequent indigenous models featured an ENGESA turret with 90mm (3.54in) gun, though the Mk II export model had the French Hispano-Suiza H-90 turret. Most modern Cascavels are fitted with computerized fire-control systems and laser range-finders. NBC protection is a further option. The Cascavel also has excellent lightweight armour developed by ENGESA and the University of São Paulo in a joint programme.

Country of origin:	Brazil
Crew:	3
Weight:	13,400kg (29,500lb)
Dimensions:	Length (with gun): 6.2m (20.34ft); width: 2.59m (8.5ft); height: 2.68m (8.79ft)
Range:	880km (545 miles)
Armour:	16mm (0.62in)
Armament:	1 x 90mm (3.54in) cannon; 1 x coaxial MG, some versions 1 x 12.7mm (0.5in) or 7.62mm (0.3in) turret-mounted MG
Powerplant:	1 x Detroit Diesel 6V-53 6-cylinder diesel developing 212hp (158kW)
Performance:	Maximum road speed: 100km/h (60mph); fording: 1m (3.3ft); gradient: 60 percent; vertical obstacle: 0.6m (2ft)

FV 721 Fox

The FV 721 Fox entered service with the British Army in 1973, having undergone development since 1965 as the replacement for the Ferret armoured car. Armament received a major upgrade from the Ferret's machine guns. The 30mm (1.18in) Rarden cannon was introduced, which when loaded with Armour-Piercing Discarding-Sabot Tracer (APDST) rounds can destroy light armoured vehicles at 1000m (3300ft) and even penetrate weaker armour points of MBTs. The Fox is a quick vehicle with a road speed of 104km/h (65mph) and can be made fully amphibious by fitting an external float screen. The wheels then power and steer the vehicle through the water. The Fox is no longer in British service.

Country of origin:	United Kingdom
Crew:	3
Weight:	6120kg (13,500lb)
Dimensions:	Length (gun included): 5.08m (16.67ft); width: 2.13m (6.99ft); height: 1.98m (6.5ft)
Range:	434km (270 miles)
Armour:	Aluminium (details classified)
Armament:	1 x 30mm (1.18in) Rarden cannon; 1 x coaxial 7.62mm (0.3in) MG; 2 x 4 smoke grenade launchers
Powerplant:	1 x Jaguar XK 4.2-litre 6-cylinder petrol, developing 190hp (142kW)
Performance:	Maximum speed: 104km/h (65mph); fording: 1m (3.3ft)/amphibious; gradient: 46 percent; vertical obstacle: 0.5m (1.6ft); trench: 1.22m (4ft)

RBY Mk1

The RBY Mk1 is a light reconnaissance vehicle first manufactured by Israel Aircraft Industries in the mid-1970s. Though the hull is all-welded steel with 8mm (0.31in) armour, there is no top cover for the crew compartment. Also, the front windscreen can be folded flat for unimpaired visibility. These features increase the RBY's vulnerability to small-arms and shell fire, but reduce the chances of occupant heat exhaustion in the hot Middle Eastern climate. A variety of machine guns and cannon, even a 106mm (4.17in) recoilless rifle, can be fitted to the rim of the hull. The RBY Mk1's bonnet and bumpers are made of fibre glass designed to disintegrate harmlessly if the vehicle strikes a mine.

Country of origin:	Israel
Crew:	2 + 6
Weight:	3600kg (7900lb)
Dimensions:	Length: 5.02m (16.47ft); width: 2.03m (6.66ft); height: 1.66m (5.45ft)
Range:	550km (340 miles)
Armour:	(Steel) 8mm (0.31in)
Armament:	Various MGs and cannons
Powerplant:	1 x Chrysler 6-cylinder petrol, developing 120hp (89kW)
Performance:	Maximum road speed: 100km/h (62mph); fording: 0.4m (1.3ft); gradient: 60 percent

MOWAG Spy

The MOWAG Spy is a 4x4 version of the excellent Piranha series of vehicles. It has a basic armoured personnel carrier shape, though the sides of the hull are angled steeply to deflect both small-arms fire and the force of mine explosions, aided by a ground clearance of 0.5m (1.64ft). Armament is located in a small turret at the rear of the vehicle. Standard fitment is a 12.7mm (0.5in) Browning M2 HB with a coaxial 7.62mm (0.3in) general-purpose machine gun. The latter can be mounted in a pair to provide extra firepower and dispense with the Browning. Other options include a 20mm (0.78in) Oerlikon GAS-AOA cannon. All weapons are remotely operated from inside the crew compartment.

Country of origin:	Switzerland
Crew:	3
Weight:	7500kg (16,500lb)
Dimensions:	Length: 4.52m (14.83ft); width: 2.5m (8.2ft); height: 1.66m (5.45ft)
Range:	700km (430 miles)
Armour:	Details classified
Armament:	1 x 12.7mm (0.5in) MG; 1 x 7.62mm (0.3in) coaxial MG
Powerplant:	1 x Detroit or Cummins 8-cylinder petrol, developing 216hp (161kW) at 2800rpm
Performance:	Maximum road speed: 110km/h (68mph); fording: amphibious; gradient: 70 percent

Spähpanzer 2 Luchs

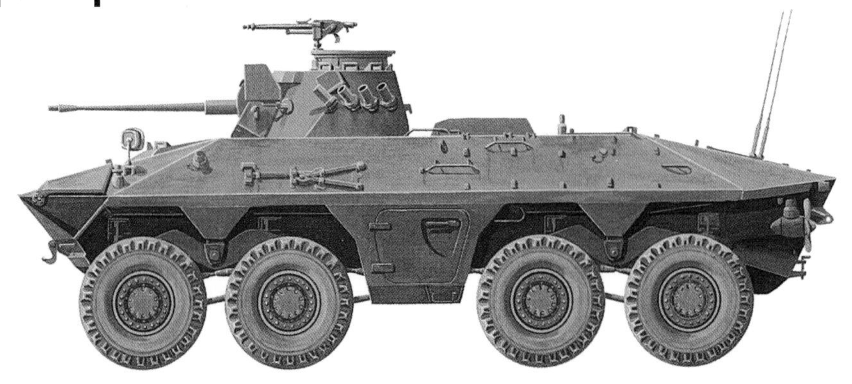

Having previously relied on American or European imports, West Germany began to develop a range of indigenous armoured vehicles during the 1960s. From 1975, Thyssen Henschel began production of an 8 x 8 armoured reconnaissance vehicle – the Luchs – completing 408 before 1978. Too expensive for significant export success, the vehicle was well-armoured and came with a range of extras such as power steering to reduce driver fatigue, night vision, a nuclear, biological and chemical (NBC) system and pre-heating for the engine, essential for winter operations. Fully amphibious, the vehicle has an exceptional operational range. In the water it is powered by two propellers mounted at the rear of the vehicle. The turret has full power traverse through 360 degrees.

Country of origin:	West Germany
Crew:	4
Weight:	19,500kg (42,900lb)
Dimensions:	length 7.743m (25ft 4.75in); width 2.98m (9ft 9.3in); height (including anti-aircraft machine gun) 2.905m (9ft 6.3in)
Range:	800km (500 miles)
Armour:	classified
Armament:	one 20mm cannon; one 7.62 machine gun
Powerplant:	one Daimler-Benz OM 403 A 10-cylinder diesel engine developing 390hp (291kW)
Performance:	maximum road speed 90km/h (56mph); fording amphibious; vertical obstacle 0.60m (1ft 11.7in); trench 1.90m (6ft 3in)

Dragoon

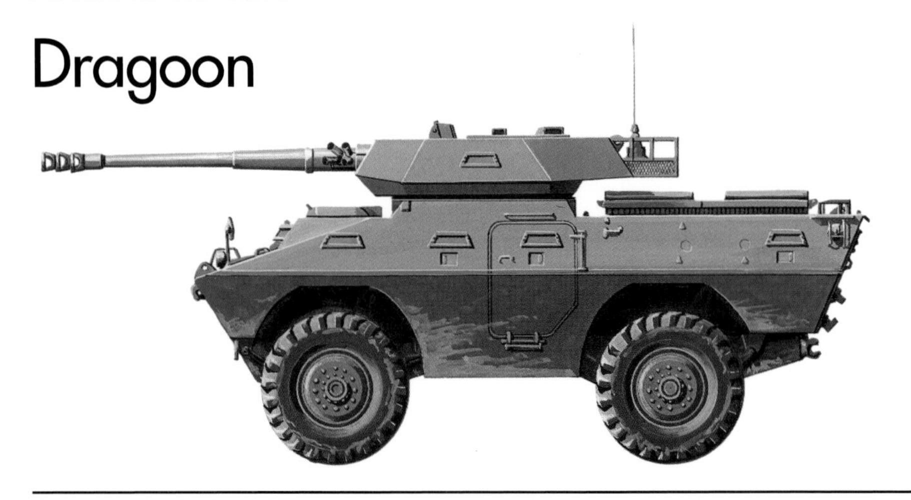

The Dragoon Armoured Fighting Vehicle is a fast 4x4 vehicle armed with a turret-mounted 90mm (3.54in) KEnerga gun and coaxial 7.62mm (0.3in) machine gun. Wheels are recessed for travel over rough terrain and the steel hull is designed for fully amphibious operations. Since 1984, when production was taken over by the merger-created AV Technology Corporation, variants have emerged including an 81mm (3.19in) Armoured Mortar Carrier, a turretless APC carrying six infantry, a TOW ATGW launcher and an ambulance. Turret armament can be altered to 40mm (1.57in) cannon or 12.7mm (0.5in) machine gun. The Dragoon is in service with security forces in the US, Thailand, Turkey and various Latin American countries.

Country of origin:	United States
Crew:	3 + 6
Weight:	12,700kg (28,000lb)
Dimensions:	Length: 5.89m (19.3ft); width: 2.44m (8ft); height: 2.13m (6.98ft)
Range:	1045km (650 miles)
Armour:	Steel (details classified)
Armament:	1 x 90mm (3.54in) KEnerga gun; 1 x coaxial 7.62mm (0.3in) MG
Powerplant:	1 x Detroit 6V-53T 6-cylinder turbo diesel, developing 300hp (223kW) at 2800rpm
Performance:	Maximum road speed: 116km/h (72mph); fording: amphibious; gradient: 60 percent; vertical obstacle: 0.6m (2ft)

AMX-10

In the 1950s, the French Army issued a requirement for a replacement for the standard Panhard EBR armoured car with a more powerful armament. The first prototype of the AMX-10 was completed in 1971, and the vehicle entered service in 1979. The two main drawbacks were cost (being more expensive to build than some main battle tanks) and level of sophistication, particularly important for a conscript army. The suspension could be adjusted for different types of terrain and the fire-control system was the most sophisticated installed in any vehicle of its class, with a laser rangefinder, computer and low-light TV system and complete amphibious capability. The internal layout is conventional, with driver at the front, a three-man turret and engine and transmission at the rear.

Country of origin:	France
Crew:	4
Weight:	15,400kg (33,880lb)
Dimensions:	length 9.15m (30ft 0.25in); width 2.95m (9ft 8in); height 2.68m (8ft 9.5in)
Range:	800km (500 miles)
Armour:	8-32mm (0.31-1.25in)
Armament:	one 105mm gun; one 7.62mm machine gun
Powerplant:	one Baudouin Model 6F 11 SRX eight-cylinder diesel developing 260hp (194kW)
Performance:	maximum road speed 85km/h (53mph); fording amphibious; vertical obstacle 0.70m (2ft 3.25in); trench 1.15m (3ft 9in)

Panhard ERC

The first Panhard ERC appeared in 1977, based on technology developed for a 1970 French Army requirement but not used. Production began in 1979 and the vehicle was quickly exported to Nigeria, Argentina and Iraq amongst others, with the French using it as part of their Rapid Intervention Force. The vehicle was fully amphibious, with six-wheel drive capability. One interesting feature was that the centre wheels could be raised or lowered to deal with different types of terrain. Other features included laser rangefinder, night vision equipment, nuclear, biological and chemical (NBC) defence systems and a land navigation system, essential for desert operations. The Panhard is fully amphibious, being propelled in the water by its wheels.

Country of origin:	France
Crew:	3
Weight:	7400kg (16,280lb)
Dimensions:	length 7.693m (25ft 2.75in); width 2.495m (8ft 2.25in); height 2.254m (7ft 4.75in)
Range:	800km (500 miles)
Armour:	10mm (0.39in)
Armament:	one 90mm gun; one 7.62mm coaxial machine gun
Powerplant:	one Peugeot V-6 petrol engine developing 166hp (116kW)
Performance:	maximum road speed 100km/h (62mph); fording amphibious; vertical obstacle 0.80m (2ft 7.5in); trench 1.10m (3ft 7.5in)

Cougar

The Cougar is essentially a Swiss MOWAG Piranha produced by the Diesel Division of General Motors of Canada between 1979 and 1982. Three basic variants exist. The Cougar Gun Wheeled Fire Support Vehicle (WFSV) is fitted with the turret of an Alvis Scorpion with 76mm (2.99in) gun. An APC variant, the Grizzly APC, has the capacity to carry three crew and six other personnel. Finally, the Husky Wheeled Maintenance and Recovery Vehicle features a roof-mounted crane for engineering projects. All variants are amphibious. The Cougars are still in service today with the Canadian Army, though most have been upgraded to an 8x8 configuration. Specifications relate to the Wheeled Fire Support Vehicle variant.

Country of origin:	Canada
Crew:	3
Weight:	9526kg (21,004lb)
Dimensions:	Length: 5.97m (19.59ft); width: 2.53m (8.3ft); height: 2.62m (8.6ft)
Range:	602km (374 miles)
Armour:	10mm (0.39in)
Armament:	1 x 76.2mm (3in) cannon; 1 x 7.62mm (0.3in) coaxial MG
Powerplant:	1 x Detroit Diesel 6V-53T 6-cylinder diesel developing 215hp (160kW)
Performance:	Maximum road speed: 102km/h (63mph); fording: amphibious; gradient: 60 percent; vertical obstacle: 0.5m (1.6ft)

EE-3 Jararaca

The EE-3 Jararaca was produced by the now-dissolved ENGESA company. It is basically a diminutive 4x4 scout car only 4.12m (13.52ft) in length and 1.56m (5.12ft) in height. Its small size and light weight give it excellent manoeuvrability and speed, qualities it can maintain over rough ground using a central tyre-pressure regulation system. All tyres are of run-flat type. The hull is constructed from double-layer steel armour plate. Inside is a three-man crew with the driver positioned centrally over the front glacis plate. Three periscopes provide him with hatch-down visibility. The EE-3 accepts various armament configurations ranging from the standard 12.7mm (0.5in) Browning machine gun to a MILAN ATGW.

Country of origin:	Brazil
Crew:	3
Weight:	5500kg (12,100lb)
Dimensions:	Length: 4.12m (13.52ft); width: 2.13m (6.99ft); height: 1.56m (5.12ft)
Range:	750km (470 miles)
Armour:	Double-layer steel (details classified)
Armament:	1 x 12.7mm (0.5in) Browning M2 HB as standard
Powerplant:	1 x Mercedes-Benz OM 314A 4-cylinder turbo diesel, developing 120hp (89kW) at 2800rpm
Performance:	Maximum road speed: 100km/h (60mph); fording: 0.6m (2ft); gradient: 60 percent; vertical obstacle: 0.4m (1.3ft); trench: 0.4m (1.3ft)

VEC Cavalry Scout Vehicle

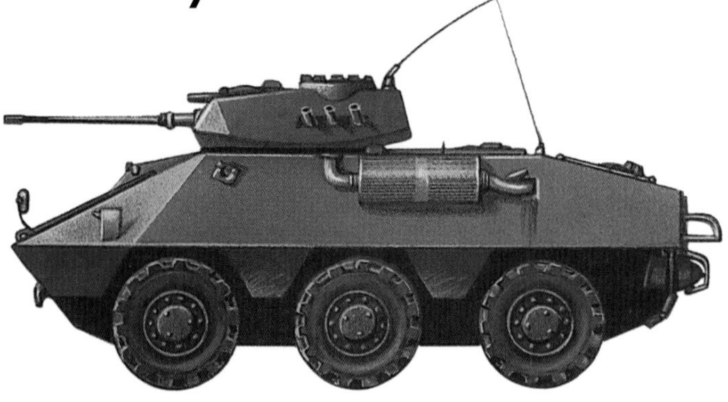

The Vehículo de Exploracíon de Caballereía (VEC) emerged in prototype stage in the late 1970s, before entering service with the Spanish Army in 1980. It is a fairly standard armoured car design, with an all-welded aluminium armour providing protection across its frontal section against small arms ammunition up to 7.62mm (0.3in) armour-piercing rounds. The VEC holds five crew comfortably; the engine is set at the rear to conserve interior space. The vehicle is defended by either a 20mm (0.78in) cannon in a FIAT-OTO Melara turret, or a 25mm (0.98in) Oerlikon cannon in an Oerlikon-Bührle GDB-COA turret. NBC options are available and the VEC is also fully amphibious.

Country of origin:	Spain
Crew:	5
Weight:	13,750kg (30,300lb)
Dimensions:	Length: 6.1m (20ft); width: 2.5m (8.2ft); height: 3.3m (10.83ft)
Range:	800km (500 miles)
Armour:	Aluminium (details classified)
Armament:	1 x 20mm (0.78in) cannon; or 1 x 25mm (0.98in) cannon; 1 x coaxial 7.62mm (0.3in) MG; 2 x 3 smoke grenade launchers
Powerplant:	(latest models) 1 x Scania DS9 diesel, developing 310hp (231kW)
Performance:	Maximum road speed: 103km/h (64mph); fording: amphibious; gradient: 60 percent; vertical obstacle: 0.6m (2ft); trench: 1.5m (4.9ft)

OTO Melara R3 Capraia

The R3 Capraia is a heavily armoured Italian reconnaissance vehicle which entered production in 1982. The basic vehicle is 4x4 configuration, with a hull that features welded aluminium armour with a thickness up to 32mm (1.26in), strong enough to deflect small-arms rounds of 7.62mm (0.3in) calibre. Many optional turrets and externally mounted weapons are available for the R3. Seen here is the T20 FA-HS turret fitted with an Oerlikon KAD-B17 20mm (0.78in) cannon. Other turret configurations include the T 7.62 FA (7.62mm (0.3in) machine gun), T 12.7 FA (12.7mm (0.5in) machine gun), T 106x2 FA (twin M40 106mm (4.17in) recoilless rifles) and a TOW turret (mounted launcher for a Hughes TOW ATGW).

Country of origin:	Italy
Crew:	4 or 5
Weight:	3200kg (7100lb)
Dimensions:	Length: 4.86m (15.94ft); width: 1.78m (5.84ft); height: 1.55m (5.09ft)
Range:	500km (300 miles)
Armour:	(Aluminium) 32mm (1.26in)
Armament:	(T 20 FA-HS turret) 1 x Oerlikon KAD-B17 20mm (0.78in) cannon
Powerplant:	1 x Fiat Model 8144.81.200 4-cylinder diesel, developing 95hp (71kW) at 4200rpm
Performance:	Maximum road speed: 120km/h (75mph); fording: amphibious; gradient: 75 percent

Cardoen Piranha 6x6D

The Chilean Piranha is a Swiss MOWAG Piranha produced under licence by Carlos Cardoen since the early 1980s (FAMAE are also heavily involved with Piranha production). The Swiss and Chilean versions are almost the same, though Cardoen has upgraded its vehicle to a 400-litre (106-gal) fuel capacity instead of the Swiss model's 250 litres (66gal). Though most 6x6 Piranhas in Chile are APCs, a small number are produced as Fire Support Vehicles. These have a Cockerill 90mm (3.54in) MK3 gun mounted on an ENGESA ET-90 90mm turret or a Cardoen 90mm turret. Other trial versions have been fitted with ATGW launchers and even Oerlikon Contraves 20mm (0.78in) GAD-AOA anti-aircraft turrets.

Country of origin:	Chile
Crew:	3 or 4
Weight:	10,500kg (23,200lb)
Dimensions:	Length: 5.97m (19.59ft); width: 2.5m (8.2ft); height: 2.65m (8.69ft)
Range:	700km (435 miles)
Armour:	Not available
Armament:	1 x 90mm (3.54in) cannon; 1 x 12.7mm (0.5in) coaxial MG
Powerplant:	1 x Detroit Diesel 6V-53T diesel, developing 300hp (224kW) at 2800rpm
Performance:	Maximum road speed: 100km/h (60mph); fording: amphibious; gradient: 70 percent; vertical obstacle: 0.5m (1.6ft)

Renault VBC 90

The Renault Vehicule Blindé de Combat 90 (VBC 90) was produced mainly for export markets. Sales of the vehicle have, however, been disappointing and it is currently in service with only the French gendarmerie and Omani military forces. Unlike many other nations, France commonly fits large-calibre guns to its armoured cars. The VBC 90 mounts a powerful 90mm (3.54in) weapon on its Giat TS-90 turret. Computerized fire-control systems and laser range-finders are also fitted, and today, VBC 90s in service have NBC technology and night-vision devices. Production of the VBC 90 is complete and no variants other than the basic model have been produced.

Country of origin:	France
Crew:	3
Weight:	13,500kg (29,800lb)
Dimensions:	Length (gun forwards): 8.8m (28.87ft); width: 2.5m (8.2ft); height: 2.55m (8.37ft)
Range:	1000km (620 miles)
Armour:	Classified
Armament:	1 x 90mm (3.54in) cannon; 1 x 7.62mm (0.3in) coaxial MG; 1 x 7.62mm (0.3in) turret-mounted MG (option); 2 x 2 smoke grenade launchers
Powerplant:	1 x Renault MIDS 06.20.45 turbo diesel, developing 220hp (164kW)
Performance:	Maximum speed: 92km/h (57mph); fording: 1.2m (3.9ft); gradient: 50 percent; vertical obstacle: 0.5m (1.6ft); trench: 1m (3.3ft)

Pandur

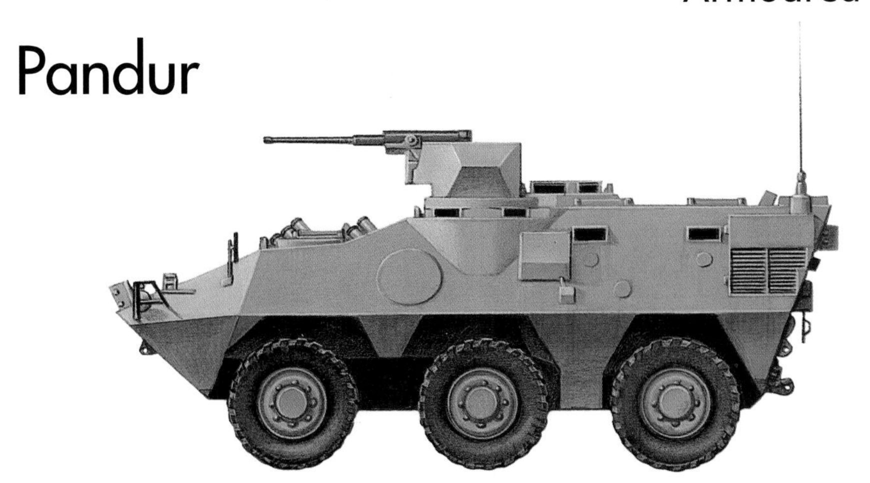

The Pandur 6x6 armoured vehicle was developed by Steyr-Daimler-Puch in the mid-1980s. It entered service with the Austrian Army in 1994 and many other armies since. A common chassis is produced in either 'A' or 'B' variants: 'A' with a raised centre roof and 'B' with a flat roof. Both house a two-man crew. The APC variant has additional space for eight personnel. Pandurs come in a range of variants according to turret or armament configuration. The Pandur Armoured Reconnaissance Fire Support Vehicle, for example, has a Mark 8 90mm (3.5in) gun mounted in a Cockerill LCTS turret, while the Light Armoured Vehicle features the MultiGun Turreted System with 25, 30 or 35mm (0.98, 1.18 or 1.38in) cannon.

Country of origin:	Austria
Crew:	2 + 8
Weight:	13,500kg (29,800lb)
Dimensions:	Length: 5.7m (18.7ft); width: 2.5m (8.2ft); height: 1.82m (5.97ft)
Range:	700km (430 miles)
Armour:	8mm (0.31in)
Armament:	1 x 12.7mm (0.5in) MG; 2 x 3 smoke grenades launchers; various other configurations
Powerplant:	Steyr WD 612.95 6-cylinder turbo diesel, developing 240hp (179kW)
Performance:	Maximum road speed: 100km/h (60mph); fording: 1.2m (3.9ft); gradient: 70 percent; vertical obstacle: 0.5m (1.6ft)

RPX-90

The Lohr RPX-90 is a 4x4 armoured car with a powerful Hispano-Suiza CNMP 90mm (3.54in) cannon as standard. This weapon enables it to tackle MBTs and fortified positions at close ranges, though armoured reconnaissance remains its primary role. Other turrets are available for the RPX-90, including variants with 20mm (0.78in) cannon, 60mm (2.36in) mortar and MATRA SATCP surface-to-air missiles. The vehicle has an all-welded steel hull and large low-pressure tyres to give good off-road traction. Wide bulletproof windows at the front provide the driver with broad visibility. These can be shuttered in combat. Despite its boat-like shape, the RPX-90 is not amphibious.

Country of origin:	France
Crew:	3
Weight:	11,000kg (24,300lb)
Dimensions:	Length (gun forwards): 7.41m (24.31ft); width: 2.56m (8.39ft); height: 2.54m (8.33ft)
Range:	1000km (620 miles)
Armour:	Classified
Armament:	1 x 90mm (3.54in) cannon; 1 x 7.62mm (0.3in) coaxial MG
Powerplant:	1 x BMW 6-cylinder turbo diesel, developing 310hp (231kW)
Performance:	Maximum road speed: 105km/h (65mph); fording: 1.4m (4.6ft); gradient: 40 percent; vertical obstacle: 0.6m (2ft)

Rooikat

The Rooikat is one of the world's most potent armoured cars. Its development programme began in 1978, but it took 12 years before it was ready to enter service in 1990. Two main versions are available. The Rooikat 76 has a stabilized 76mm (2.99in) gun, and the Rooikat 105 has an even more powerful 105mm (4.13in) anti-tank gun which can fire six rounds per minute. Such firepower allows the Rooikat to make aggressive seek-and-destroy missions as well as combat reconnaissance. The classified armoured type protects the crew from anti-tank mines and small arms ammunition up to 24mm (0.94in) calibre. All tyres have run-flat inserts – mobility is maintained even with loss of pressure in all eight tyres.

Country of origin:	South Africa
Crew:	4
Weight:	28,000kg (61,700lb)
Dimensions:	Length: 7.09m (23.26ft); width: 2.9m (9.51ft); height: 2.8m (9.19ft)
Range:	1000km (620 miles)
Armour:	Classified
Armament:	1 x 76mm (2.99in) gun (Rooikat 76); 1 x 105mm (4.13in) gun (Rooikat 105); 1 x coaxial 7.62mm (0.3in) MG; 1 x turret-mounted 7.62mm (0.3in) MG; 2 x 4 smoke grenade launchers
Powerplant:	1 x V-10 diesel, developing 563hp (420kW)
Performance:	Maximum road speed: 120km/h (75mph); fording: 1.5m (4.9ft); gradient: 70 percent; vertical obstacle: 1m (3.3ft); trench: 2m (6.6ft)

LGS Fennek

The LGS Fennek is a joint project of Krauss-Maffei Wegmann of Germany and SP Aerospace and Vehicle Systems B.V. of the Netherlands. It is an Armed Reconnaissance Vehicle, and uses the latest Tactical Command and Control System (TCSS). Battlefield observation is conducted using the STN Atlas Elektronik BAA technology. This combines a thermal imager, day camera and laser rangefinder in a single unit extended on a mast 1.5m (4.9ft) above the vehicle roof. A GPS system plots the position of enemy/friendly units on constantly updated digitized maps. Standard armament is an electrically controlled machine gun or 40mm (1.57in) grenade launcher. Some Dutch vehicles mount the Rafael Gill ATGW unit.

Country of origin:	Germany/Netherlands
Crew:	3
Weight:	7900kg (17,400lb)
Dimensions:	Length: 5.72m (18.77ft); width: 2.49m (8.17ft); height: 2.18m (7.15ft)
Range:	860km (530 miles)
Armour:	Details classified
Armament:	1 x 7.62mm (0.3in) or 12.7mm (0.5in) MG; or 1 x 40mm (1.57in) cannon
Powerplant:	1 x Deutz diesel, developing 240hp (179kW) at 2800rpm
Performance:	Maximum road speed: 115km/h (71mph); fording: 1m (3.3ft); gradient: 60 percent

Scout

The Cadillac Gage Commando Scout, to give it its proper title, has a boat-like appearance which belies the fact that it is not amphibious (its maximum fording depth is 1.17m/3.84ft). Its name suggests a reconnaissance role, which is its primary duty, but it can also perform anti-tank and command post missions with different fitments. Turret options include a TOW ATGW launcher, a combination of a 40mm (1.58in) grenade launcher and a 12.7mm (0.5in) machine gun, or a twin machine gun. Its light weight and aerodynamic shape give the Scout an operating range of 1290km (800 miles), greater than most reconnaissance vehicles. It also has run-flat tyres as standard.

Country of origin:	United States
Crew:	2–3
Weight:	7240kg (15,960lb)
Dimensions:	Length: 5m (16.4ft); width: 2.05m (6.73ft); height: 2.16m (7.09ft)
Range:	1290km (800 miles)
Armour:	Steel (details classified)
Armament:	1 x 7.62mm (0.3in) MG
Powerplant:	1 x Cummins V6 diesel, developing 155hp (115kW) at 3300rpm
Performance:	Maximum road speed: 96km/h (60mph); fording: 1.17m (3.84ft); gradient: 60 percent; vertical obstacle: 0.6m (2ft)

Humber 'Pig'

Designed to supplement the Alvis Saracen, the Humber 'Pig' was based on the chassis of the Humber FV1600 truck chassis and entered service with the British Army in the 1950s. It was intended purely for transport to and from the battlefield rather than for any combat role. Carrying six men and equipped with firing ports, the Pig found itself being phased out with the arrival of the FV432 into service. However, the conflict in Northern Ireland rescued it from the scrapheap – the British needed a riot-control vehicle. It was given additional armour for the internal security role and equipped with barricade-removal equipment at the front. It remained in service in Northern Ireland until the 1980s. Variants included an ambulance and an anti-tank version equipped with Malkara missiles.

Country of origin:	United Kingdom
Crew:	2 + 6 (or 2 + 8)
Weight:	5790kg (12,738lb)
Dimensions:	length 4.926m (16ft 2in); width 2.044 (6ft 8.5in); height 2.12m (6ft 11.5in)
Range:	402km (250 miles)
Armour:	8mm (0.31in)
Armament:	2 x 4 smoke dischargers
Powerplant:	one Rolls-Royce B60 Mk 5A six-cylinder petrol engine developing 120hp (89kW)
Performance:	maximum road speed 64km/h (40mph); fording 0.5m (1ft 7in); vertical obstacle 0.23m (9in); trench not applicable

Sonderwagen SWI

The Geschützer Sonderwagen SWI was part of the MOWAG MR 8-01 series of armoured personnel carriers developed in the 1950s. It was specifically made for the Federal German Border Police as a security APC. Its armed counterpart was the SW2, which featured a 20mm (0.78in) cannon mounted on the turret. Both vehicles had two sets of three smoke grenade launchers. The basic vehicle had an all-welded steel hull with the engine located in the rear. It could carry three to five personnel including the crew. Because it was mainly intended for urban duties, the SW1 was not amphibious and did not have NBC fittings or night-vision systems.

Country of origin:	Switzerland
Crew:	3–5
Weight:	8200kg (18,100lb)
Dimensions:	Length: 5.31m (17.42ft); width: 2.25m (7.38ft); height: 1.88m (6.17ft)
Range:	400km (250 miles)
Armour:	Steel
Armament:	None
Powerplant:	1 x Chrysler R 318-233 4-cylinder petrol, developing 161hp (120kW)
Performance:	Maximum road speed: 80km/h (50mph); fording: 1.1m (3.6ft); gradient: 60 percent

BLR

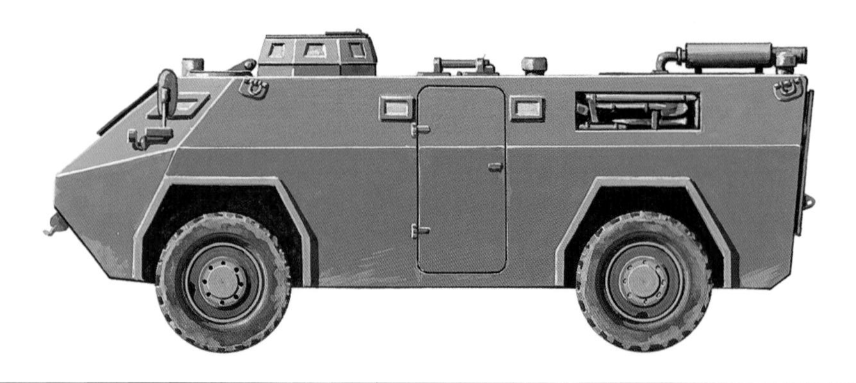

The Santa Barbara BLR armoured personnel carrier is an internal security vehicle in service with the Spanish Marines and Guardia Civil, as well as security forces in Ecuador. It is a 4x4 vehicle with a steel armoured hull, bullet-proof windows and security-minded extras such as bullet-proof tyres and automated fire-extinguishers for the engine and wheels. There is no standard armament but a cupola mount is available for various machine-gun and cannon configurations. Also available is a 90mm (3.54in) cannon in a dedicated turret. In addition, smoke- and gas-grenade launchers can be fitted. Unlike many APCs, the BLR is not amphibious, which indicates its security rather than military role.

Country of origin:	Spain
Crew:	1 + 12
Weight:	12,000kg (26,500lb)
Dimensions:	Length: 5.65m (18.54ft); width: 2.5m (8.2ft); height: 1.99m (6.53ft)
Range:	570km (350 miles)
Armour:	(Steel) 8mm (0.31in)
Armament:	See text
Powerplant:	1 x Pegaso 9220 6-cylinder diesel, developing 210hp (157kW)
Performance:	Maximum road speed: 93km/h (58mph); fording: 1.1m (3.3ft); gradient: 60 percent

TM 90

The TM 90 was one in a series of security vehicles/armoured personnel carriers produced by Thyssen in the 1970s. It was particularly designed for police use in anti-terrorist and riot-control contexts. The chassis was an all-wheel-drive Daimler-Benz model. On top of this was an armoured superstructure with specially angled joints and panels to deflect blows from hand-held weapons. Bullet-proof windows were fitted, and to accommodate the police market, a siren, blue light and a loudspeaker were also standard. The basic vehicle was unarmed, though a machine gun could be mounted next to the roof hatch. Because of better-suited vehicles in the marketplace, the TM 90 achieved few domestic or export sales.

Country of origin:	West Germany
Crew:	4
Weight:	4200kg (9300lb)
Dimensions:	Length: 4.4m (14.44ft); width: 2.05m (6.73ft); height: 1.85m (6.07ft)
Range:	600km (370 miles)
Armour:	Not available
Armament:	None
Powerplant:	1 x 6-cylinder diesel, developing 134hp (100kW)
Performance:	Maximum road speed: 110km/h (68mph)

Commando Ranger

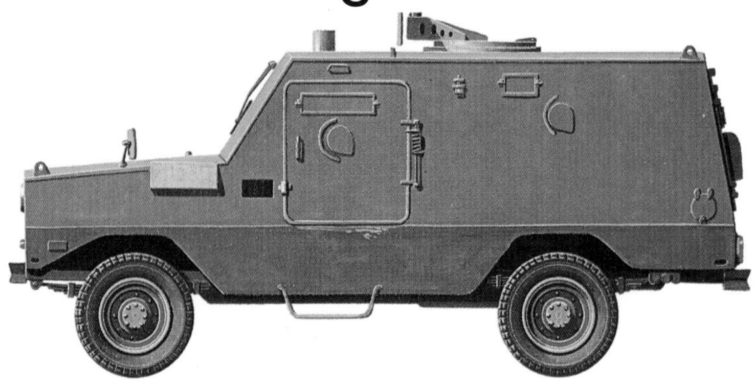

In 1979, Cadillac Gage was selected to meet the US Air Force's requirement for an armoured vehicle to provide security and protect its foreign air bases from attack by terrorists or other groups, and escort ordnance to and from bases. The Ranger entered service in 1980, based on a standard Chrysler truck chassis. The fully armoured compartment carried six men, who could fire from within the vehicle through firing ports, and this compartment was insulated and air-conditioned to reduce crew fatigue on lengthy patrols. Known to the USAF as the Peacekeeper, the vehicle was exported to Luxembourg and Indonesia. Optional equipment includes grenade launchers, spotlight and front-mounted winch. Variants included a command vehicle and an ambulance.

Country of origin:	United States
Crew:	2 + 6
Weight:	4536kg (9979lb)
Dimensions:	length 4.699m (15ft 5in); width 2.019 (6ft 7.5in); height 1.981m (6ft 6in)
Range:	556km (345 miles)
Armour:	7mm (0.27in)
Armament:	one or two 7.62mm machine guns
Powerplant:	one Dodge 360 CID V-8 petrol engine developing 180hp (134kW)
Performance:	maximum road speed 112.5km/h (70mph); fording 0.457 (1ft 6in); vertical obstacle 0.254m (10in); trench not applicable

Bravia Commando Mk III

The Commando Mk III is an armoured personnel carrier ideally suited to urban security use. It is manufactured by Bravia, based in Lisbon, Portugal, and was originally developed for the Portuguese National Guard. The chassis is actually that of a truck, the 4x4 Bravia Gazela, with a hull superstructure of armoured steel plate. With a thickness of between 6.35mm (0.25in) and 7.94mm (0.31in), the armour is sufficiently thick to stop low-powered small-arms fire and hand-thrown missiles. Windows can be covered with armoured shutters in action. A turret surmounting the hull carries a 12.7mm (0.5in) MG and a 7.62mm (0.3in) coaxial machine gun. The vehicle can also mount a 60mm (2.36in) grenade launcher pod.

Country of origin:	Portugal
Crew:	3 + 5
Weight:	4855kg (10,700lb)
Dimensions:	Length: 4.97m (16.31ft); width: 1.93m (6.33ft); height: 2.05m (6.73ft)
Range:	800km (500 miles)
Armour:	(Steel) 7.94mm (0.31in) maximum
Armament:	1 x 12.7mm (0.5in) MG; 1x 7.62mm (0.3in) coaxial MG
Powerplant:	1 x Perkins 4-cylinder diesel, developing 81hp (60kW) at 2800rpm
Performance:	Maximum road speed: 90km/h (56mph); gradient: 70 percent

Sandringham 6

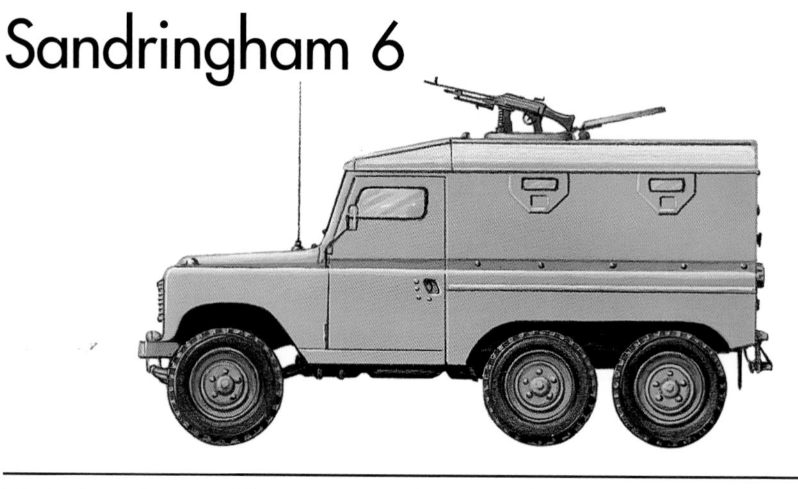

The Sandringham 6 is an armoured personnel carrier based on the long-wheelbase Land Rover but in 6x6 configuration. Despite its soft-skinned appearance, the Sandringham 6 is heavily clad in an all-welded steel armour body, resistant to most small-arms fire and shell splinters. The two-man crew are seated behind transparent armour screens, which are equal in strength to the metal armour. Armoured shutters can also be dropped over these windows. Six firing ports are provided around the vehicle – four in the hull and two in the rear doors – and a 7.62mm (0.3in) machine gun can be fitted onto a cupola on the roof. This is aimed by periscope. For riot-control duties, a gas-grenade launcher can replace this gun.

Country of origin:	United Kingdom
Crew:	2 + 8
Weight:	3700kg (8200lb)
Dimensions:	Length: 4.44m (14.57ft); width: 1.69m (5.54ft); height: 2.08m (6.82ft)
Range:	300km (190 miles)
Armour:	Not available
Armament:	Optional (see text)
Powerplant:	1 x Rover V8 petrol, developing 91hp (68kW) at 3500rpm
Performance:	Maximum road speed: 95km/h (59mph)

Shorland SB401

The Shorland SB401 armoured personnel carrier is recognizably derived from the standard British Army Land Rover. Its chassis is the Land Rover's long-wheelbase version (2.77m/9.09ft), and most of its components are from the standard Land Rover vehicle. However, the addition of a heavy armour-plated body meant that the chassis had to be strengthened. Powering this heavy vehicle requires a Rover V8 engine developing 91hp (68kW) at 3500rpm. The armour plate gives protection against high-velocity 7.62mm (0.3in) rifle and machine-gun rounds at above 25m (82ft) range. A glass-fibre interior floor reduces the risk of shrapnel wounds from explosives thrown under the vehicle.

Country of origin:	United Kingdom
Crew:	2 + 6
Weight:	3545kg (7800lb)
Dimensions:	Length: 4.29m (14.07ft); width: 1.78m (5.84ft); height: 2.16m (7.09ft)
Range:	368km (229 miles)
Armour:	Not available
Armament:	None
Powerplant:	1 x Rover V8 petrol, developing 91hp (68kW) at 3500rpm
Performance:	Maximum road speed: 104km/h (65mph); vertical obstacle: 0.23m (0.75ft)

ASA Guardian

The ASA Guardian is used mainly in security and police work, particularly for counter-terrorist and riot-control operations. It was developed by stretching the wheelbase of the Fiat Campagnola light vehicle, upgrading to a more powerful engine and adding sturdier armour plate. The vehicle is resistant to small-arms fire and even tyres and windows are bullet-proof. No weapon is fitted as standard, but there is the option to mount a machine gun on the rim of the hatch in the centre of the roof. In addition, both driver and front-seat passenger have firing ports in the doors. The Guardian is used throughout Italy and also in various Middle Eastern countries.

Country of origin:	Italy
Crew:	6
Weight:	2730kg (6019lb)
Dimensions:	Length: 3.68m (12.07ft); width: 1.75m (5.74ft); height: 2.12m (6.96ft)
Range:	380km (240 miles)
Armour:	Not available
Armament:	None (see text)
Powerplant:	1 x Mercedes-Benz, Fiat or Rover 4-cylinder petrol, developing 80hp (60kW)
Performance:	Maximum road speed: 120km/h (75mph)

13pdr 9cwt AA Gun

One of the very first British field AA guns to be developed was the 13-pounder (76mm/3in) horse artillery gun on a high-angle mounting. When more power was subsequently required, the same mounting was tried with an 18-pdr (83.8mm/3.3in) horse artillery gun, but for various ballistic reasons it proved to be a failure. The correct solution, it appeared, was to re-line the 18pdr gun to 76mm (3in) calibre and fire the 13-pdr shell with the 18-pdr cartridge. This 13pdr 9cwt AA Gun was highly successful and thus became the most common British field AA gun of World War I. It was almost always mounted upon a motor truck, although ground platform carriages began to appear towards the end of the war. This example is seen mounted on a Thornycroft Type J lorry.

Country of origin:	United Kingdom
Crew:	2 + gun crew
Weight:	7620kg (7.5 tons)
Dimensions:	Not known
Range:	Not known
Armour:	None
Armament:	1 x 76mm (3.0in) anti-aircraft gun
Powerplant:	Not available
Performance:	Maximum road speed: 23km/h(14mph)

SdKfz 8

In 1939, the German Army ordered ten 88mm (3.46in) Flak 18 guns to be mounted upon the cargo bed of the Daimler-Benz 18-ton semi-tracked carrier. This was done by simply removing the gun and its pedestal from the four-legged AA mounting and bolting it to the chassis. A three-sided shield was added to protect the gunners, and armour was applied around the engine and the driver's position. The resulting vehicles were issued as anti-aircraft defence for moving columns and were used in the Polish and French campaigns. Their secondary role was as assault guns to attack fortified positions with direct fire, and it was a short step to using them as tank destroyers. Fifteen were built in 1940, but plans to build 112 more in 1941–2 were cancelled as it was clear that a full-tracked, fully-armoured vehicle was a better idea.

Country of origin:	Germany
Crew:	13
Weight:	925,300kg (25 tons)
Dimensions:	Length: 7.34m (24.1ft); width 2.53m (8.3ft); height: 2.83m (9.3ft)
Range:	200km (125 miles)
Armour:	None
Armament:	1 x Flak 18 88mm (3.46in) gun
Powerplant:	Maybach HL85
Performance:	Maximum road speed: 51km/h (32mph)

Flakpanzer 38 (t)

The Flakpanzer 38 (t) was produced from the chassis of the Czech LT-38 tracked vehicle in 1943, though it did not enter service until 1944. By locating the engine in the front of the chassis, an armoured section could be constructed at the rear. This held a Flak 38 20mm (0.78in) cannon suitable for low-level air defence. The Flakpanzer 38 (t) was totally inadequate for its role, with limited mobility and firepower. Only 160 were made during WWII, and most of these were sent out to the Russian front where they were used in ground-assault roles in support of infantry units. The Flak 38 cannon proved particularly useful against soft-skinned vehicles.

Country of origin:	Germany
Crew:	5
Weight:	9800kg (21,600lb)
Dimensions:	Length: 4.61m (15.12ft); width: 2.13m (6.98ft); height: 2.25m (7.38ft)
Range:	210km (130 miles)
Armour:	10–50mm (0.39–1.96in)
Armament:	1 x Flak 38 20mm (0.78in) cannon
Powerplant:	1 x Praga AC 6-cylinder petrol, developing 147hp (110kW)
Performance:	Maximum road speed: 42km/h (26mph)

Möbelwagen

The Flakpanzer IV Möbelwagen had a troubled pre-production stage. Its original configuration of four Flak 38 20mm (0.78in) cannon mounted on a PzKpfw IV chassis was produced by Krupp in early 1943. The cannon operators were protected by four hinged 20mm (0.78in) armour shields which could be lowered for 360-degree gun traverse. However, the design was not given official approval, and it took until 1944 before a new version was accepted, this time armed with a 37mm (1.46in) Flak 43 gun. Production began in April 1944, and about 240 were made by the end of the war. The Möbelwagen was technologically superseded by the Ostwind and Wirbelwind AAA systems.

Country of origin:	Germany
Crew:	5
Weight:	25,000kg (55,100lb)
Dimensions:	Length: 4.61m (15.12ft); width: 2.88m (9.44ft); height: 2.7m (8.86ft)
Range:	200km (125 miles)
Armour:	60mm (2.63in)
Armament:	4 x 20mm (0.78in) Flak 38 L/112.5 cannon (prototype); 1 x 37mm (1.46in) Flak 43 cannon (production model)
Powerplant:	1 x HL 120 Maybach 12-cylinder petrol, developing 268hp (200kW)
Performance:	Maximum road speed: 38km/h (24mph); fording: 1m (3.3ft); gradient: 60 percent; vertical obstacle: 0.6m (2ft); trench: 2.2m (7.2ft)

Wirbelwind

The Wirbelwind was an attempt to enhance the mobile firepower of frontline German units in the face of an increasing Allied air supremacy in 1944. Four 20mm (0.78in) Flak 38 L/112.5 cannon were set into a nine-sided armoured turret, which was then mounted on the chassis of battle-damaged Panzer IV tanks. While the Wirbelwind did prove effective against low-flying aircraft, its competitor, the Flakpanzer IV Ostwind, armed with a single 37mm (1.46in) Flak 43 L/89 cannon, proved to have superior knockdown power and replaced the Wirbelwind. Plans to upgrade the Wirbelwind were halted by the collapse of German industry towards the end of the war.

Country of origin:	Germany
Crew:	3
Weight:	22,000kg (48,510lb)
Dimensions:	Length: 5.92m (19.42ft); width: 2.9m (9.51ft); height: 2.7m (8.86ft)
Range:	200km (125 miles)
Armour:	60mm (2.63in)
Armament:	4 x 20mm (0.78in) Flak 38 L/112.5 cannon
Powerplant:	1 x HL 120 Maybach 12-cylinder petrol, developing 268hp (200kW)
Performance:	Maximum road speed: 38km/h (24mph); fording: 1m (3.3ft); gradient: 60 percent; vertical obstacle: 0.6m (2ft); trench: 2.2m (7.2ft)

M42

The M42 anti-aircraft system, commonly known as the 'Duster', was based on the M41 Bulldog tank and was one of a family of vehicles developed after the end of World War II. Between 1951 and 1956, around 3700 were built, mainly by Cadillac. The main drawback of the vehicle was its petrol engine, which restricted its operating range and its lack of a radar fire-control system, the gunner being forced to rely on optic sights. In addition, the open-topped turret afforded the crew little protection. However, it saw extensive service in Vietnam, albeit mainly in a ground-support rather than anti-aircraft role, and continued to serve with the National Guard into the 1980s. Its power-assisted twin 40mm turret was the same as that used on the M19 self-propelled anti-aircraft gun system used in World War II.

Country of origin:	United States
Crew:	6
Weight:	22,452kg (49,394lb)
Dimensions:	length 6.356m (20ft 10in); width 3.225m (10ft 7in); height 2.847m (9ft 4in)
Range:	161km (100 miles)
Armour:	12-38mm (0.47-1.5in)
Armament:	twin 40mm anti-aircraft guns; one 7.62mm machine gun
Powerplant:	one Continental AOS-895-3 six-cylinder air-cooled petrol engine developing 500hp (373kW)
Performance:	maximum road speed 72.4km/h (45mph); fording 1.3m (4ft 3in); vertical obstacle 1.711m (2ft 4in); trench 1.829m (6ft)

ZSU-57-2

The ZSU-57-2 was the first Soviet self-propelled anti-aircraft gun to see service on a significant scale after World War II. The chassis was a lightened version of the T-54 main battle tank with thinner armour, the distinctive feature of the vehicle being the large, open-topped turret. This created a greater power-to-weight ratio than the T-54 and, coupled with extra fuel tanks, gave the gun good mobility and operating range. Practical firing rate was around 70 rounds per minute, with the empty cartridge cases being transported to a wire basket at the rear by a conveyor belt. The vehicle was exported widely to other Warsaw Pact countries, North Africa and the Middle East, seeing extensive action with Syrian forces during the fighting in Lebanon against the Israelis in 1982.

Country of origin:	USSR
Crew:	6
Weight:	28,100kg (61,820lb)
Dimensions:	length 8.48m (27ft 10in); width 3.27m (10ft 9in); height 2.75m (9ft)
Range:	420km (260 miles)
Armour:	15mm (0.59in)
Armament:	twin 57mm anti-aircraft cannon
Powerplant:	one Model V-54 V-12 diesel engine developing 520hp (388kW)
Performance:	maximum road speed 50km/h (31mph); fording 1.4m (4ft 7in); vertical obstacle 0.80m (2ft 7in); trench 2.70m (8ft 10in)

M53/59

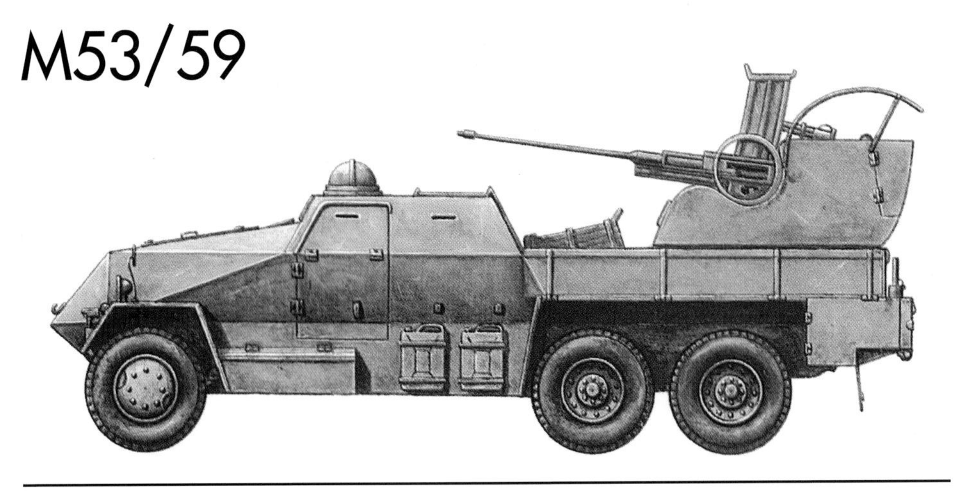

In the 1950s, Czechoslovakia developed and began production of the M53/59 self-propelled anti-aircraft gun. Based on the Praga V3S 6 x 6 truck chassis with an armoured cab, the vehicle was used in place of the Soviet ZSU-57-2. Essentially a clear-weather system, the vehicle carried neither infrared night vision equipment nor a nuclear, biological and chemical (NBC) defence system. Both armour-piercing incendiary ammunition for ground targets and high-explosive incendiary for aircraft were carried. Other than its reliance on clear-weather systems, the other main drawback was its poor cross-country mobility, which prevented effective operation with tracked vehicles. In addition to the Czech Army, the M53/59 saw service with both the former Yugoslavia and Libya.

Country of origin:	Czechoslovakia
Crew:	6
Weight:	10,300kg (22,660lb)
Dimensions:	length 6.92m (22ft 8in); width 2.35m (7ft 9in); height 2.585m (8ft 6in)
Range:	500km (311 miles)
Armour:	none (vehicle as a whole)
Armament:	twin 30mm cannon
Powerplant:	one Tatra T912-2 six-cylinder diesel engine developing 110hp (82kW)
Performance:	maximum road speed 60km/h (37mph); vertical obstacle 0.46m (1ft 6in); trench 0.69m (2ft 3in)

M727 HAWK

In 1997, the US military disposed of the last of its HAWK ('Homing All the Way to the Kill') missiles after almost 40 years of service. It first entered US Army service in August 1960, the launcher unit first being towed by a 2.5-ton 6x6 truck. In the early 1970s, the HAWK was produced in a self-propelled version, the M727 SP HAWK. This used a modified M548 tracked cargo carrier, which supported the three-missile launcher mounted on its rear hull. HAWK missiles were tracked to their target by following electro-magnetic energy reflected off the target by a Continuous-wave Illuminator radar, part of the HAWK battery. The HAWK system remains operational in a number of allied countries such as Germany and the Republic of Korea.

Country of origin:	United States
Crew:	4
Weight:	12,925kg (28,494lb)
Dimensions:	Length: 5.87m (19.26ft); width: 2.69m (8.83ft); height: 2.5m (8.2ft)
Range:	489km (304 miles)
Armour:	Not available
Armament:	3 x HAWK SAM
Powerplant:	1 x Detroit 6V53 6-cylinder diesel, developing 214hp (160kW)
Performance:	Maximum road speed: 61km/h (38mph); fording: 1m (3.3ft); gradient: 60 percent; vertical obstacle: 0.61m (2ft); trench: 1.68m (5.51ft)

M163 Vulcan

In the early 1960s, Rock Island Arsenal developed a self-propelled air-defence system based on the M113 armoured personnel carrier chassis. GEC began production and the vehicle was soon being deployed to Vietnam, where it was widely used by both US and South Vietnamese troops in a ground-support role. An electrically operated turret was mounted on the M113 chassis and armed with a six-barrelled Gatling-type cannon. This had adjustable rates of fire depending on whether it was being used for ground attack or anti-aircraft defence, and was the same weapon used by F-16 fighter aircraft. In the direct-fire role the Vulcan has a rate of fire of 1180 rounds per minute. The vehicle was exported to Ecuador, Israel, Morocco, North Yemen, South Korea and Tunisia.

Country of origin:	United States
Crew:	4
Weight:	12,310kg (27,082lb)
Dimensions:	length 4.86m (15ft 11in); width 2.85m (9ft 4in); height 2.736m (9ft 11in)
Range:	83km (300 miles)
Armour:	38mm (1.5in)
Armament:	one 20mm six-barrelled M61 series cannon
Powerplant:	one Detroit 6V-53 six-cylinder diesel engine developing 215hp (160kW)
Performance:	maximum road speed 67km/h (42mph); fording amphibious; vertical obstacle 1.61m (2ft); trench 1.68m (5ft 6in)

Type 63

To meet its needs for a self-propelled anti-aircraft gun, the Chinese took the chassis of the Soviet T-34 tank (supplied to them in large numbers before relations were broken off between the two countries) and added an open-topped turret with twin anti-aircraft guns. The vehicle was severely limited in that it had no provision for radar control and had to be sighted and elevated manually, a major drawback when faced with fast, low-flying aircraft, particularly as the gun had to be loaded manually with five-round clips. The Type 63 was supplied to the Viet Cong during the Vietnam War in the 1960s, but otherwise was only used in numbers by the People's Liberation Army. Amazingly, given its mediocre qualities, it continued in use with Chinese force until the late 1980s.

Country of origin:	China
Crew:	6
Weight:	32,000kg (70,400lb)
Dimensions:	length 6.432m (21ft 1in); width 2.99m (9ft 10in); height 2.995m (9ft 10in)
Range:	300km (186 miles)
Armour:	18-45mm (0.7-1.8in)
Armament:	twin 37mm anti-aircraft cannon
Powerplant:	one V-12 water-cooled diesel engine developing 500hp (373kW)
Performance:	maximum road speed 55km/h (34mph); fording 1.32m (4ft 4in); vertical obstacle 0.73m (2ft 5in); trench 2.5m (8ft 2in)

SA-4 Ganef

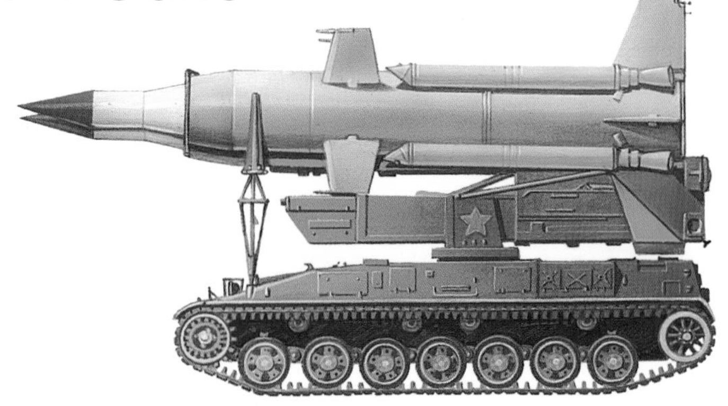

The SA-4 Ganef SAM system entered Soviet service in 1964. The launch vehicle (designated 2P24) is the tracked chassis of both the GMZ armoured minelayer and, later, the M1973 152mm (5.98in) self-propelled howitzer (though the latter vehicle used a shortened version of the SA-4 chassis). Each carrier is powered by a 12-cylinder diesel engine providing the 520hp (388kW) necessary to move the two Ganef missiles mounted above, each weighing 1800kg (4000lb). The missiles sit on a turntable mounting capable of 360-degree traverse and 45-degree elevation. NBC, air filtration and infrared night-vision devices are standard equipment on the 2P24 to enable operations in hazardous environments.

Country of origin:	USSR
Crew:	3–5
Weight:	30,000kg (66,150lb)
Dimensions:	Length (with missiles): 9.46m (31.03ft); width: 3.2m (10.5ft); height (with missiles): 4.47m (14.67ft)
Range:	450km (280 miles)
Armour:	15–20mm (0.59–0.78in)
Armament:	2 x SA-4 Ganef SAM missiles
Powerplant:	1 x V-59 12-cylinder diesel, developing 520hp (388kW)
Performance:	Maximum road speed: 45km/h (28mph)

M48 Chaparral

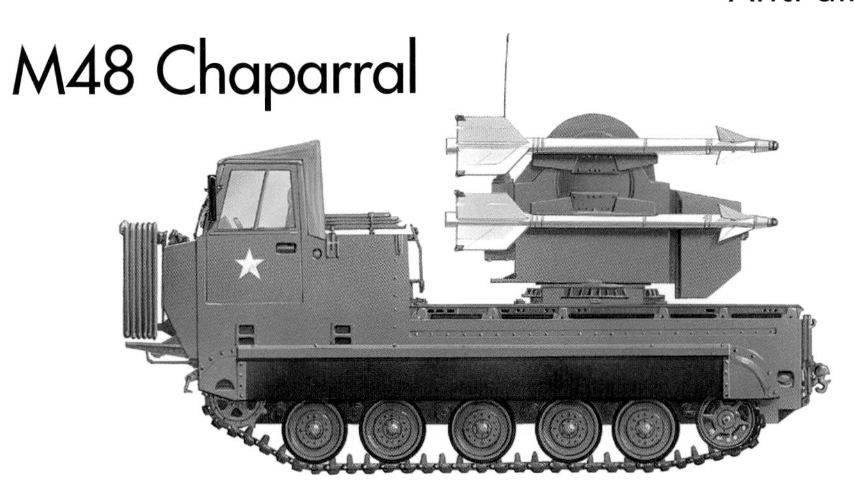

The M48 Chaparral went into production in the late 1960s using the MIM-72C SAM for short-range low-altitude interception missions. Guidance to target was via a fire-and-forget infrared system, later fitted with a Rosette Scan Seeker to resist enemy ECM. The M48 Chaparral system comprised a four-missile launcher on the back of an M-730A2 tracked cargo-carrier based on the M113 APC, with eight missiles stored. An amphibious capability was optional through a swim kit. An enemy aircraft warning system for the Chaparral was provided by a Forward Area Alerting Radar (FAAR) using a pulse-Doppler radar. All remaining Chaparral systems were deactivated in 1997.

Country of origin:	United States
Crew:	5
Weight:	11,500kg (25,360lb)
Dimensions:	Length: 6.06m (19.88ft); width: 2.69m (8.83ft); height: 2.68m (8.79ft)
Range:	489km (304 miles)
Armour:	Not applicable
Armament:	12 x MIM-72C SAM
Powerplant:	1 x Detroit 6V53 6-cylinder diesel, developing 214hp (160kW)
Performance:	Maximum road speed: 61km/h (38mph); fording: 1m (3.3ft); gradient: 60 percent; vertical obstacle: 0.61m (2ft); trench: 1.68m (5.51ft)

ZSU-23-4

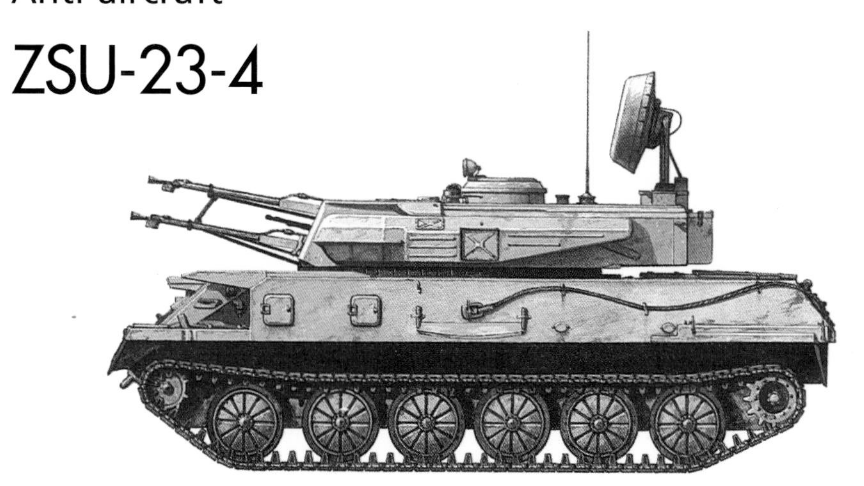

The ZSU-23-4 was developed in the 1960s as the replacement for the ZSU-57-2. Although having a shorter firing range, radar fire-control and an increased firing rate made the weapon much more effective. The chassis was similar to that of the SA-6 surface-to-air missile (SAM) system and used components of the PT-76 tank. Known to the Soviets as the 'Shilka', the vehicle can create an impassable wall of anti-aircraft fire over a 180-degree arc. Widely exported, the ZSU-23-4 was particularly effective in Egyptian hands during the Yom Kippur War of 1973, bringing down Israeli aircraft who were forced to fly low by the Egyptian missile defence system. It also saw extensive combat service with the North Vietnamese during the Vietnam War, bringing down numerous American aircraft.

Country of origin:	USSR
Crew:	4
Weight:	19,000kg (41,800lb)
Dimensions:	length 6.54m (21ft 5in); width 2.95m (9ft 8in); height (without radar) 2.25m (7ft 4in)
Range:	260km (162 miles)
Armour:	10-15mm (0.39-0.6in)
Armament:	four AZP-23 23mm anti-aircraft cannon
Powerplant:	one V-6R diesel engine developing 280hp (210kW)
Performance:	maximum road speed 44km/h (27mph); fording 1.4m (4ft 7in); vertical obstacle 1.10m (3ft 7in); trench 2.80m (9ft 2in)

SA-6 Gainful

The SA-6 Gainful was developed in the early 1960s and entered active service in 1967. It went on to be one of the most successful anti-aircraft weapons of the 20th century, exported worldwide and combat-proven by Egypt and Syria in the 1973 Yom Kippur war. Three SA-6 missiles are transported on the modified chassis of a ZSU-23-4, also used to form the ZSU-23-4 Shilka self-propelled anti-aircraft gun system. Both vehicles have radiation warning systems, NBC protection and fire-control equipment. The typical SA-6 battery consists of one 'Straight Flush' fire-control vehicle, four actual launcher vehicles and two ZIL-131 6x6 resupply trucks. SA-6 missiles are radar-guided and have a maximum range of 22,000m (72,200ft).

Country of origin:	USSR
Crew:	3
Weight:	14,000kg (30,900lb)
Dimensions:	Length: 7.39m (24.25ft); width: 3.18m (10.43ft); height: (with missiles) 3.45m (11.32ft)
Range:	260km (160 miles)
Armour:	15mm (0.59in)
Armament:	3 x SA-6 Gainful SAMs
Powerplant:	1 x model V-6R 6-cylinder diesel, developing 240hp (179kW)
Performance:	Maximum road speed: 44km/h (27mph); fording: 1m (3.3ft); gradient: 60 percent; vertical obstacle: 1.1m (3.6ft); trench: 2.8m (9.2ft)

AMX-13 DCA

The AMX-13 DCA entered production in the late 1960s to meet French requirements for a self-propelled anti-aircraft gun. It is essentially an AMX-13 main battle tank chassis fitted with a cast-steel turret. The vehicle entered service with the French Army in 1969. A total of 60 were delivered before production ceased and up to the 1980s, the AMX-13 DCA was the only self-propelled anti-aircraft gun in use with French forces. To aid fire control, there is an Oeil Noir 1 radar scanner fitted to the back of the turret, which is retractable while on the move. The DCA turret was fitted to the improved AMX-30 chassis for export to Saudi Arabia in the late 1970s and 1980s. The AMX-13 DCA is an adequate air defence vehicle, though now rather long in the tooth.

Country of origin:	France
Crew:	3
Weight:	17,200kg (37,840lb)
Dimensions:	length 5.40m (17ft 11in); width 2.50m (8ft 2in); height (radar up) 3.80m (12ft 6in); height (radar down) 3.00m (9ft 10in)
Range:	300km (186 miles)
Armour:	25mm (0.98in)
Armament:	twin 30mm Hispano (now Oerlikon) cannon
Powerplant:	one SOFAM Model 8Gxb eight-cylinder water-cooled petrol engine developing 250hp (186kW)
Performance:	maximum road speed 60km/h (37mph); fording 0.6m (1ft 11in); vertical obstacle 0.65m (2ft 2in); trench 1.70m (5ft 7in)

Roland

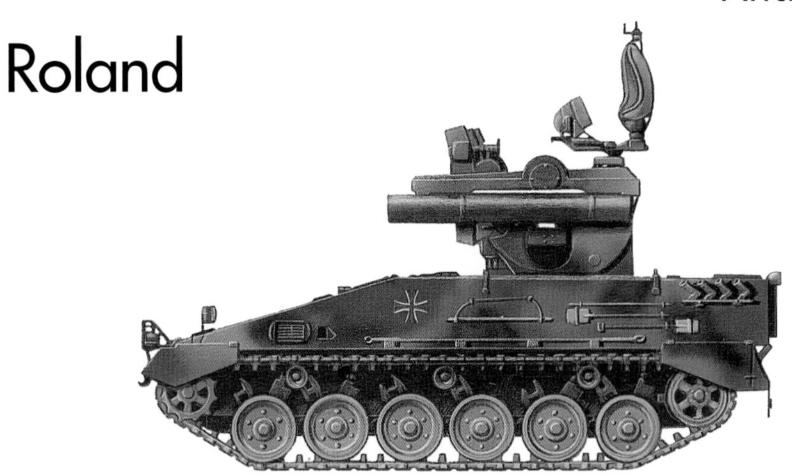

The Roland SAM system is a Franco-German production which began in the 1960s and involved France's Aérospatiale and West Germany's Messerschmitt-Bölkow-Blohm. Known collectively as Euromissile, the two companies developed the clear-weather (Roland 1) and all-weather (Roland 2) versions of the missile. The German Army's TELAR vehicle is the chassis of the Marder MICV (pictured here), while the French opted for the chassis of the AMX-30 MBT. Both versions carry two launch-ready missiles, one either side of the pulse-Doppler radar turret, with eight more stored. The radar system features an Identification Friend or Foe (IFF) assessment computer which on the Marder version can detect targets at distances of up to 18km (11 miles).

Country of origin:	France/West Germany
Crew:	3
Weight:	34,800kg (76,7004lb)
Dimensions:	Length: 6.92m (22.7ft); width: 3.24m (10.63ft); height: 2.92m (9.58ft)
Range:	600km (370 miles)
Armour:	Steel (details classified)
Armament:	2 + 8 Roland SAM missiles
Powerplant:	1 x MTU mB 833Ea-500 6-cylinder diesel, developing 590hp (440kW)
Performance:	Maximum road speed: 60km/h (37mph); fording: 1.5m (4.9ft); gradient: 60 percent; vertical obstacle: 1m (3.3ft); trench: 2.5m (8.2ft)

SA-8 Gecko

The SA-8 Gecko was the first Soviet air-defence system to combine surveillance, target acquisition and missile launcher in one vehicle. It has proved to be a popular system, particularly in the Middle East, and in the Soviet Army it replaced the 57mm (2.24in) anti-aircraft gun. The Gecko's transportation is handled by the chassis of the ZIL-167 6x6 vehicle. This is fully amphibious, propulsion coming from two waterjets. It features an NBC-protected crew compartment and a central tyre-pressure regulation system. Two Gecko infrared- and active-seeker-guided missiles are mounted ready to fire, controlled by two tracking and two guidance radars. An updated version of the Gecko, the SA-8B, has six missiles in enclosed containers.

Country of origin:	USSR
Crew:	5
Weight:	17,499kg (38,587lb)
Dimensions:	Length: 9.14m (30ft); width: 2.8m (9.19ft); height (with radar lowered): 4.2m (13.92ft)
Range:	250km (155 miles)
Armour:	Not known
Armament:	6 x SA-8 Type 9M33 SAMs
Powerplant:	1 x 5D20 B-300 diesel with gas-turbine auxiliary drive, developing 299hp (223kW)
Performance:	Maximum road speed: 80km/h (50mph); fording: amphibious

BRDM-2 with SA-9

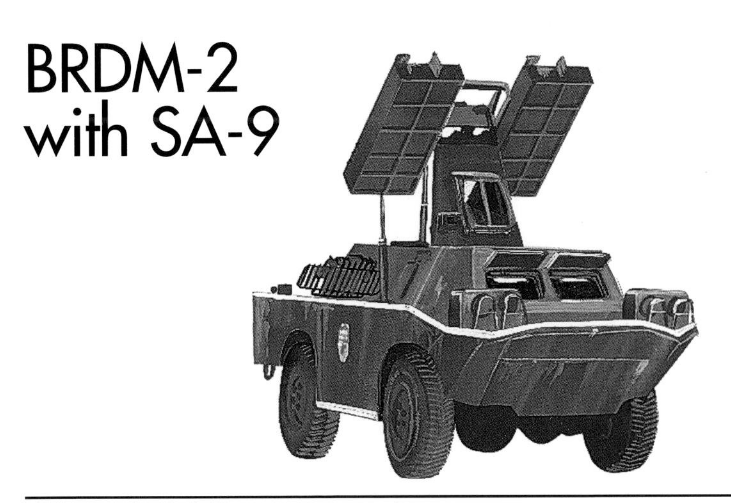

The success of the BRDM-2 design resulted in a rash of variants amongst Soviet forces, particularly in the role of guided-missile launcher. In 1972 the BRDM was issued with its standard turret removed and replaced by an SA-9 Gaskin SAM system. The unit consists of four launcher tubes mounted on a dedicated turret, each holding an SA-9 Gaskin infrared-seeker missile with an engagement altitude of around 4000m (13,123ft). In the early 1980s the vehicle acquired a Gun Dish radar on the front of the turret to give the SAM system all-weather capability, something it previously lacked. Two ATGW variants of the BRDM-2 were also launched in 1973 and 1977, mounting Swatter-B and Spandrel command-to-line-of-sight missiles.

Country of origin:	USSR
Crew:	4
Weight:	7000kg (15,435lb)
Dimensions:	Length: 5.75m (18.86ft); width: 2.35m (7.71ft); height: 2.31m (7.58ft)
Range:	750km (465 miles)
Armour:	(Steel) 10mm (0.39in) maximum
Armament:	4 x SA-9 Gaskin SAMs
Powerplant:	1 x GAZ-41 V8 petrol, developing 140hp (104kW)
Performance:	Maximum road speed: 100km/h (62mph); fording: amphibious; gradient: 60 percent; vertical obstacle: 0.4m (1.3ft); trench: 1.25m (4.1ft)

GDF-CO3

Produced by Oerlikon-Bührle, the GDF series was designed to be a highly mobile anti-aircraft defence system to protect rear-area targets such as factories and air bases. The chassis for the tracked version is derived from the M113 series of armoured vehicles; the wheeled version is based on the 4 x 4 HYKA cross-country vehicle. The GDF-CO3 has a day/night fire-control system with laser rangefinder, in addition to a Contraves search radar. The vehicle fires a range of ammunition, including armour-piercing discarding sabot-tracer rounds for use against ground targets. Its layout is unusual in that the crew compartment is at the front with the guns behind them. Nevertheless, as a mobile air-defence platform the vehicle is ideally suited to Switzerland's needs.

Country of origin:	Switzerland
Crew:	3
Weight:	18,000kg (39,600lb)
Dimensions:	length 6.70m (22ft 0in); width 2.813m (9ft 3in); height 4.00m (13ft 2in)
Range:	480km (297 miles)
Armour:	8mm (0.31in)
Armament:	twin 35mm KDF cannon
Powerplant:	one GMC 6V-53T 6-cylinder diesel engine developing 215hp (160kW)
Performance:	maximum road speed 45km/h (28mph); fording 0.6m (1ft 11in); vertical obstacle 0.609m (2ft 0in); trench 1.80m (5ft 11in)

Crotale

The Crotale was developed to fulfil a South African order for an advanced all-weather SAM system. Designated 'Cactus' in South Africa, the Crotale missile has sold well around the world and has recently been updated in the Crotale Next-Generation Air Defence Missile System. The original-format vehicle is a Hotchkiss-Brandt-designed 4x4 armoured hull, used for both the target-acquisition and firing vehicles. The firing vehicle mounts four R.440 missiles, each with a range of approximately 8500m (28,000ft) and a blast radius of 8m (26ft). The target-acquisition vehicle carries a Doppler pulse search and surveillance radar with an 18km (11-mile) acquisition range.

Country of origin:	France
Crew:	3
Weight:	(launcher vehicle) 27,300kg (60,200lb)
Dimensions:	Length: 6.22m (20.4ft); width: 2.65m (8.69ft); height (vehicle): 2.04m (6.69ft)
Range:	500km (310 miles)
Armour:	3–5mm (0.12–0.2in)
Armament:	4 x Matra R.440 SAM missiles
Powerplant:	1 x diesel generator and 4 x electric motors, developing 236hp (176kW)
Performance:	Maximum road speed: 70km/h (43mph); fording: 0.68m (2.23ft); gradient: 40 percent; vertical obstacle: 0.3m (1ft)

Flakpanzer 1 Gepard

The Gepard emerged in the late 1960s as an indigenous self-propelled anti-aircraft gun (SPAAG) for the West German Army, which had formerly used the US M42 40mm (1.57in) system. It entered service in 1976 and was subsequently bought by the Belgians and Dutch, as well as the Germans. The Gepard chassis is based on the Leopard 1 MBT with downgraded armour requirements, while the Contraves turret mounts twin 35mm (1.38in) Oerlikon KDA cannon and a retractable search radar. Fire-control is fully computerized with ground- or aerial-engagement options and, amongst latest models, a Siemens laser rangefinder. The Oereikon cannon have a cyclical rate of fire of 550rpm, in 20- or 40-round bursts.

Country of origin:	Germany
Crew:	4
Weight:	47,300kg (104,000lb)
Dimensions:	Length: 7.68m (25.19ft); width: 3.27m (10.72ft); height: 3.01m (9.87ft)
Range:	550km (340 miles)
Armour:	40mm (1.57in)
Armament:	2 x 35mm (1.38in) cannon; eight smoke dischargers
Powerplant:	1 x MTU MB 838 Ca M500 10-cylinder multi-fuel, developing 830hp (619kW)
Performance:	Maximum road speed: 64km/h (40.5mph); fording: 2.5m (8.2ft)

SA-13 Gopher

The ZRK-BD Strela 10 (NATO reporting name SA-13 Gopher) was introduced into Soviet forces in the late 1970s as a replacement for the SA-9 Gaskin. It consists of four SA-13 infrared-guided missiles transported by a modified MT-LB Multipurpose Armoured Vehicle acting as a TELAR (Transporter Erector Launcher and Radar). The MT-LB was chosen for its exceptional mobility and fully amphibious hull (power in the water comes from the MT-LB's wide tracks). Each TELAR vehicle usually carries eight missile reloads in a cargo compartment at the rear. SA-13 missiles have an effective range of 5000m (16,400ft) to an altitude of 3500m (11,500ft).

Country of origin:	USSR
Crew:	3
Weight:	12,080kg (26,636lb)
Dimensions:	Length: 6.93m (22.74ft); width: 2.85m (9.35ft); height: 3.96m (13ft)
Range:	500km (310 miles)
Armour:	7–14mm (0.28–0.55in)
Armament:	4 + 4 9M37 SAM missiles
Powerplant:	1 x YaMZ-239V 8-cylinder diesel, developing 709hp (529kW)
Performance:	Maximum road speed: 61.5km/h (38mph); fording: amphibious; gradient: 60 percent; vertical obstacle: 0.7m (2.3ft); trench: 2.7m (8.9ft)

SA-10 Grumble

The S-300PMU1 (NATO reporting name SA-10 Grumble) is a cutting-edge air-defence system developed in the early 1970s, operational service beginning in 1980. The key advantage of the SA-10 is that it can acquire and engage multiple targets simultaneously across a very broad spectrum of altitude – 25m (82ft) to 30,000m (98,400ft). The four-missile erector-launcher is mounted on a 5P85SE2 or 5P85TE2 semi-trailer pulled by a MAZ-7910 8x8 tractor truck. Three missiles can be launched in one second, each for different targets. During deployment, the missile battery consists of an engagement control centre, a Doppler target-acquisition radar, a trailer-mounted FLAP LID radar system, and up to 12 erector launchers.

Country of origin:	USSR
Crew:	4
Weight:	43,300kg (95,500lb)
Dimensions:	Length: 11.47m (37.63ft); width: 10.17m (33.36ft); height: 3.7m (12.14ft)
Range:	650km (400 miles)
Armour:	None
Armament:	4 x 5V55K SA-10 SAMs
Powerplant:	1 x D12A-525A 12-cylinder diesel, developing 517hp (386kW)
Performance:	Maximum road speed: 60km/h (37mph)

SA-11 Gadfly

The 9K37M1 BUK-1 SAM system (NATO reporting name SA-11 Gadfly), is a replacement for the SA-6 Gainful and was introduced into service in 1980. It is a medium-range radar-guided missile with a 90 percent kill probability against aircraft, 40 percent against cruise missiles. The target is acquired by a SNOW DRIFT warning and acquisition radar at ranges of up to 70km (43 miles), though the TELAR system takes over the tracking of the missile to target. The TELAR vehicle itself is a modified GM-539 tracked chassis carrying a Fire Dome radar unit and four missiles in a turntable launcher. The fully tracked configuration allows the Gadfly to keep up with Russian armoured units even in off-road manoeuvres.

Country of origin:	USSR
Crew:	4
Weight:	(launch vehicle) 32,340kg (71,309lb)
Dimensions:	Length: 9.3m (30.51ft); width: 3.25m (10.66ft); height: 3.8m (12.47ft)
Range:	500km (310 miles)
Armour:	Not applicable
Armament:	4 x Type 9M38M1 (SA-11) SAM missiles
Powerplant:	1 x V-64-4 12-cylinder diesel, developing 709hp (529kW)
Performance:	Maximum road speed: 65km/h (40mph)

Shahine

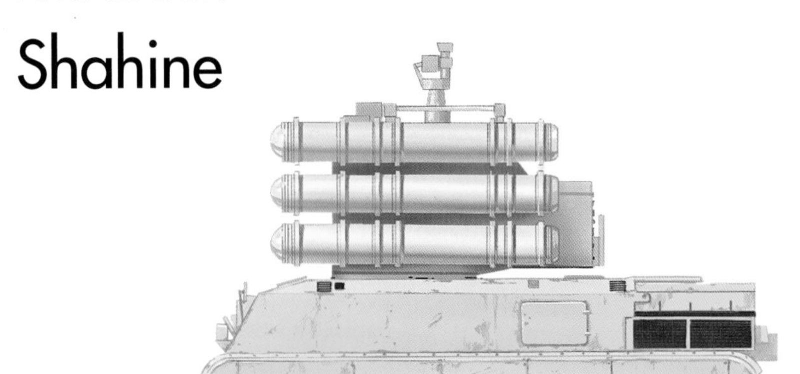

Unlike many mobile SAM systems, the Shahine is heavily armoured. Its firing and acquisition units are both mounted on an AMX-30 MBT chassis with armour 15–80mm (0.59–3.15in) thick. The traction and power of the AMX-30 chassis give the Shahine great versatility in deployment and excellent cross-country mobility. Target acquisition is performed by a separate vehicle mounting a pulse-Doppler surveillance radar and acquisition electronics. The launcher contains six Matra R.460 SAM missiles, each being guided by the command-control centre to its target. A reloading vehicle accompanies the Shahine unit, and can reload the entire system using an onboard crane.

Country of origin:	France
Crew:	3
Weight:	(launcher vehicle) 38,799kg (85,554lb)
Dimensions:	Length: 6.59m (21.62ft); width: 3.1m (10.17ft); height: 5.5m (18ft)
Range:	600km (370 miles)
Armour:	15–80mm (0.59–3.15in)
Armament:	6 x Matra R.460 SAM missiles
Powerplant:	1 x Hispano-Suiza HS110 12-cylinder multi-fuel, developing 690hp (515kW)
Performance:	Maximum road speed: 65km/h (40mph); fording: 1.3m (4.3ft); gradient: 60 percent; vertical obstacle: 0.93m (3.05ft)

Wildcat

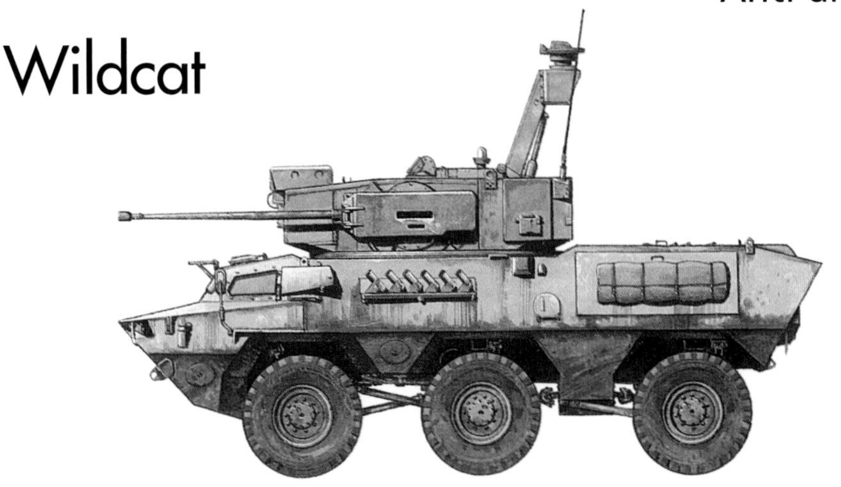

Realising that the self-propelled gun based on the Leopard 1 chassis and the American Sergeant York M247 would be too expensive for many countries, Krauss-Maffei decided to build a new family of anti-aircraft guns for sale abroad to tap into the lucrative market for arms outside of Europe. It was decided to use the automotive components of the 6 x 6 Transportpanzer already in production for the West German Army. With a laser rangefinder, radar scanner and automatic target-tracking, the fully computerised fire-control system makes the Wildcat an effective weapon, either against aircraft or against ground targets. It is also relatively inexpensive to maintain and spares are easy to come by – two attributes which make it attractive to countries with tight defence budgets.

Country of origin:	West Germany
Crew:	3
Weight:	18,500kg (40,700lb)
Dimensions:	length 6.88m (22ft 7in); width 2.98m (9ft 9in); height (radar down) 2.74m (9ft)
Range:	600km (373 miles)
Armour:	classified
Armament:	twin 30mm Mauser Mk 30-F cannon
Powerplant:	one Mercedes-Benz turbocharged eight-cylinder diesel engine developing 320hp (239kW)
Performance:	maximum road speed 80km/h (50mph); fording amphibious; vertical obstacle 0.6m (1ft 11in); trench 1.1m (3ft 7in)

Sergeant York

The Vulcan was noted for its short range and relative inaccuracy (though not poor rate of fire), so in 1978 the US Army issued a requirement for a self-propelled anti-aircraft gun based on the M48 main battle tank chassis to replace it. The first production M247 arrived in 1983, built by FAC. The vehicle had a comprehensive fire-control system including both surveillance and tracking radar. The M247 was capable of engaging both aircraft and helicopters, as well as tactical missiles (the latter capability being very important on the modern battlefield). However there were development problems and the programme was controversially cancelled, leading the US Army to rely on the Patriot SAM system for its air defence capability.

Country of origin:	United States
Crew:	3
Weight:	54,430kg (119,746lb)
Dimensions:	length 7.674m (25ft 2in); width 3.632m (11ft 11in); height (radar up) 4.611m (15ft 2in)
Range:	500km (311 miles)
Armour:	up to 120mm (4.72in)
Armament:	twin 40mm L/70 Bofors guns
Powerplant:	one Teledyne Continental AVDS-1790-2D diesel engine developing 750hp (559kW)
Performance:	maximum road speed 48km/h (30mph); fording 1.219m (4ft); vertical obstacle 1.914m (3ft); trench 2.591m (8ft 6in)

Tracked Rapier

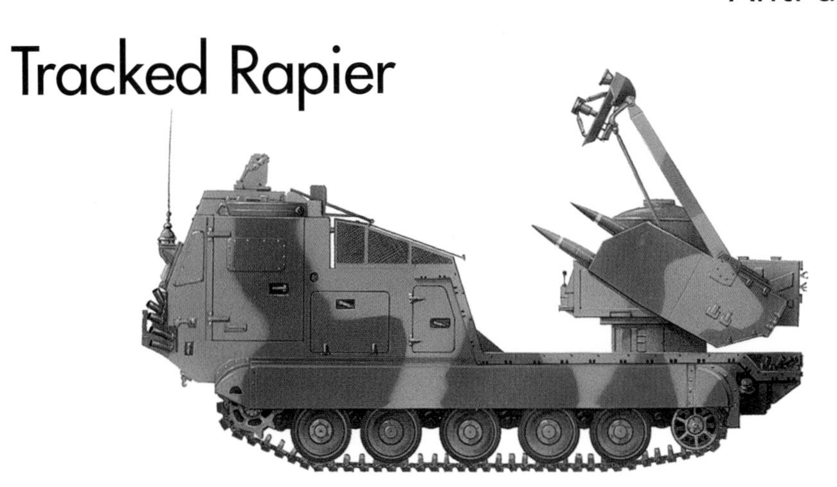

Tracked Rapier is the self-propelled version of the British Rapier SAM which first entered service with the British Army in 1971. The towed version consists of an optical tracker, power generator and the four-missile launch unit. In the case of the Tracked Rapier, all three of these elements are transplanted to the back of an M548 tracked cargo chassis, part of the M113 armoured vehicle series. The Tracked Rapier, however, carries eight missiles on its launcher, and the optical tracker is located in the cab, exiting to the outside through the roof. The tracking antenna elevates above the launcher itself. Protection for the Tracked Rapier crew is provided by a fully armoured cab.

Country of origin:	United Kingdom
Crew:	3
Weight:	14,010kg (30,892lb)
Dimensions:	Length: 6.4m (21ft); width: 9.19m (30.14ft); height: 2.5m (8.2ft)
Range:	300km (190 miles)
Armour:	Aluminium (details classified)
Armament:	8 x Rapier SAMs
Powerplant:	1 x GMC 6-cylinder turbocharged diesel, developing 250hp (186kW) at 2600rpm
Performance:	Maximum road speed: 80km/h (50mph); fording: amphibious; gradient: 60 percent; vertical obstacle: 0.6m (2ft); trench: 1.75m (5.74ft)

M1 Tunguska

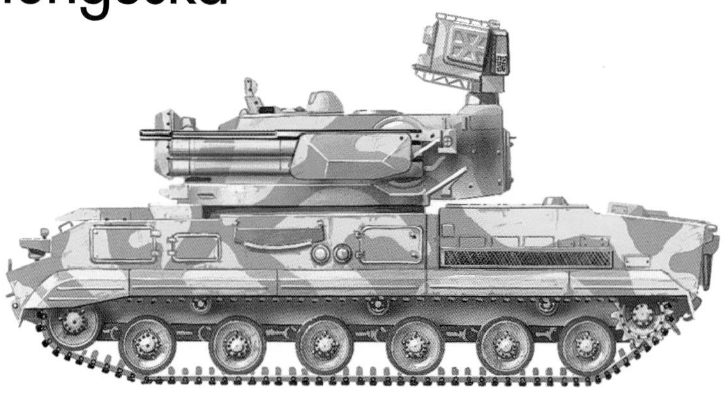

The Tunguska is a low-level air-defence system introduced in 1986 which mixes SAM and cannon technology to make a versatile aerial-interception platform. Eight SA-19 Grison missiles are mounted on the turret for medium-range (up to 10,000m/32,800ft) interception, along with two twin-barrel 2A38M 30mm (1.18in) cannon for close-range (up to 4000m/13,100ft) targets. The Tunguska has full onboard fire-control, including target acquisition radar and automated cannon targeting. Mobility is provided by the chassis of a 34-ton GM-352M tracked vehicle, which has hydropneumatic suspension and full NBC protection for the crew. Tunguska is used by both the Russian military and the Indian Army.

Country of origin:	USSR
Crew:	4
Weight:	34,000kg (75,000lb)
Dimensions:	Length: 7.93m (26ft); width: 3.24m (10.63ft); height: 4.02m (13.1ft)
Range:	500km (310 miles)
Armour:	Classified
Armament:	2 x twin-barrel 2A38M 30mm (1.18in) cannon; 8 x SA-19 Grison SAMs
Powerplant:	1 x V-64-4 12-cylinder diesel, developing 709hp (529kW)
Performance:	Maximum road speed: 65km/h (40mph)

Type 87 AWSP

The Type 87 Automatic Western Self-Propelled (AWSP) was developed in the late 1970s as a replacement for the obsolete US M42 Duster AAA system, then in use with the Japanese military. Looking abroad for inspiration, Japanese engineers took the turret system of the German Gepard air-defence system and mounted it on the Type 74 MBT chassis. Testing was completed in 1987 from when Mitsubishi Heavy Industries started to produce the first of 180 AWSP vehicles. Like the Gepard, the Type 87 is armed with two 35mm (1.38in) Oerlikon KDA cannon, but with a much-improved fire-control system. The tower at the back of the turret mounts the acquisition and tracking radar.

Country of origin:	Japan
Crew:	3
Weight:	36,000kg (79,400lb)
Dimensions:	Length: 7.99m (26.21ft); width: 3.18 m (10.43ft); height: 4.4m (14.44ft)
Range:	500km (310 miles)
Armour:	Steel (details classified)
Armament:	2 x 35mm (1.38in) Oerlikon KDA cannon
Powerplant:	1 x 10F22WT 10-cylinder diesel, developing 718hp (536kW)
Performance:	Maximum road speed: 60km/h (37mph); fording: 1m (3.3ft); gradient: 60 percent; vertical obstacle: 1m (3.3ft); trench: 2.7m (8.9ft)

MIM-104 (GE) Patriot

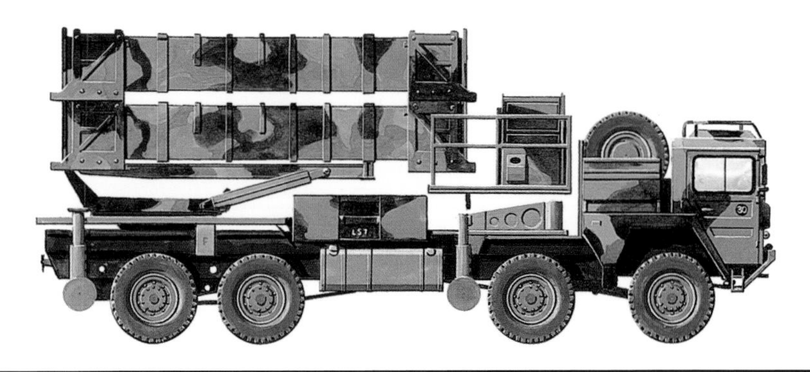

The Raytheon MIM-104 (GE) Patriot is an advanced SAM system introduced in the late 1980s. Using a track-via-missile (TVM) onboard guidance system in tandem with a ground-based tracking unit, each missile can engage aircraft targets and incoming ballistic and cruise missiles. Patriots were successfully used in the Gulf War to intercept incoming Iraqi Scud missiles fired at Israel, though their success did not equal media hype. Four pre-loaded Patriot missiles are transported in an M901 launcher fitted to an M860 two-axle semi-trailer. This in turn is pulled by an M818 6x6 tractor. A Patriot battery also features a MSQ-104 Engagement Control Centre (ECC) pulled by a M814 6x6 truck. An upgraded variant of the Patriot served in the Iraq war of 2003.

Country of origin:	United States
Crew:	2
Weight:	(M109 launcher) 26,867kg (59,241lb)
Dimensions:	Length: 10.4m (34.12ft); width: 2.49m (8.17ft); height: 3.96m (13ft)
Range:	800km (500 miles)
Armour:	Not applicable
Armament:	4 x Patriot SAM missiles
Powerplant:	1 x MAN D2866 LGF 6-cylinder diesel, developing 355hp (265kW)
Performance:	Maximum road speed: 80km/h (50mph)

76mm Otomatic Air Defence Tank

The 76mm (3in) Otomatic Air Defence Tank was developed primarily as a weapon for keeping helicopters and ground attack aircraft off the back of ground troops, and secondarily as a useful weapon against light armoured vehicles should they appear. The Otomatic System consists of a turret assembly with a 76mm gun, surveillance and tracking radars, electro-optical sights, fire control computer and all the sundry equipment that ties these items together. This complete unit can then be dropped into any tank with a large enough turret ring. For the purposes of the Italian Army trials, the Leopard 1 was selected and the whole ensemble fits together well and has performed successfully.

Country of origin:	Italy
Crew:	4
Weight:	47,000kg (46.26 tons)
Dimensions:	length 7.08m (23ft 3in); width 3.25m (10ft 8in); height 3.07m (10ft 1in) (radar stowed)
Range:	500km (310 miles)
Armour:	not disclosed
Armament:	one 76mm (3in) gun
Powerplant:	MTU V-10 multi-fuel, 830bhp at 2200 rpm
Performance:	maximum road speed 60km/h (37mph); fording 1.2m (47in); vertical obstacle 1.15m (45in); trench 3m (9ft 10in)

Sidam 25

The OTOBREDA Sidam 25 entered production in 1989. It is basically four Oerlikon KBA 25mm (0.98in) automatic cannon turret-mounted on the ever-popular M113 APC. Using an optronic fire-control system, the weapon is highly accurate against low-flying aerial targets within its 2000m (6650ft) effective range. Rate of fire is 2400 rounds per minute and the turret takes 600 rounds when fully loaded, enough ammunition for around eight two-second bursts. Thirty armour-piercing rounds are also held in an internal magazine for use against ground targets. Using the almost ubiquitous M113 vehicle meant simple logistics and affordable spare parts.

Country of origin:	Italy
Crew:	3
Weight:	15,100kg (33,300lb)
Dimensions:	Length: 5.04m (16.54ft); width: 2.67m (8.76ft); height (without turret): 1.82m (5.97ft)
Range:	550km (342 miles)
Armour:	(Aluminium) – 38mm (1.49in)
Armament:	4 x 25mm (0.98in) Oerlikon KBA cannon
Powerplant:	1 x Detroit 6V-53T 6-cylinder diesel, developing 266hp (198kW)
Performance:	Maximum road speed: 69km/h (40mph); fording: amphibious; gradient: 60 percent; vertical obstacle: 0.61m (2ft); trench: 1.68m (5.51ft)

ADATS

The Air Defense Anti-Tank System (ADATS) is a troubled experiment by the Swiss Oerlikon-Bührle-Gruppe and the US Martin-Marietta to produce a combined anti-tank/anti-aircraft missile system. Production began in 1989, but combat-conditions testing in the early 1990s led to the US Army abandoning the vehicle in favour of dedicated anti-tank/anti-aircraft weaponry. However, some remain in service with the Canadian Army and Swiss military forces. The chassis of the ADATS is a modified M113A2 APC. Eight ADATS missiles are mounted on the top of the hull with a Doppler pulse radar and an electro-optical target-acquisition system. ADATs missiles have a range of 10km (6 miles) and can penetrate 900mm (35in) of armour.

Country of origin:	Switzerland/United States
Crew:	3
Weight:	15,800kg (34,800lb)
Dimensions:	Length: 4.86m (15.94ft); width: 2.68m (8.79ft); height (with radar antenna): 4.48m (14.7ft)
Range:	400km (250 miles)
Armour:	12–38mm (0.47–1.49in)
Armament:	8 x ADATS SAMs
Powerplant:	1 x Detroit 6V-53N 6-cylinder diesel, developing 211hp (158kW)
Performance:	Maximum road speed: 58km/h (36mph); fording: amphibious; gradient: 60 percent; vertical obstacle: 0.61m (2ft); trench: 1.68m (5.51ft)

Armoured Starstreak

The Starstreak SAM is a close-range anti-aircraft missile designed for low-level defence against targets such as ground-attack aircraft and helicopters. It is a versatile missile which can be launched from multiple platforms: shoulder, attack helicopter, and a vehicular version, the Starstreak Self-Propelled High-Velocity Missile (SP HVM). The SP HVM entered into service with the British Army in 1997. Eight Starstreak missiles are mounted in a turntable launcher on top of an Alvis Stormer vehicle. A roof-mounted Air Defence Alerting Device (ADAD) performs infrared targeting. The missiles themselves break into three darts as they approach the target, each tracked to impact by a laser-guidance system.

Country of origin:	United Kingdom
Crew:	3
Weight:	12,700kg (28,000lb)
Dimensions:	Length: 5.33 m (17.49ft); width: 2.4m (7.87ft); height: 3.49m (11.45ft)
Range:	650km (400 miles)
Armour:	Aluminium (details classified)
Armament:	8 +12 Starstreak SAMs
Powerplant:	1 x Perkins T6/3544 6-cylinder turbocharged diesel, developing 250hp (186kW) at 2600rpm
Performance:	Maximum road speed: 80km/h (50mph); fording: amphibious; gradient: 60 percent; vertical obstacle: 0.6m (2ft); trench: 1.75m (5.74ft)

Somua MCG/S307(f)

The French were extremely active in half-track design during the inter-war period. Though Somua specialized in civilian utility vehicles, in the 1930s it produced a series of artillery tractors using a Kegresse-type half-track configuration. In 1935, the Somua MCG went into production, and 2543 vehicles were built before World War II. The MCG had a rubber track like the Kegresse vehicles, though substantial metal reinforcing meant it could run for up to 8000km (4970 miles) before a track change. Under the Germans, requisitioned MCGs were designated S307(f) and many were converted into weapons platforms, carrying, for example, 75mm (2.95in) PaK 40 L/46 guns, 80mm (3.15in) rocket launchers and mortars.

Country of origin:	France
Crew:	4
Weight:	7300kg (16,100lb)
Dimensions:	Length: 5.3m (17.39ft); width: 1.88m (6.17ft); height: 1.95m (6.39ft)
Range:	170km (105 miles)
Armour:	Not available
Armament:	Various (see text)
Powerplant:	1 x Somua 4-cylinder petrol, developing 60hp (45kW)
Performance:	Maximum road speed: 36km/h (22mph)

28/32cm Wurfkörper SdKfz 251

The Wurfkörper was one of the earliest German rocket systems, entering service in 1940. It offered two sizes of rocket, the Wurfkörper Spreng with a 28cm (11in) high-explosive rocket and the Wurfkörper M F1 50, a 32cm (12.6in) rocket with liquid incendiary warhead. Crude, inaccurate, and underpowered – maximum range was around 2000m (6600ft) – the rockets nonetheless proved useful in action, particularly in urban combat. Mobility for the Wurfkörper system was achieved by mounting the missiles in their packing crates on the side of a SdKfz 251 half-track. Aiming the rockets was a simple matter of aligning the vehicle with the target. The mobile Wurfkörper tended to operate within Panzer units.

Country of origin:	Germany
Crew:	Up to 12
Weight:	8000kg (17,600lb)
Dimensions:	Length: 5.8m (19ft); width: (without rockets) 2.1m (6.9ft); height: 1.75m (5.74ft)
Range:	300km (190 miles)
Armour:	(Steel) 15mm (0.59in)
Armament:	6 x 28cm (11in) or 32cm (12.6in) Wurfkörper rockets; 1 x MG
Powerplant:	1 x Maybach HL 42 6-cylinder petrol, developing 101hp (75kW)
Performance:	Maximum road speed: 53km/h (33mph); fording: 0.6m (2ft); gradient: 24 percent

BM-13

The BM-13, or 'Katyusha', consisted of a battery of 16 M-13 fin-stabilized rockets which could be launched over a 8500m (27,900ft) maximum range. Though individually inaccurate, as an area saturation weapon the rockets created a terrifying HE salvo. The missiles were launched from a simple iron rail system mounted on the back of a truck and manually targeted. The first truck used in this role was the Russian ZiS-5 (pictured here), of which over 83,000 units were produced between 1942 and 1945. As the war went on, Katyushas were mounted on any available truck, including the Russian ZiS-6 STZ-5 artillery tractor, and US Lend-Lease Fords, Studebakers and Chevrolets.

Country of origin:	USSR
Crew:	2
Weight:	8900kg (19,600lb)
Dimensions:	Length: 6.55m (21.49ft); width: 2.24m (7.35ft); height: 2.76m (9.06ft)
Range:	370km (230 miles)
Armour:	Not applicable
Armament:	16 x 132mm (5.2in) M-13 rockets
Powerplant:	1 x Hercules JXD 6-cylinder petrol, developing 87hp (65kW)
Performance:	Maximum road speed: 72km/h (45mph)

BM-31-12 on ZiS-6

In late 1942, the M-31 rocket was introduced to enhance the performance of the earlier M-8 and M-13 weapons. These were deemed to contain too little explosive force, so whereas the M-13 had a 4.9kg (10.8lb) warhead, the M-31 contained 28.9kg (63.7lb) of explosive. Mobile launchers for the M-31 did not emerge until March 1944. The best vehicles for the job were ZiS-6 6x6 or Studebaker US-6 6x6 trucks. Twelve rockets were held in the rack mounted upon the rear. While the US trucks received armoured shutters to protect the cab windows during firing, the Soviet vehicles tended to be naked against the backblast. Over 1200 BM-31-12s were produced in 1944 alone, and another 600 in 1945.

Country of origin:	USSR
Crew:	2
Weight:	8900kg (19,600lb)
Dimensions:	Length: 6.55m (21.49ft); width: 2.24m (7.35ft); height: 3.2m (10.49ft)
Range:	350km (220 miles)
Armour:	Not applicable
Armament:	1 x M31 rocket-launcher system
Powerplant:	1 x 6-cylinder petrol, developing 87hp (65kW)
Performance:	Maximum road speed: 70km/h (43mph)

Wurfgranate 41

Nebelwerfer units were originally formed to lay down smoke screens for tactical use. The launchers were later adapted to fire artillery rockets, whose droning sound led to the Allied nickname 'Moaning Minnie'. The 15cm-Nebelwerfer 41 was mounted on a 3.7cm anti-tank gun carriage, but in 1942 the launcher was fitted to the half-tracked SdKfz 4/1 Maultier. This was a more effective system, as rockets betrayed their location immediately on firing and thus tended to draw swift retaliation. The Panzerwerfer 42, as it was known, allowed rapid escape from the point of firing and thus greater survivability. In the main, the mobile launchers were used to give fire support for armoured operations.

Country of origin:	Germany
Crew:	3
Weight:	7100kg (15,653lb)
Dimensions:	Length 6m (19.7ft); width 2.2m (7.2ft); height 3.05m (10ft)
Range:	130km (81 miles)
Armour:	8 to 10mm (0.31 to 0.39in)
Armament:	1 x 150mm (5.9in) Nebelwerfer 41 ten-barrelled rocket launcher, 1 x 7.92mm (0.31in) MG42 machine gun
Powerplant:	1 x Opel 6-cylinder petrol
Performance:	Maximum road speed: 40km/h (25mph)

Honest John

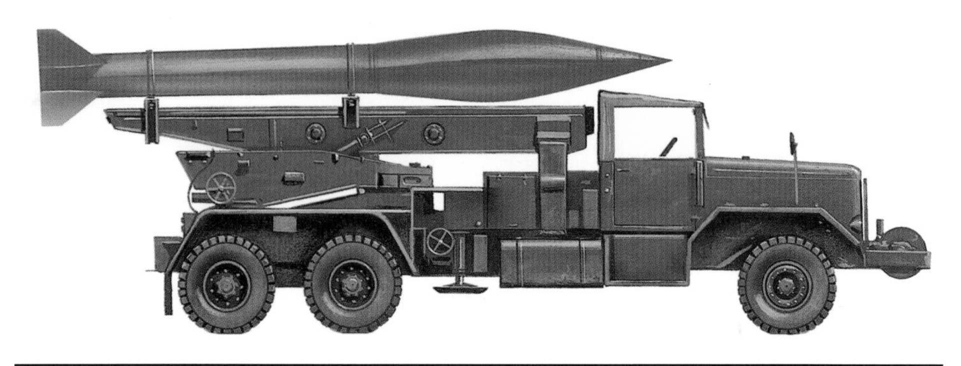

The Douglas MGR-1A Honest John was the earliest of the US tactical battlefield nuclear weapons. It received its first test firing in 1951 at the White Sands testing range and entered service two years later. Both the MGR-1A and the improved MGR-1B (introduced in 1960) were unguided rockets used in a similar manner to conventional tube artillery. Range was up to 19km (12 miles). Besides 2-, 20-, or 40-kiloton W31 nuclear warheads, conventional warheads could be fitted, including 680kg (1500lb) HE and 564kg (1243lb) chemical. The Honest John was launched from the chassis of a 6x6 truck TEL vehicle. Being an unguided missile, it was fired from a simple hydraulically raised rail.

Country of origin:	United States
Crew:	3
Weight:	16,400kg (36,200lb)
Dimensions:	Length: 9.89m (32.45ft); width: 2.9m (9.51ft); height: 2.67m (8.76ft)
Range:	480km (300 miles)
Armour:	None
Armament:	4 x tactical battlefield missiles supplied from independent transport truck
Powerplant:	1 x AM General 6-cylinder petrol, developing 139hp (104kW)
Performance:	Maximum road speed: 90km/h (56mph)

BM-24

The BM-24 was the BM-21's predecessor, introduced into service during the early 1950s. Originally mounted on a ZIL-151 6 x 6 truck, the system was later transferred to a ZIL-157. The system consisted of two rows of six tubular frame rails. Two stabiliser jacks were fitted which had to be lowered before firing. The BM-24 saw widespread use with Arab armies against the Israelis, the latter being so impressed with the system that they pressed the large numbers of captured launchers into service and designed a new rocket for it, with shorter range but a more effective warhead. This version saw service in the 1973 Yom Kippur War and in Lebanon in 1982. Rocket types include high-explosive, smoke and chemical, with a typical range being 11km (6.84 miles).

Country of origin:	USSR
Crew:	6
Weight:	9200kg (20,240lb)
Dimensions:	Length 6.7m (21ft 11in); width 2.3m (7ft 6in); height 2.91m (9ft 6in)
Range:	430km (269 miles)
Armour:	None
Armament:	12 240mm rocket-launcher tubes
Powerplant:	one six-cylinder water-cooled petrol engine developing 109hp (81kW)
Performance:	Maximum road speed 65km/h (40.6mph); fording 0.85m (2ft 9in); vertical obstacle 0.46m (1ft 6in); trench 0.69m (2ft 3in)

Type 70

The Type 63 was developed in the late 1950s. It consisted of three rows of four barrels. For firing the wheels were removed and the launcher was supported by two legs at the front, with a spade attached at the rear to absorb recoil. It could be fired independently, or mounted on a 4 x 4 truck chassis, this version being known as the Type 81. A smaller version was developed for use by airborne forces, which could be broken down for transport by men or horses. The Type 63 has seen extensive combat service around the world, being used by the Mujahideen in Afghanistan, by the North Vietnamese in Vietnam, by the Iranians in the Iran–Iraq War and by the PLO against the Israelis. The Type 70 rocket launcher, shown above and specified below, uses components of the YW 531C armoured personnel carrier.

Country of origin:	China
Crew:	2
Weight:	12,600kg (27,720lb)
Dimensions:	Length: 5.4m (17ft 9in); width 3m (9ft 9in); height 2.58m (8ft 6in)
Range:	500km (312 miles)
Armour:	10mm (0.39in)
Armament:	12 107mm rocket-launcher tubes
Powerplant:	one V-8 diesel engine developing 320hp (238kW)
Performance:	Maximum road speed 65km/h (38mph); fording amphibious; vertical obstacle 0.6m (1ft 11in); trench 2m (6ft 6in)

SS-1c Scud B Launcher

The Scud B is a medium-range tactical missile with nuclear or conventional high-explosive warheads. Introduced in 1961, it has a poor operational record. Its gyroscopic guidance system is only active for the first 80 seconds of flight. After this period, the warhead detaches and makes an unguided flight to the target at speeds of up to Mach 9. The Scud is consequently extremely inaccurate, as was demonstrated by Iraqi Scud attacks against Israeli cities during the first Gulf War. A single Scud is carried on a modified MAZ-543 truck acting as a transporter-erector-launcher. Initially a JS-3 tracked chassis was used, but the MAZ-543 was introduced from 1965 to give improved off-road mobility.

Country of origin:	USSR
Crew:	4
Weight:	37,400kg (82,500lb)
Dimensions:	Length: 13.36m (43.83ft); width: 3.02m (9.91ft); height: 3.33m (10.93ft)
Range:	450km (280 miles)
Armour:	Not applicable
Armament:	1 x Scud B tactical ballistic missile
Powerplant:	1 x D12A-525A 12-cylinder diesel, developing 525hp (391kW) at 2100rpm
Performance:	Maximum road speed: 45km/h (28mph)

BM-21

The BM-21 entered service in the early 1960s and became the standard multiple rocket-launcher of Warsaw Pact armies, as well as most Soviet client states. Variants were produced in China, India, Egypt and Romania. The 40-round launcher was mounted on a URAL-375 6 x 6 truck (later a on a ZIL-131 in a modified 36-round form). For airborne troops, a smaller 12-round version was developed to be mounted on a 4 x 4 truck. Most BM-21 variants have been used in action, particularly in Afghanistan. In addition, customised versions were used by the PLO in battles around Beirut from 1982 onwards. The BM-21 is symbolic of Russian multiple rocket launchers, being crude and simple to operate. Nevertheless, when used in batteries it could deliver devastating firepower.

Country of origin:	USSR
Crew:	6
Weight:	11,500kg (25,300lb)
Dimensions:	length 7.35m (24ft 1in); width 2.69m (8ft 9in); height 2.85m (9ft 4in)
Range:	405km (253 miles)
Armour:	none
Armament:	40 122mm rocket-launcher tubes
Powerplant:	one V-8 water-cooled petrol engine developing 180hp (134kW)
Performance:	maximum road speed 75km/h (46.8mph); fording 1.5m (4ft 11in); vertical obstacle 0.65m (2ft 1in); trench 0.875m (2ft 10in)

Pershing

The Martin Marietta MGM-31A Pershing tactical nuclear missile was conceived in 1958 and introduced in 1963. Its primary purpose was to deliver 60- to 400-kiloton W50 airburst nuclear warheads at ranges of between 160 and 740km (100 and 460 miles). Initially, deployment of the Pershing was made using an M474 tracked launch vehicle. On firing, this would hydraulically raise the missile into position and extend a blast plate with two hydraulic stabilizers out of the rear of the vehicle. In 1985, when the MGM-31B Pershing II was introduced, the launcher vehicle was changed to an M656 series truck with faster road speed. Under nuclear weapon treaties, the last Pershings were destroyed in 1991.

Country of origin:	United States
Crew:	1
Weight:	8100kg (17,900lb)
Dimensions:	Length (with rocket): 10.6m (34.78ft); width: 2.5m (8.2ft); height: 3.79m (12.43ft)
Range:	320km (200 miles)
Armour:	Not applicable
Armament:	1 x Pershing tactical nuclear missile
Powerplant:	1 x Chrysler A-710-B 8-cylinder petrol, developing 215hp (160kW)
Performance:	Maximum road speed: 65km/h (40mph)

FROG-7

The ZIL-135 became one of the Soviet Union's most successful missile-launch vehicles, exported to Algeria, Egypt, Cuba, Iraq, North Korea, Yemen, Yugoslavia and many other countres. It was chosen to carry battlefield missile systems because its 8x8 configuration gives decent off-road mobility, and also because it is relatively cheap at around $25,000 (£15,600) per vehicle. The FROG-7 is the last unguided nuclear-capable battlefield rocket produced by the Soviet Union, and has a range of up to 69km (43 miles). The circular error probability of the rocket is 500–700m (1650–2300ft). Having entered service in 1965, FROG-7s are now mostly replaced in the Russian Federation by the guided SS-21.

Country of origin:	USSR
Crew:	4
Weight:	20,300kg (44,900lb)
Dimensions:	Length: 10.69m (35.07ft); width: 2.8m (9.19ft); height (with missile): 3.35m (11ft)
Range:	650km (400 miles)
Armour:	Not applicable
Armament:	1 x FROG-7 rocket
Powerplant:	2 x ZIL-375 8-cylinder petrol, each developing 177hp (132kW)
Performance:	Maximum road speed: 40km/h (25mph)

LARS II

The Light Artillery Rocket System II (LARS II) was an upgrade to the 110mm (4.33in) LARS I which entered service with the West German Army in 1969. Whereas the LARS I rocket launcher was mounted on a simple 4x4 truck, the upgrade in 1980 placed it on the back of a MAN 6x6 truck and gave it an updated fire-control system. The weapon itself consists of two banks of launcher tubes situated side by side, each bank having 18 tubes. Munitions include DM-711 mine dispensers, DM-21 HE-fragmentation and DM-701 anti-tank mine dispenser. All 36 rockets can be fired in 17.5 seconds and have a maximum range of up to 14km (9 miles). A cab-mounted 7.62mm (0.3in) machine gun provides crew defence.

Country of origin:	West Germany
Crew:	2
Weight:	19,100kg (42,100lb)
Dimensions:	Length: 8.26m (27.09ft); width: 2.49m (8.17ft); height: 2.99m (9.8ft)
Range:	450km (280 miles)
Armour:	Not applicable
Armament:	36 x 110mm (4.33in) rockets; 1 x 7.62mm (0.3in) MG
Powerplant:	1 x Deutz BF8L 413F V8 turbo diesel, developing 315hp (235kW)
Performance:	Maximum road speed: 90km/h (56mph)

M548 Carrier

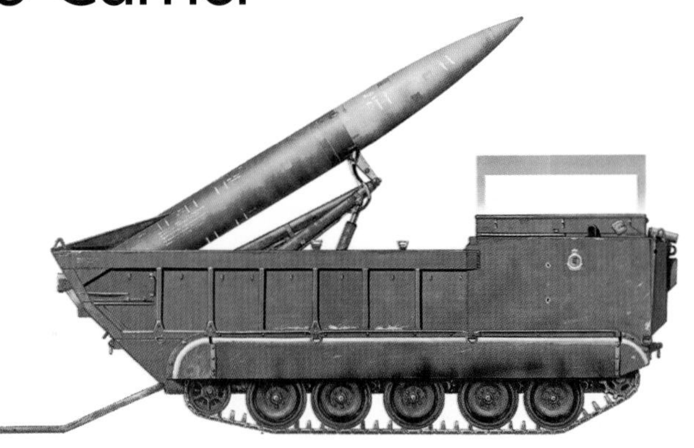

The M548 was developed as a result of a requirement from the US Army Signal Corps for a tracked vehicle to carry specialised equipment. Using many of the automotive components of the M113 armoured personnel carrier, the vehicle was designed either for carrying cargo cross-country or for towing trailers or weapons. The M 548 was fully amphibious, propelled in the water by its tracks and was equipped with infrared night vision. The M548 has been used for many specialised vehicles including: the Vought Lance missile-launcher (as shown above); radar and electronic warfare vehicle; mine layer; 35mm self-propelled anti-aircraft gun; mine clearance and recovery vehicle. Over a dozen countries bought variants based on the M548 chassis, including Germany, Spain and Italy.

Country of origin:	United States
Crew:	1 + 3
Weight:	12,882kg (28,340lb)
Dimensions:	length 5.893m (19ft 4in); width 2.692m (8ft 10in); height 2.82m (9ft 3in)
Range:	483km (300 miles)
Armour:	44mm (1.73in)
Armament:	one 7.62mm or 12.7mm anti-aircraft machine gun
Powerplant:	one Detroit-Diesel Model 6V-53 six-cylinder liquid-cooled diesel engine developing 215hp (160kW)
Performance:	maximum road speed 64km/h (40mph); fording amphibious; vertical obstacle 0.61m (2ft 0in); trench 1.68m (5ft 6in)

XLF-40

The XLF-40 is the largest rocket launcher in the Brazilian arsenal. The vehicular component is a modified version of the US M3A1 light tank chassis. Large numbers of M3s were sold to South America after World War II. In Brazil, 100 subsequently underwent conversion in the 1970s to create the X1A1 vehicle, a lengthened M3 with an additional road wheel. The X1A1 became the basis of the XLF-40. It carries three launcher rails mounting SS-60 missiles and extends three hydraulic stabilizing columns during launching to provide a rigid base. Each rocket weighs 595kg (1312lb), contains either a high explosive or submunition warhead and has a tactical range of 60km (37 miles).

Country of origin:	Brazil
Crew:	4
Weight:	17,070kg (37,639lb)
Dimensions:	Length 6.5m (21.3ft); width: 2.6m (8.5ft); height: 3.2m (10.5ft)
Range:	600km (370 miles)
Armour:	(Steel) 58mm (2.28in)
Armament:	3 x SS-60 rockets
Powerplant:	1 x Saab Scania DS-11 6-cylinder turbo diesel, developing 295hp (220 kW)
Performance:	Maximum road speed: 55km/h (34mph); fording: 1.3m (4.3ft); gradient: 60 percent; vertical obstacle: 0.8m (2.6ft)

Pluton

The Pluton is a short-range tactical nuclear weapons system developed by France in the late 1960s. During this period, defence disagreements with the United States and other NATO nations led France to concentrate on producing its own nuclear weaponry. The Pluton was a replacement for the US Honest John battlefield missile, and entered service in 1974. It was a 7.6m (24.9ft) long, 2400kg (5300lb) missile in a power-operated launcher box mounted on an AMX-30 main battle tank chassis. An accompanying Berliet 6x6 truck provided the fire-control centre. The missile had a range of up to 150km (90 miles) and was powered by a single-propellant rocket. Pluton systems were dismantled during the 1990s.

Country of origin:	France
Crew:	4
Weight:	36,000kg (79,400lb)
Dimensions:	Length (with rocket): 7.76m (25.46ft); width: 3.1m (10.17ft); height: 3.64m (11.94ft)
Range:	600km (370 miles)
Armour:	80mm (3.14in) max
Armament:	1 x short-range nuclear missile
Powerplant:	1 x Renault-Saviem HS110 12-cylinder diesel, developing 691hp (515kW)
Performance:	Maximum road speed: 65km/h (40mph); fording: 2m (6.5ft); gradient: 60 percent; vertical obstacle: 0.93m (3.05ft)

BM-22 Uragan

The BM-22 Uragan was one of the later generation of Soviet multiple rocket launchers. It entered active service with Soviet artillery regiments and tank units in the mid-1970s. Sixteen missiles can be launched in one salvo, the number of launch tubes configured 4-6-6 from top to bottom of the three-layer stack. Reloading the entire system takes around 20 minutes. Transportation is provided by a ZIL-135 8x8 truck chassis. Designed in the ZIL Moscow Automobile Plant, the ZIL-135 was produced for various battlefield haulage tasks, particularly missile carriage. It carried the Soviet Union's first tactical battlefield missile system, the Luna, as well as the Uragan MLRS, and features a 70-ton carrying capacity.

Country of origin:	USSR
Crew:	4
Weight:	20,000kg (44,100lb)
Dimensions:	Length: 9.63m (31.59ft); width: 2.8m (9.19ft); height: 3.22m (10.56ft)
Range:	570km (350 miles)
Armour:	Not applicable
Armament:	16 x 220mm (8.66in) rockets
Powerplant:	2 x ZIL-375 8-cylinder petrol, each developing 177hp (132kW)
Performance:	Maximum road speed: 65km/h (40mph)

Type 75

The Type 75 is the mobile rocket-launching version of the Type 73 Japanese armoured personnel carrier. This was developed in the late 1960s by Mitsubishi Industries, and became the standard armoured personnel carrier of the Japanese Ground Self-Defence Force. It has an all-welded hull made of lightweight aluminium armour. The conversion to rocket launcher took place in 1975. A 130mm (5.12in) hydraulically operated rocket-launching battery was mounted on the rear of the hull. In addition, a Type 75 ground-wind measuring vehicle was developed to operate alongside the attack system. It is fitted with a 12.5m (41ft) vertical mast for measuring wind speeds up to 30km/h (19mph).

Country of origin:	Japan
Crew:	3
Weight:	16,500kg (36,400lb)
Dimensions:	Length: 5.78m (18.96ft); width: 2.8m (9.19ft); height: 2.67m (8.76ft)
Range:	300km (190 miles)
Armour:	Aluminium (details classified)
Armament:	1 x 130mm (5.12in) rocket-launcher system
Powerplant:	1 x Mitsubishi 4ZF 4-cylinder diesel, developing 300hp (224kW) at 2200rpm
Performance:	Maximum road speed: 53km/h (33mph); fording: amphibious; gradient: 60 percent; vertical obstacle: 0.7m (2.3ft); trench: 2m (6.6ft)

Walid

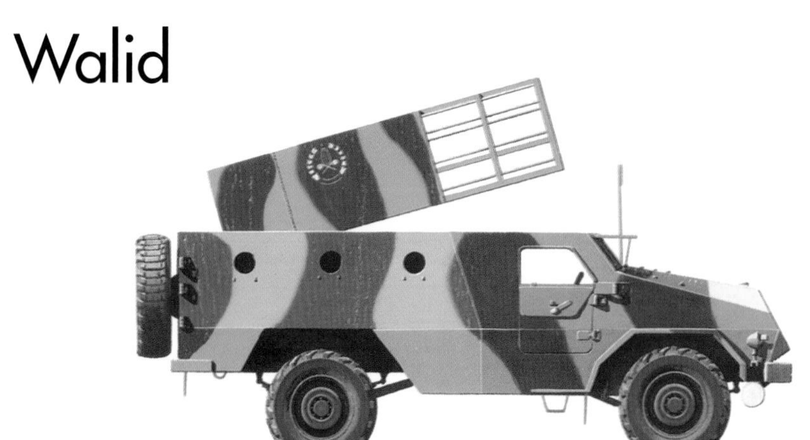

The Egyptian Army has relied in the main on copies of Soviet-produced multiple rocket launcher systems, reflecting the heavy Russian influence in the country in the 1950s and 1960s. However, since Egypt has moved closer to the West, a number of indigenous programmes have been initiated, in particular the Sakr-18 and Sakr-30 Multiple Rocket Launchers, as well as a specialised system for laying down smoke screens. Based on the Walid 4 x 4 armoured personnel carrier, a full salvo of D-3000 rockets is able to produce a smoke screen 1000m (3280ft) long, lasting for up to 15 minutes, sufficient to cover most activities on the battlefield. The same system can be mounted onto a T-62 tank. The rockets are carried in a ready-to-launch position (there is also a six-round version).

Country of origin:	Egypt
Crew:	2
Weight:	unknown
Dimensions:	length 6.12m (20ft); width 2.57m (8ft 5in); height 2.3m (7ft 6in)
Range:	800km (500 miles)
Armour:	8mm (0.31in)
Armament:	12 80mm rocket-launcher tubes
Powerplant:	one diesel engine developing 168hp (125kW)
Performance:	maximum road speed 86km/h (54mph); fording 0.8m (2ft 7in); vertical obstacle 0.5m (1ft 7in)

BMG-109 Tomahawk GLCM

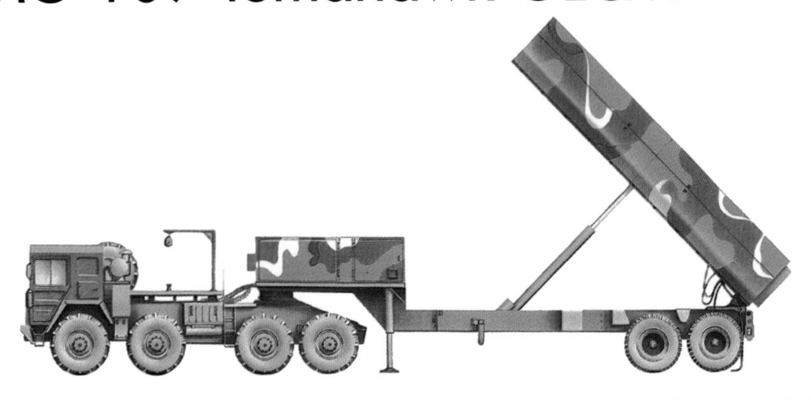

The BMG-109 Tomahawk cruise missile was developed in the 1970s by General Dynamics, and successfully submarine-launched in 1981. Land- and air-launched variants were subsequently produced, the Ground-Launched Cruise Missile (GLCM) entering service in 1983. The GLCM is a towed launcher unit capable of firing four Tomahawks from a 2500km (1550-mile) range. Even at this distance, the Tomahawk will hug the terrain throughout its flight using TERRCOM (Terrain Contour Matching) and DSMAC (Digital Scene Matching Area Correlation) systems. The launcher vehicle is commonly towed by a MAN Cat I AI 8x8 truck. These vehicles also carry Patriot missile systems and Roland air defence missile systems.

Country of origin:	United States
Crew:	4
Weight:	(Vehicle only) 13,400kg (29,550lb)
Dimensions:	Length: (vehicle only) 10.27m (33.7ft); width: 2.5m (8.2ft); height: 2.93m (9.61ft)
Range:	600km (370 miles)
Armour:	Not applicable
Armament:	4 x BMG-109 Tomahawk cruise missiles
Powerplant:	1 x Deutz BF8L 413 8-cylinder turbo diesel, developing 339hp (253kW)
Performance:	Maximum road speed: 90km/h (56mph)

Valkiri

South Africa began development of an indigenous multiple rocket launcher in 1977 as a counter to the various Soviet systems in service with neighbouring African countries. The Valkiri entered service in 1981, deployed in batteries of eight, to be used against guerrilla camps, troop concentrations and soft-skinned vehicle convoys. Mounted on a 4 x 4 SAMIL truck chassis, the full 24-round complement could be fired in 24 seconds, with a 10-minute reloading time. Highly mobile and with minimal launch signature, the Valkiri proved an ideal weapon for cross-border raids and counter-insurgency work, especially as the system could be easily camouflaged to resemble a standard truck. Each of the rockets the system fired had a maximum range of 22km (13.67 miles).

Country of origin:	South Africa
Crew:	2
Weight:	6440kg (14,168lb)
Dimensions:	length 5.41m (17ft 9in); width 1.985m (6ft 6in), height 3.2m (10ft 6in)
Range:	650km (406 miles)
Armour:	none
Armament:	24 127mm rocket-launcher tubes
Powerplant:	one six-cylinder diesel engine developing 120hp (89kW)
Performance:	maximum road speed 80km/h (50mph); fording 0.5m (1ft 7in); vertical obstacle 0.6m (1ft 11in); trench 0.6m (1ft 11in)

MLRS

The Vought Multiple Launch Rocket System (MLRS) had its origins in a 1976 feasibility study into what was known as a General Support Rocket System. Following trials the Vought system was chosen and entered service with the US Army in 1982. These Self-Propelled Launcher Loaders on the chassis of the M2 Infantry Fighting Vehicle carry two pods of six rounds each. These rounds might consist of fragmentation bomblets, anti-tank mines, chemical warheads or mine-dispensing munitions. The Vought MLRS was licensed to the UK, France, Italy, West Germany and the Netherlands for production. It saw action during the 1991 Gulf War, when Allied MLRS batteries tore large holes in Iraqi defence lines prior to the ground offensive to free Kuwait, and again in the 2003 Iraq war.

Country of origin:	United States
Crew:	3
Weight:	25,191kg (55,420lb)
Dimensions:	length 6.8m (22ft 4in); width 2.92m (9ft 7in); height 2.6m (8ft 6in)
Range:	483km (302 miles)
Armour:	classified
Armament:	two rocket pod containers, each holding six rockets
Powerplant:	one Cummings VTA-903 turbo-charged eight-cylinder diesel engine developing 500hp 373kW)
Performance:	maximum road speed 64km/h (40mph); fording 1.1m (3ft 7in); vertical obstacle 1m (3ft 4in); trench 2.29m (7ft 6in)

Astros II

The Astros II is a conventional truck-based multiple rocket launcher built by Tectran in Brazil. The 10-tonnes (9.9-tons) 6 x 6 cross-country vehicle is equipped with armoured shutters to protect the crew cabin. In service with the Brazilian Army and exported in large numbers to Iraq during the Iran-Iraq War, the Astros system uses a common launcher, command and fire-control vehicle to deliver three different types of rocket, the SS-30, SS-40 and SS-60. The rockets range in weight from 68kg to 595kg (149.6lb to 1309lb), all of which are unguided. An ammunition resupply vehicle is always attached to the Astros system. Though less sophisticated than the MLRS, for example, the Astros does provide an excellent rocket launcher system for Third World and developing states.

Country of origin:	Brazil
Crew:	3
Weight:	10,000kg (22,000lb)
Dimensions:	length 7m (22ft 11in); width 2.9m (9ft 6in); height 2.6m (8ft 6in)
Range:	480km (300 miles)
Armour:	classified
Armament:	one battery of four, 16 or 32 rocket-launcher tubes
Powerplant:	one six-cylinder water-cooled diesel engine developing 212hp (158kW)
Performance:	maximum road speed 65km/h (40.62mph); fording 1.1m (3ft 7in); vertical obstacle 1m (3ft 4in); trench 2.29m (7ft 6in)

SS-23 Spider

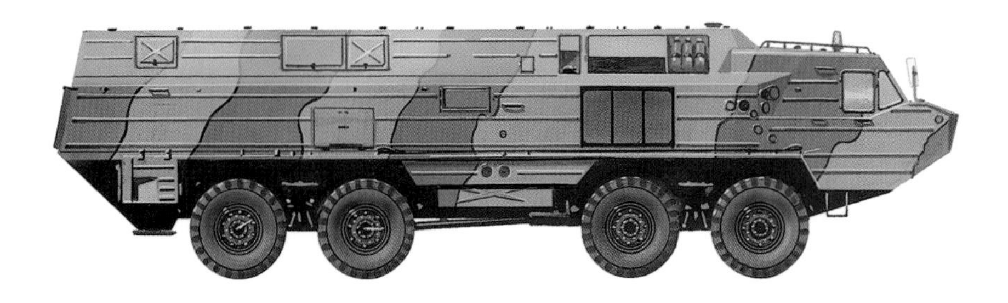

The SS-23 Spider was a tactical ballistic missile deployed in 1985, but scrapped in 1989 under the Intermediate-Range and Shorter-Range Nuclear Forces (INF) Treaty. Destroyed with them were the SS-23s' transport-erector-launcher vehicles – modified BAZ-6944 8x8 trucks. Unusually for mobile tactical-missile launchers, the BAZ-6944 was fully amphibious and could travel at 10km/h (6mph) in the water. On land, its maximum speed was 70km/h (43mph) and a central tyre-pressure regulation system allowed it to maintain good cross-country speeds. In a four-year service life, 239 SS-23s were produced. With a range of 500km (310 miles) and accurate to 100m (328ft), the SS-23s were of genuine concern to NATO forces.

Country of origin:	USSR
Crew:	3
Weight:	29,000kg (63,900lb)
Dimensions:	Length: 11.76m (38.58ft); width: 3.19m (10.47ft); height: 3m (9.84ft)
Range:	1000km (620 miles)
Armour:	Not available
Armament:	1 x SS-23 ballistic missile
Powerplant:	1 x UTD-25 8-cylinder diesel, developing 394hp (294kW)
Performance:	Maximum road speed: 70km/h (43mph)

M-77 Oganj

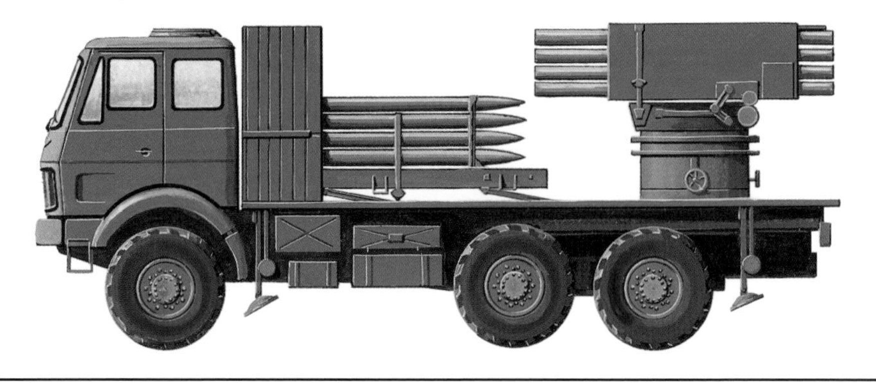

The M-77 Oganj consists of a YMRL 32 (Yugoslav Multiple Rocket Launcher, 32-barrel) rocket system mounted on the back of a FAP-2026 6x6 truck. Each M-77 rocket carries a 19.5kg (43lb) high-explosive warhead which it fires to a distance of 20km (12.5 miles). A full salvo can devastate an area 167 x 213m (548 x 699ft). The truck can carry 32 missiles preloaded in the launcher tubes, and another 32 in a reloading pack just behind the cab. The Oganj later received the M-91 cluster-warhead missile, which dramatically increases the kill zone for a single salvo. Each missile contains 48 bomblets or four anti-tank mines. These warheads were combat tested during the civil war in Yugoslavia.

Country of origin:	Yugoslavia
Crew:	5
Weight:	22,400kg (49,400lb)
Dimensions:	Length: 11.5m (37.56ft); width: 2.49m (8.17ft); height: 3.1m (10.17ft)
Range:	600km (370 miles)
Armour:	Not applicable
Armament:	32 + 32 x M-77 or M-91 rockets; 1 x 12.7mm (0.5in) MG
Powerplant:	1 x 8-cylinder diesel, developing 256hp (191kW)
Performance:	Maximum road speed: 80km/h (50mph)

9A52 Smerch

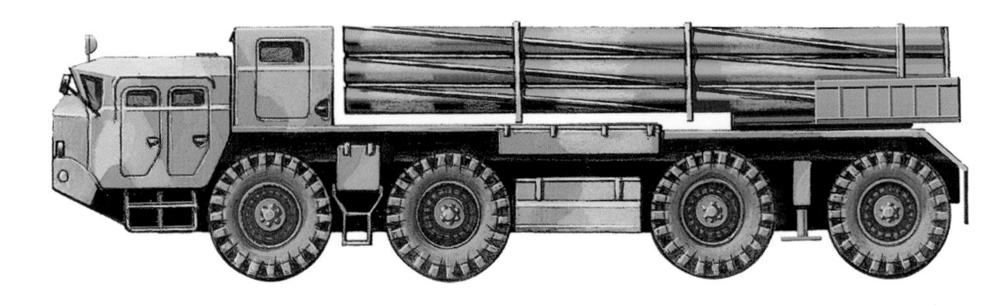

The 9A52 Smerch is Russia's equivalent to the US Multiple Launch Rocket System. Twelve launch tubes can fire salvos of 300mm (11.81in) rockets to distances of 70km (43 miles). Specialist munitions include the Bazalt parachute-retarded warhead which hangs in the air, detects armoured targets and shoots a 1kg (2.2lb) penetrator through the weaker upper armour. The Smerch is carried on a MAZ-543 series 8x8 truck. This vehicle was developed from the MAZ-535/537 series as a specialist carrier vehicle for missile and rocket systems such as the SS-1 Scud and SS-3 Scaleboard. For its size, the MAZ-543 has good cross-country capability owing to ground clearance of 0.45m (1.48ft).

Country of origin:	USSR
Crew:	4
Weight:	43,700kg (96,400lb)
Dimensions:	Length: 12.1m (39.7ft); width: 3.05m (10ft); height: 3.05m (10ft)
Range:	850km (530 miles)
Armour:	Not applicable
Armament:	12 x 300mm (11.81in) rockets
Powerplant:	1 x D12A-525 12-cylinder diesel, developing 517hp (386kW)
Performance:	Maximum road speed: 60km/h (37mph)

BAK 1906

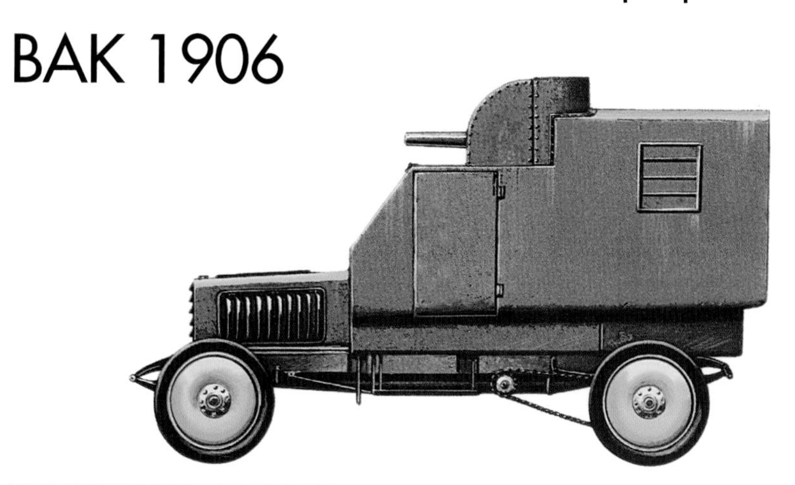

The Ballon-Abwehr-Kanonenwagen (BAK) 1906 was designed by the Ehrhardt company for use against enemy observation balloons in World War I. It was essentially a commercial truck chassis on which was mounted a 50mm (1.97in) cannon firing high-explosive shrapnel shells. The cannon was seated on a rotating turret with a 60 degree traverse and could engage static balloon targets up to several hundred metres in altitude. With the advent of aircraft observation, however, the BAK 1906 was upgraded to a 75mm (2.95in) cannon and became possibly the first self-propelled anti-aircraft vehicle, the BAK 1909. The open crew compartment made the BAK 1906 vulnerable to infantry fire.

Country of origin:	Germany
Crew:	5
Weight:	3200kg (7100lb)
Dimensions:	Length: 5.27m (17.29ft); width: 1.93m (6.33ft); height: 3.07m (10.07ft)
Range:	Not available
Armour:	Not available
Armament:	1 x 50mm (1.97in) cannon
Powerplant:	1 x Ehrhardt 4-cylinder petrol, developing 60hp (45kW)
Performance:	Maximum road speed: 45km/h (28mph)

194mm Gun GPF

GPF stands for 'Grand Puissance, Filloux', or 'gun of great power'. This one was designed by Colonel Filloux, and is one of a number of heavy guns he designed for the French Army during World War I. Developed in 1917, this was simply a heavier barrel fitted to the carriage of the existing 155mm (6.1in) GPF which Filloux had designed. In broad terms, the 194mm (7.63in) weapon had about twice the shell-power of the 155mm gun, when weight of shell, explosive content and range were all taken into consideration. Transportation was in two units, the barrel being removed from the carriage and placed on a special transport wagon. The towing tractor was provided with a winch which was used to transfer the barrel from the wagon and on to the carriage, or vice versa. They remained in service until 1940.

Country of origin:	France
Crew:	8
Weight:	28 tonnes (27.5 tons)
Dimensions:	Length: 8.12m (26ft 7in); width: 2.7m (8ft 9in); height: 2.35m (7ft 8in)
Range:	50km (30 miles)
Armour:	None
Armament:	1 x 194mm (7.6in) GPF gun
Powerplant:	1 x Panhard 6-cylinder petrol, developing 110hp (82kW)
Performance:	Maximum road speed: 10km/h (6mph)

St Chamond Mortier de 280 sur Chenilles

The French considered the tank to be nothing but a gun carrier, and thus began looking at ways of mounting even heavier guns on tracks. This design was quite revolutionary – the gun carriage had electric motors driving the two tracks. The current was supplied from another vehicle, similar to the gun carriage but without a gun, and was provided with a petrol engine driving an electric generator. This hooked on to the gun carriage, a cable was plugged in, and the tractor fed electric current to its own tracks and to those of the gun carriage. All the driver of the gun carriage had to do was steer. A number of these guns were made and used in 1918, though reports of their activities are scarce. A number also carried the 194mm (7.6in) GPF gun; they were last seen being used by the Germans in Russia in 1943.

Country of origin:	France
Crew:	8
Weight:	28 tonnes (27.5 tons)
Dimensions:	Length: 8.12m (26ft 7in); width: 2.7m (8ft 9in); height: 2.35m (7ft 8in)
Range:	50km (30 miles)
Armour:	None
Armament:	1 x 280mm (11in) Schneider howitzer
Powerplant:	1 x Panhard 6-cylinder petrol, developing 110hp (82kW)
Performance:	Maximum road speed: 10km/h (6mph)

Birch Gun Mk II

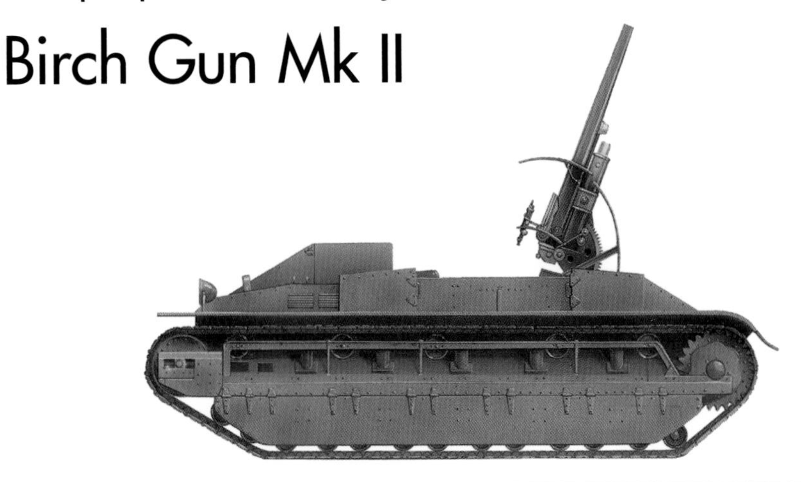

The Birch Gun was the world's first effective example of self-propelled artillery. It was named after General Sir Noel Birch, Master General of the Ordnance, and it emerged from the Woolwich Arsenal as an experimental model in 1925. The Birch Gun consisted of an unmodified Vickers medium tank chassis on which was mounted an 18-pounder (83.8mm/3.3in) field gun. A second version, the Mk II of 1926, featured better elevation for the gun, allowing it to engage either ground or aerial targets. British high command response to the Birch Gun was not favourable, mainly from prejudice rather than reasoned complaint, and after a third version in 1928, the project was abandoned.

Country of origin:	United Kingdom
Crew:	6
Weight:	12,000kg (26,500lb)
Dimensions:	Length: 5.8m (19ft); width: 2.4m (7.9ft); height: 2.3m (7.6ft)
Range:	192km (119 miles)
Armour:	6mm (0.24in)
Armament:	1 x 75mm (2.95in) gun
Powerplant:	1 x Armstrong-Siddeley 8-cylinder petrol, developing 90hp (67 kW)
Performance:	Maximum road speed: 45km/h (28mph)

203mm Howitzer M1931 (L/25)

During World War II the Russians did not waste any time in the manufacture of super-heavy artillery; they had an effective ground attack aircraft, the Stormovik, which was directly under army control just as the Stuka dive-bomber was in the German Army, and this acted as the heavy artillery. The heaviest gun put into the field was this 203mm (8in) Howitzer M1931 (L/25), and one suspects that had it not already existed, it would not have been built during the war. There were a number of versions of this weapon, but the most common was this model on the tracked carriage. When inspected closely, it can be seen that this carriage has been derived directly from an agricultural tractor design, and was ideal for floating such a heavy gun across the snow and mud of the Russian winter and spring.

Country of origin:	USSR
Crew:	15
Weight:	17,700kg (17.42 tons)
Dimensions:	Length of gun: 5.09m (16ft); width: not known; height: not known
Range:	Not applicable
Armour:	None
Armament:	1 x 203mm (8.0in) gun
Powerplant:	None
Performance:	Maximum road speed (towed): 15km/h (9mph)

sIG 33

The sIG 33 was a self-propelled howitzer used to equip German infantry battalions of World War II. The first version appeared during the French Campaign of May 1940, and was simply the standard sIG 33 heavy infantry gun mounted on a PzKpfw I chassis and fitted with armoured shields to protect the crew. It was developed to provide armoured infantry with close fire support from a self-propelled armoured platform. The centre of gravity was rather high, though, and the chassis was overloaded. In consequence, the PzKpfw II chassis was converted for use in 1942, giving better armour protection, followed by the PzKpfw III. The vehicle served throughout the war and was still in production in 1944, with over 370 vehicles being made.

Country of origin:	Germany
Crew:	4
Weight:	11,505kg (25,300lb)
Dimensions:	length 4.835m (15ft 10.4in); width 2.15m (7ft 0.6in); height 2.40m (7ft 10.5in)
Range:	185km (115 miles)
Armour:	6-13mm (0.23-0.5in)
Armament:	one 15cm sIG 33 howitzer
Powerplant:	one Praga six-cylinder petrol engine developing 150hp (111.9kW)
Performance:	maximum road speed 35km/h (21.75mph); fording 0.914m (3ft); vertical obstacle 0.42m (1ft 5in); trench 1.75m (5ft 9in)

M41M90/53

The Semovente M41M90/53 was one of several self-propelled guns developed by Italy during the early years of World War II. Its original purpose was as an anti-aircraft gun, but like the German 88mm (3.46in) Flak weapons it was equally useful against ground targets. The 90mm (3.54in) Model 39 cannon was set to the rear of an M14/41 chassis, the engine relocated to the front of the vehicle. An L.6 light tank accompanied the M41M90/53 as an ammunition resupply vehicle, carrying 26 rounds internally and another 40 in a trailer. The M41M90/53 saw most action in North Africa in 1941 and 1942, but after the Italian armistice, it continued in use in German hands in Italy's mountainous northern regions.

Country of origin:	Italy
Crew:	2
Weight:	17,000kg (37,500lb)
Dimensions:	Length: 5.21m (17.09ft); width: 2.20m (7.22ft); height: 2.15m (7.05ft)
Range:	200km (125 miles)
Armour:	25mm (0.98in)
Armament:	1 x Ansaldo Model 39 90mm (3.54in) cannon
Powerplant:	1 x SPA 15-TM-41 8-cylinder petrol, developing 145hp (108kW)
Performance:	Maximum road speed: 35km/h (22mph)

Type 4

The Japanese produced few heavy armoured vehicles, partly because they were deemed unnecessary based on experiences in China and Manchuria, and partly because their industrial capacity was inadequate for the task. The Type 4 was a self-propelled howitzer using the Type 97 medium tank as a base. The howitzer itself dated from 1905 and had been with withdrawn from service in 1942 but continued to be used in the self-propelled version. The Type 4 was poorly armoured and a had a slow rate of fire, mainly because of the breech mechanism employed. The Japanese were unable to produce them on a mass scale, being deployed in ones and twos, mainly for island defence. They were hopelessly outnumbered against American artillery in the Pacific battles in World War II.

Country of origin:	Japan
Crew:	4 or 5
Weight:	13,300kg (29,260lb)
Dimensions:	length 5.537m (18ft 2in); width 2.286m (7ft 6in); height to top of shield 1.549m (5ft 1in)
Range:	250km (156miles)
Armour:	25mm (0.98in)
Armament:	one Type 38 150mm howitzer
Powerplant:	one V-12 diesel engine developing 170hp (126.8kW)
Performance:	maximum road speed 38km/h (23.6mph); fording 1.0m (3ft 3in); vertical obstacle 0.812m (2ft 8in); trench 2.0m (6ft 7in)

SdKfz 135/1 15cm Howitzer

The origins of the SdKfz 135/1 actually lay with a French vehicle, the Tracteur Blinde 37L (Lorraine). This served as a French armoured personnel carrier and artillery tractor, and a total of 315 were captured by the Germans when France was occupied in 1940. Initially the vehicles were converted into self-propelled anti-tank guns – the original crew compartment was removed and replaced by a gun shield and a PaK 40/1 L-46 75mm (2.95in) cannon. This vehicle was the SdKfz 135. The 135/1 variant was of similar construction but mounted a 150mm (5.9in) howitzer. All such converted vehicles suffered from thin upper armour, and the crews were especially vulnerable to artillery or air attack.

Country of origin:	Germany
Crew:	5
Weight:	8100kg (17,900lb)
Dimensions:	Length (with gun): 5.31m (17.42ft); width: 1.88m (6.17ft); height: 2.08m (6.82ft)
Range:	135km (85 miles)
Armour:	Not available
Armament:	1 x 150mm (5.9in) howitzer
Powerplant:	1 x Delahaye 103 TT diesel, developing 79hp (59kW)
Performance:	Maximum road speed: 34km/h (21mph)

Bishop

The Bishop was designed to relieve the 25-pounder batteries in North Africa of their role as anti-tank weapons, in which role they were taking a pounding from the Germans. A 25mm gun was therefore mounted on the chassis of a Valentine tank – it was not a success. The new vehicle had a high, slab-sided turret which made an excellent target for enemy gunners. The gun was mounted in a fixed turret with limited elevation. By the time they were introduced, the 25-pounder was no longer being used in an anti-tank role, so the Bishops were diverted for artillery use. The Bishop was the first British effort at a self-propelled gun and was useful in showing the potential of the type and what to avoid in future designs. When the M7 Priest arrived, the Bishop soon fell out of use.

Country of origin:	United Kingdom
Crew:	4
Weight:	7879kg (17,333lb)
Dimensions:	length 5.64m (18ft 6in); width 2.77m (9ft 1in); height 3.05m (10ft)
Range:	177km (110 miles)
Armour:	8-60mm (0.315-2.36in)
Armament:	one 25-pounder gun
Powerplant:	one AEC six-cylinder diesel engine developing 131hp (97.7kW)
Performance:	maximum road speed 24km/h (15mph); fording 0.91m (3ft); vertical obstacle 0.83m (2ft 9in): trench 2.28m (7ft 6in)

StuG III Ausf F

The StuG III Ausf F was developed from 1941, by personal order of Adolf Hitler himself, to regain superiority over the Soviet KV-1 and T-34 tanks on the Eastern Front. The armour of the Ausf A-E series was upgraded and a new long StuK40 L/48 7.5cm gun was fitted in place of the original short 7.5cm version, which significantly improved the vehicle's anti-tank capability. The basic hull and superstructure remained the same, other than the addition of an exhaust fan to remove gun fumes. The gun mantlet was also redesigned to allow for the recoil mechanism of the larger gun. The Ausf F proved highly effective against the Soviet KV-1s and T-34s and the vehicle remained in service throughout the war –its low silhouette giving it an added advantage in tank-versus-tank combats.

Country of origin:	Germany
Crew:	4
Weight:	21,800kg (47,960lb)
Dimensions:	length 6.31m (19ft 2in); width 2.92m (8ft 11in); height: 2.15m (6ft 7in)
Range:	140km (92 miles)
Armour:	11-50mm (0.4-2in)
Armament:	one 75mm Stuk40 L/48 gun; one 7.92mm machine gun
Powerplant:	one Maybach HL120TRM engine
Performance:	maximum road speed 40km/h (25mph); fording 0.8m (2ft 8in); vertical obstacle 0.6m (2ft); trench 2.59m (8ft 6in)

T19

The T19 was produced between 1941 and 1944. Its weapon was a 105mm (4.13in) M2A1 howitzer. This had a maximum range of 10,698m (35,097ft) and could fire HE, HEAT, smoke and illumination rounds. The gun was mounted on an M3 half-track to create the T19, and the vehicle chassis required considerable strengthening to cope with the impact of firing. Eight rounds of 105mm (4.13in) ammunition were carried on board, with more being transported in a towed trailer. The T19 saw service in North Africa, Italy and northern Europe, but it was replaced by the M7 GMC during 1944. Existing T19s were often stripped of their howitzers to supply the M7 and converted back to standard M3s.

Country of origin:	United States
Crew:	5 or 6
Weight:	10,500kg (23,150lb)
Dimensions:	Length: 6.18m (20.28ft); width: 2.22m (7.28ft); height: 2.55m (8.37ft)
Range:	282km (175 miles)
Armour:	(Steel) 13mm (0.51in) maximum
Armament:	1 x 105mm (4.13in) M2A1 howitzer
Powerplant:	1 x White 160AX 6-cylinder diesel, developing 128hp (95kW)
Performance:	Maximum road speed: 65km/h (40mph); fording: 0.81m (2.66ft)

SU-76

The battles of 1941 showed the Soviet light tanks to be virtually useless. It was thus decided to combine the T-70 already in production with the excellent ZIS-3 and ZIS-76 guns to create a highly mobile anti-tank weapon. A wartime expedient, there were few comforts for the crew and it was known to troops as 'The Bitch'. The first SU-76s appeared in late 1942 and by mid-1943 they were deployed in appreciable numbers. Better German armour had by this time reduced the effectiveness of the ZIS gun and thus the vehicle's role was changed from anti-tank to infantry support. By 1945, many SU-76s were converted into ammunition carriers or recovery vehicles. After the war, many were transferred to China and North Korea, seeing service during the Korean War.

Country of origin:	USSR
Crew:	4
Weight:	10,600kg (23,320lb)
Dimensions:	length 4.88m (16ft 0.1in); width 2.73m (8ft 11.5in); height 2.17m (7ft 1.4in)
Range:	450km (280 miles)
Armour:	up to 25mm (0.98in)
Armament:	one ZIS-3 76mm gun
Powerplant:	two GAZ six-cylinder petrol engines each developing 70hp (52.2kW)
Performance:	maximum road speed 45km/h (28mph); fording 0.89m (2ft 11in); vertical obstacle 0.70m (2ft 3.6in); trench 3.12m (10ft 2.8in)

Sexton

In 1941, the British were searching for a suitable armoured vehicle to mount the standard British 25-pounder gun. The Canadians were producing the Ram tank, soon to be replaced by American M3s, and these were altered to accommodate the 25-pounder, becoming known as the Sexton. Used mainly as a field artillery weapon to support armoured divisions, the Sexton saw action in Northwest Europe in 1944 and 1945. By the time production ceased shortly after the war, a total of 2150 had been built. The main variant was a purpose-built command tank with the weapon removed and extra radios added. A reliable, rugged and effective weapon, the Sexton continued in service until the 1950s with the British Army, and until very recently with some other armies.

Country of origin:	Canada
Crew:	6
Weight:	25,300kg (55,660lb)
Dimensions:	length 6.12m (20ft 1in); width 2.72m (8ft 11in); height 2.44m (8ft 0in)
Range:	290km (180 miles)
Armour:	up to 32mm (1.25in)
Armament:	one 25-pounder howitzer; two.303in Bren Guns; one 0.5in Browning machine gun
Powerplant:	one nine-cylinder radial piston engine developing 400hp (298.3kW)
Performance:	maximum road speed 40.2km/h (25mph); fording 1.01m (3ft 4in); vertical obstacle 0.61m (2ft); trench 1.91m (6ft 3in)

M7 Priest

Nicknamed the 'Priest' by British crews because of its pulpit-shaped machine-gun turret at the front, the M7 grew from US experience with howitzers mounted on half-tracked vehicles. A fully tracked carriage was required, and the M3 tank was modified to fill the role. The British received many under the Lend-Lease scheme and deployed them first at the second battle of El Alamein in 1942. Some measure of their popularity is suggested by the British order for 5500 to be delivered within one year of their first use. The drawback was that the howitzer was not standard British issue, and thus required separate supplies of ammunition. Mobile and reliable, the M7 fought to the end of the war and remained in service in the role of armoured personnel carrier – it was also widely exported.

Country of origin:	United States
Crew:	5
Weight:	22,500kg (49,500lb)
Dimensions:	length 6.02m (19ft 9in); width 2.88m (9ft 5.25in); height 2.54m (8ft 4in)
Range:	201km (125 miles)
Armour:	up to 25.4mm (1in)
Armament:	one 105mm howitzer; one 12.7mm machine gun
Powerplant:	one Continental nine-cylinder radial piston engine developing 375hp (279.6kW)
Performance:	maximum road speed 41.8km/h (26mph); fording 1.219m (4ft); vertical obstacle 0.61m (2ft); trench 1.91m (6ft 3in)

M40

The M40 entered development in December 1943 and was based on the M4 tank chassis and used the 155mm 'Long Tom' gun. A heavy spade was attached to the rear which could be dug into the ground to help absorb recoil after firing. The first production vehicles appeared in January 1945, and arrived just as World War II in Europe was ending. It continued in service, with a total of 311 being built, and saw its main action in the Korean War (1950-53), where it proved an excellent weapon, and in Indochina with the French Army. The M40 appeared at a time when nuclear warfare was making its debut, and thus it was used extensively for post-war trials designed to provide protection against fallout for the crew, forming the blueprint for modern self-propelled vehicles.

Country of origin:	United States
Crew:	8
Weight:	36,400kg (80,080lb)
Dimensions:	length 9.04m (29ft 8in); width 3.15m (10ft 4in); height 2.84m (9ft 4in)
Range:	161km (100 miles)
Armour:	up to 12.7mm (0.5in)
Armament:	one 155mm (6.1in) gun
Powerplant:	one Continental nine-cylinder radial piston engine developing 395hp (294.6kW)
Performance:	maximum road speed 38.6km/h (24mph); fording 1.067m (3ft 6in); vertical obstacle 0.61m (2ft); trench 2.26m (7ft 5in)

StuG III Ausf G

The StuG III Ausf G was the last StuG to enter production in World War II. Based predominantly on the chassis of the PzKpfw III, which was being phased out of tank service in favour of the much more lethal Panther, the Ausf G carried thicker armour than its predecessors, which was fortunate, as the Stug III was called upon more and more to fill the role of a tank, being cheaper and easier to build. However, its lack of mobility proved a liability as it was vulnerable to infantry with anti-tank projectiles. The addition of armoured 'skirts' (Schützen) went some way towards improving protection, but despite a valiant effort, the StuG IIIs were not really suited for the tank role in which they found themselves. Nevertheless, the Ausf G version was the best of the bunch, and performed well on the battlefield.

Country of origin:	Germany
Crew:	4
Weight:	24,100kg (53,020lb)
Dimensions:	length 6.77m (20ft 7in); width 2.95m (9ft); height 2.16m (6ft 7in)
Range:	155km (97 miles)
Armour:	16-80mm (0.62-3.14in)
Armament:	one 75mm (2.95in) Stuk40 L/48 gun; one 7.92mm (0.31in) MG42 machine gun
Powerplant:	one Maybach HL120TRM engine
Performance:	maximum road speed 40km/h (25mph); fording 0.8m (2ft 8in); vertical obstacle 0.6m (2ft); trench 2.59m (8ft 6in)

Hummel

The Hummel ('Bumble Bee') was a hybrid of the PzKpfw III and IV hulls, with a lightly armoured open superstructure, which formed the heavy artillery element of German panzer and panzergrenadier divisions from 1942 onwards. The Hummel first saw action at the Battle of Kursk in July 1943. They were useful and popular weapons and were used on all fronts, having plenty of room for the crew of five and the mobility to keep up with the panzer divisions. Well over 600 had been produced by late 1944, and 150 were converted into ammunition carriers as lorries proved inadequate for the task. Other variants included the Oskette, a wider-tracked version produced for winter fighting on the Russian Front. It was usual for 18 rounds of ammunition to be carried in the vehicle.

Country of origin:	Germany
Crew:	5
Weight:	23,927kg (52,640lb)
Dimensions:	length 7.17m (23ft 6.3in); width 2.87m (9ft 5in); height 2.81m (9ft 2.6in)
Range:	215km (134 miles)
Armour:	up to 50mm (1.97in)
Armament:	one 15cm (5.9in) sIG 33 howitzer or one 88mm (3.46in) anti-tank gun
Powerplant:	one Maybach V-12 petrol engine developing 265hp (197.6kW)
Performance:	maximum road speed 42km/h (26.1mph); fording 0.99m (3ft 3in); vertical obstacle 0.6m (2ft); trench 2.20m (7ft 3in)

ISU-152

The ISU-152 was the first of the Soviet heavy self-propelled artillery carriages of World War II, entering service in 1943, just in time to take part in the Battle of Kursk in July. Built on a KV-2 heavy tank chassis, it was intended for a dual role as an anti-tank weapon and heavy assault gun. The vehicle was in the vanguard of the Soviet advances of 1944 and 1945, and the vehicles were amongst the first to enter Berlin at the end of the war. The ISU-152's major drawback was a lack of internal stowage space for ammunition, and each vehicle thus required constant supply by ammunition carriers, which was hazardous and affected tactical mobility. Nevertheless, the ISU-152 remained in service after the war, being used during the crushing of the 1956 Hungarian uprising.

Country of origin:	USSR
Crew:	5
Weight:	45,500kg (100,100lb)
Dimensions:	length overall 9.80m (32ft 1.8in) and hull 6.805m (22ft 3.9in); width 3.56m (11ft 8.2in); height 2.52m (8ft 3.2in)
Range:	180km (112 miles)
Armour:	35-100mm (1.38-3.94in)
Armament:	one 152mm (6in) howitzer; one 12.7mm (0.5in) anti-aircraft machine gun
Powerplant:	one V-12 diesel engine developing 520hp (387.8kW)
Performance:	maximum road speed 37km/h (23mph); fording 1.3m (4ft 3.2in); vertical obstacle 1.20m (3ft 8in); trench 2.59m (8ft 6in)

M56

After World War II, the US Army issued a requirement for a highly mobile anti-tank gun which could be dropped with the first wave of airborne troops and have a firepower similar to that of a tank. Cadillac began production of the M56 (also known as the Scorpion) in 1953 and ceased production in 1959. The M56 was deployed with the 82nd and 101st Airborne Divisions and saw action in the Vietnam War (although not on a large scale), mainly in a fire-support role. In addition, small numbers were exported to Spain and Morocco. The main drawbacks were a lack of armour and the massive recoil, which often moved the vehicle several feet and obscured the target with dust. In the 1960s, the vehicle was replaced by the M551, another flawed armoured fighting vehicle design.

Country of origin:	United States
Crew:	4
Weight:	7000kg (15,400lb)
Dimensions:	length 5.841m (19ft 2in); width 2.577m (8ft 5.5in); height 2.067m (6ft 9.3in)
Range:	225km (140 miles)
Armour:	classified
Armament:	one 90mm (3.54in) gun
Powerplant:	one Continental six-cylinder petrol engine developing 200hp (149kW)
Performance:	maximum road speed 45km/h (28mph); vertical obstacle 0.762m (2ft 6in); trench 1.524m (5ft)

ASU-57

The ASU-57 was developed in the 1950s specifically for use by Soviet airborne divisions (54 vehicles per division) and was designed to be parachuted with the troops, using pallets fitted with retro-rocket systems to soften impact on landing. The gun was a development of the World War II ZIS-2, while its engine was taken from the Pobeda civilian car. Despite its drawbacks – a hull made of welded aluminium which affords little protection for the crew, a rather underpowered engine and weaponry – the ASU-57 remained in service for around 20 years before being replaced by the ASU-85. For airborne troops such vehicles are invaluable, giving lightly armed soldiers, who are invariably isolated behind enemy lines, mobile artillery support on the battlefield.

Country of origin:	USSR
Crew:	3
Weight:	3300kg (7260lb)
Dimensions:	length 4.995m (16ft 4.7in); width 2.086m (6ft 10in); height 1.18m (3ft 10.5in)
Range:	250km (155 miles)
Armour:	6mm (0.23in)
Armament:	one 57mm (2.24in) CH-51M gun; one 7.62mm (0.3in) anti-aircraft machine gun
Powerplant:	one M-20E four-cylinder petrol engine developing 55hp (41kW)
Performance:	maximum road speed 45km/h (28mph);vertical obstacle 0.5m (20in); trench 1.4m (4ft 7in)

M109

The M109 was developed following a 1952 requirement for a self-propelled howitzer to replace the M44. The first production vehicles were completed in 1962 and survived numerous adaptations and upgrades to become the most widely used howitzer in the world, seeing action in Vietnam, in the Arab-Israeli Wars and the Iran-Iraq War, and being exported to nearly 30 countries worldwide. It has an amphibious capability and fires a variety of projectiles including tactical nuclear shells. To date some 4000 are in use around the world, and the M109 has undergone numerous upgrades, including a new gun mount, new turret with longer barrel ordnance, automatic fire control, upgraded armour and improved armour. It will continue to serve well into the next century.

Country of origin:	United States
Crew:	6
Weight:	23,723kg (52,192lb)
Dimensions:	length 6.612m (21ft 8.25in); width 3.295m (10ft 9.75in); height 3.289m (10ft 9.5in)
Range:	390km (240 miles)
Armour:	classified
Armament:	one 155mm (6.1in) howitzer; one 12.7mm (0.5in) AA machine gun
Powerplant:	one Detroit Diesel Model 8V-71T diesel engine developing 405hp (302kW)
Performance:	maximum road speed 56km/h (35mph); fording 1.07m (3ft 6in); vertical obstacle 0.533m (1ft 9in); trench 1.828m (6ft)

M107

The M107 was designed in the 1950s along with the M110 203mm self-propelled howitzer, which has the same chassis and gun mount. The first production models rolled off the factory line in 1962, and eventually a total of 524 M107s were built by the time production ceased in 1980. Though it is no longer in frontline service with the United States and the United Kingdom, it is still in first-line use with the forces of Greece, Iran, Israel, South Korea and Turkey. The M107 has a total crew of 13, but only the commander, driver and three gunners are carried on the vehicle itself, which has no crew protection. The rest are transported in a truck, along with the rounds, charges and fuses. The 175mm gun has a range of 32km (20 miles), firing a high-explosive round.

Country of origin:	United States
Crew:	5
Weight:	28,168kg (61,970lb)
Dimensions:	length 11.256m (36ft 7.75in); width 3.149m (10ft 4in); height 3.679m (12ft)
Range:	725km (450 miles)
Armour:	classified
Armament:	one 175mm (6.9in) gun
Powerplant:	one Detroit Diesel Model 8V-71T diesel engine developing 405hp(302kW)
Performance:	maximum road speed 56km/h (35mph); fording 1.06m (3ft 6in); vertical obstacle 1.016m (3ft 4in); trench 2.326m (7ft 9in)

Abbot

Post-war British designs for self-propelled guns focused on the excellent Centurion tank chassis with 25-pounder or 140mm guns. However, NATO required a standard 105 or 155mm gun. As a result, Vickers developed the 105mm Abbot self-propelled gun during the 1950s for deployment with the British Army of the Rhine. Fully armoured, the Abbot served with the Royal Artillery until being replaced by the American M109 in the 1980s. Like most British post-war armoured fighting vehicle designs, the Abbot was reliable, rugged and a potent force on the battlefield. One variant was the Value Engineered Abbot, produced for the Indian Army without extras such as flotation screen, night vision and nuclear, biological and chemical (NBC) protection.

Country of origin:	United Kingdom
Crew:	4
Weight:	16,494kg (36,288lb)
Dimensions:	length 5.84m (19ft 2in); width 2.641m (8ft 8in); height 2.489m (8ft 2in)
Range:	390km (240 miles)
Armour:	6-12mm (0.23-0.47in)
Armament:	one 105mm (4.1in) gun; one 7.62mm (0.3in) anti-aircraft machine gun; three smoke dischargers
Powerplant:	one Rolls-Royce six-cylinder diesel engine developing 240hp (179kW)
Performance:	maximum road speed 47.5km/h (30mph); fording 1.2m (3ft 11in); vertical obstacle 0.609m (2ft); trench 2.057m (6ft 9in)

Mk F3 155mm

In the 1960s, the French Army replaced their American M41 howitzers with an indigenous design, based on the AMX-13 tank chassis and known as the Mk F3. It was equipped with two rear spades which were reversed into the ground to give added stability. The F3 fired a standard 155mm high-explosive projectile, other types of ammunition being rocket-assisted, smoke and illumination. There was no nuclear, chemical and biological protection (NBC), though. It remained in production until the 1980s, being exported to a number of South American and Middle East countries. One drawback of the vehicle, apart from the lack of protection for the crew, was that it could only carry two people, the rest of the crew having to follow behind in support vehicles.

Country of origin:	France
Crew:	2
Weight:	17,410kg (38,304lb)
Dimensions:	length 6.22m (20ft 5in); width 2.72m (8ft 11in); height 2.085m (6ft 10in)
Range:	300km (185 miles)
Armour:	20mm (0.78in)
Armament:	one 155mm (6.1in) gun
Powerplant:	one SOFAM 8Gxb eight-cylinder petrol engine developing 250hp (186kW)
Performance:	maximum road speed 60km/h (37mph); vertical obstacle 0.6m (2ft); trench 1.5m (4ft 11in)

Type 54-1

The Type 54-1 consists of a 122mm (4.8in) howitzer mounted on the chassis of the YW 531 armoured personnel carrier, though the Type 54-1 differs in that it has a fifth road wheel on each side. Armoured protection is provided by the shield from the howitzer's towed version. The gun itself is actually a copy of the Soviet M-30 122mm (4.8in) howitzer, an ageing weapon now obsolete amongst modern field artillery. With a maximum gun range of 11.8km (7.33 miles), the Type 54-1 is outclassed by most NATO and Russian artillery. Nonetheless, the simplicity of the Type 54-1 vehicle makes it a dependable weapon, though one now being replaced by the Type 85 self-propelled gun.

Country of origin:	China
Crew:	7 (max)
Weight:	15,400kg (34,000lb)
Dimensions:	Length: 5.65m (18.54ft); width: 3.06m (10.04ft); height: 2.68m (8.79ft)
Range:	500km (310 miles)
Armour:	Not available
Armament:	1 x 122mm (4.8in) howitzer
Powerplant:	1 x Deutz 6150L 6-cylinder diesel, 257hp (192kW)
Performance:	Maximum road speed: 56km/h (35mph)

SM-240

The SM-240 self-propelled mortar is a weapon unique to the former Soviet Union. Using the chassis of an SA-4 SAM launcher, Russian designers in the mid-1970s created a moving platform for a massive 2B8 240mm (9.45in) mortar, the vehicle requiring nine crew in total. The mortar is carried on the rear of the hull when in transit, but hydraulically lowered to the ground for firing (though the mortar remains connected to the vehicle). Two 20-round magazines feed the mortar through automatic breech-loading. Ammunition types include HE, fragmentation, smoke and even nuclear warheads. The 2B8 can fire a 131kg (289lb) shell just under 10km (6.2 miles).

Country of origin:	USSR
Crew:	9
Weight:	27,500kg (60,600lb)
Dimensions:	Length: 7.94m (26.05ft); width: 3.25m (10.66ft); height: 3.22m (10.56ft)
Range:	500km (310 miles)
Armour:	15–20mm (0.59–0.78in)
Armament:	1 x 2B8 240mm (9.45in) mortar
Powerplant:	1 x V-59 12-cylinder diesel, 520hp (388kW)
Performance:	Maximum road speed 45km/h (28mph)

Bandkanon

Bofors produced the prototype of the Bandkanon 1A in 1960, but with extensive trials and modifications being carried out, the first production models did not appear until 1966. It had the distinction of being the first fully automatic self-propelled gun to enter service with any army. Ammunition is kept in a 14-round clip carried externally at the rear of the hull. Once the first round is loaded manually, remaining rounds are loaded automatically. However, it was not produced in quantity (production ceased after only two years) mainly because its size and lack of mobility hindered its performance on the battlefield and made it very difficult to conceal. It has undergone some improvements, such as the addition of a Rolls Royce diesel engine and a new fire-control system.

Country of origin:	Sweden
Crew:	5
Weight:	53,000kg (116,600lb)
Dimensions:	length 11.00m (36ft 1in); width 3.37m (11ft 0.7in); height 3.85m (12ft 7.5in)
Range:	230km (143 miles)
Armour:	10-20mm (0.4-0.8in)
Armament:	one 155mm (6.1in) gun; one 7.62mm (0.3in) AA machine gun
Powerplant:	one Rolls-Royce diesel engine developing 240hp (179kW) and Boeing gas turbine, developing 300hp (224kW)
Performance:	maximum road speed 28km/h (17.4mph); fording 1m (3ft 3in); vertical obstacle 0.95m (3ft 1.5in); trench 2.00m (6ft 6.75in)

M1974

After World War II the USSR concentrated development on towed artillery pieces, in contrast to NATO's drift towards self-propelled guns. It was not until 1974 that the first Soviet self-propelled howitzer made an appearance in public, hence its Western designation. Known as the Gvozdika in the USSR, the vehicle was deployed in large numbers (36 per tank division, 72 per motorised rifle division). Differing from the M1973 in being fully amphibious, the chassis has been used for a number of armoured command and chemical warfare reconnaissance vehicles, as well as a mine-clearing vehicle. It can also be fitted with wider tracks to allow it to operate in snow or swamp conditions. The M1974 was widely exported to Soviet client states as well as Angola, Algeria and Iraq.

Country of origin:	USSR
Crew:	4
Weight:	15,700kg (34,540lb)
Dimensions:	length 7.30m (23ft 11.5in); width 2.85m (9ft 4in); height 2.40m (7ft 10.5in)
Range:	500km (310 miles)
Armour:	15-20mm (0.59-0.78in)
Armament:	one 122mm (4.8in) gun; one 7.62mm (0.3in) AA machine gun
Powerplant:	one YaMZ-238V V-8 water-cooled diesel engine developing 240hp (179kW)
Performance:	maximum road speed 60km/h (37mph); fording amphibious; vertical obstacle 1.10m (3ft 7in); trench 3.00m (9ft 10in)

2S3

Known as the 2S3 Akatsiya in the former Soviet Union (designated M1973 in US Army terms), 18 vehicles were deployed as support for each tank division and motorised rifle division in the Red Army. The chassis was a shortened version of that used for the SA-4 surface-to-air missile system and the GMZ armoured minelayer, both of which were used in the USSR for many years. Fitted with nuclear, biological and chemical (NBC) protection and with a tactical nuclear capability, the vehicle was not equipped for amphibious operations. During operation it was normal for two of the crew to stand at the rear of vehicle and act as ammunition handlers, feeding projectiles via two hatches in the hull rear. The 2S3 proved a popular vehicle amongst Soviet client states and was exported to Iraq and Libya.

Country of origin:	USSR
Crew:	6
Weight:	24,945kg (54,880lb)
Dimensions:	length 8.40m (27ft 6.7in); width 3.20m (10ft 6in); height 2.80m (9ft 2.25in)
Range:	300km (186 miles)
Armour:	15-20mm (0.59-0.78in)
Armament:	one 152mm (6in) gun; one 7.62mm (0.3in) anti-aircraft machine gun
Powerplant:	one V-12 diesel engine developing 520hp (388kW)
Performance:	maximum road speed 55km/h (34mph); fording 1.5m (4ft 11in); vertical obstacle 1.10m (3ft 7in); trench 2.50m (8ft 2.5in)

2S7

The 2S7 is a massive vehicle stretching to 13.12m (43.04ft) when its long-barrelled 2A44 203mm (8in) gun is taken into account. Firing conventional ammunition, the gun has a range of over 37km (23 miles). Coping with the recoil of the 43kg (95lb) shells requires three recoil pistons with maximum travel of 140cm (55.11in). Unusually, no muzzle brake is fitted to the gun. Reloading is fully mechanized using a power-assisted loader. Two rounds per minute is the maximum rate of fire. The vehicle itself has the largest chassis of any Russian armoured vehicle, using seven rubber-tyred road wheels. Its engine sits at the rear, while the crew occupy an enclosed compartment at the front.

Country of origin:	USSR
Crew:	7
Weight:	46,500kg (102,500lb)
Dimensions:	Length (with gun): 13.12m (43.04ft); width: 3.38m (11.09ft); height: 3m (9.8ft)
Range:	650km (400 miles)
Armour:	Not known
Armament:	1 x 2A44 203mm (8in) gun
Powerplant:	1 x V-46I 12-cylinder diesel, developing 839hp (626kW)
Performance:	Maximum road speed: 50km/h (31mph); fording: 1.2m (3.9ft); gradient: 22 percent; vertical obstacle: 1m (3.3ft)

GCT 155mm

The GCT 155mm was the designated successor to the Mk F3 in the French Army. Production began in 1977. Saudi Arabia received deliveries first, before the French Army, but it finally entered service in the 1980s and was deployed in regiments of 18 guns each. By 1995 some 400 had been built for the home and export markets. The main improvements over the Mk F3 were an automatic loading system, giving a rate of fire of eight rounds a minute, and protection for the increased on-board crew of four, as well as night vision, nuclear, biological and chemical (NBC) protection and the ability to fire a range of projectiles, including a round carrying multiple anti-tank mines. The GCT 155mm saw active service during the Iran-Iraq War, Iraq having received 85 of the vehicles.

Country of origin:	France
Crew:	4
Weight:	41,949kg (92,288lb)
Dimensions:	length 10.25m (33ft 7.5in); width 3.15m (10ft 4in); height 3.25m (10ft 8in)
Range:	450km (280 miles)
Armour:	20mm (0.78in)
Armament:	one 155mm (6.1in) gun; one 7.62mm/12.7mm (0.3in/0.5in) AA machine gun
Powerplant:	one Hispano-Suiza HS 110 12-cylinder water-cooled multi-fuel engine developing 720hp (537kW)
Performance:	maximum road speed 60km/h (37mph); vertical obstacle 0.93m (3ft 0.7in); trench 1.90m (6ft 3in)

M110A2

The 203mm (8in) howitzer is commonly used as a 'partner piece' to the 155mm (6.1in) gun, using the same carriage, but for some reason the US Army did not produce a partner for the M109, but put the 8 inch on the same tracked carriage as the M107 175mm (6.88in) gun. The latter did not live up to expectations and was withdrawn from service. This left a gap in the US artillery armoury as there was no heavy SP gun capable of reaching deep into enemy territory or firing a nuclear shell. A new, longer 8 inch howitzer barrel was developed which replaced the earlier M110, turning it into the M110A1. Produced in 1978, the M110A2 had the addition of a muzzle brake, allowing the use of a more powerful propelling charge and increasing the maximum range of the gun to 22.9km (14.22 miles).

Country of origin:	United States
Crew:	5
Weight:	28,350kg (27.91 tons)
Dimensions:	length 5.72m (18ft 9in); width 3.14m (1ft 4in); height 2.93m (9ft 8in)
Range:	520km (325 miles)
Armour:	not disclosed
Armament:	one 203mm (8in) howitzer
Powerplant:	one Detroit Diesel V-8, turbocharged, developing 405hp (335.5kW) at 2300 rpm
Performance:	maximum road speed 56km/h (34mph); fording 1.06m (3ft 6in); vertical obstacle 1.01m (3ft 4in); trench 2.32m (7ft 9in)

DANA

The DANA was the first wheeled self-propelled howitzer to enter service in modern times. Wheeled vehicles have the advantage of being cheaper to build and easier to maintain, with greater strategic mobility. First seen in 1980, the DANA was built by Skoda and was based on the 8 x 8 Tatra 815 truck, the best off-road truck in existence at the time. Tyre pressure can be regulated to allow good mobility over rough terrain, and steering is power-assisted on the front four wheels. It carries three hydraulic stabilisers to be lowered into the ground before firing, and carries a crane on the roof to assist with loading the ammunition. Rate of fire is three rounds per minute for a period of 30 minutes, and the vehicle is in service in Libya, Poland, Russia, the Czech Republic and Slovakia.

Country of origin:	Czechoslovakia
Crew:	4 to 5
Weight:	23,000kg (50,600lb)
Dimensions:	length 10.5m (34ft 5in); width 2.8m (9ft 2in); height 2.6m (8ft 6in)
Range:	600km (375 miles)
Armour:	12.7mm (0.5in)
Armament:	one 152mm (6in) gun; one 12.7mm (0.5in) machine gun
Powerplant:	one V-12 diesel engine developing 345hp (257kW)
Performance:	maximum road speed 80km/h (49.71mph); fording 1.4m (4ft 7in); vertical obstacle 1.5m (4ft 11in); trench 1.4m (4ft 7in)

Palmaria

The Palmaria was developed by OTO Melara specifically for the export market and included Libya as its first purchaser. The prototype appeared in 1981, based heavily on the OF-40 main battle tank already in service with Dubai, and the first production vehicles were completed a year later. One unusual feature is the auxiliary power unit for the turret, thus conserving fuel for the main engine. It comes equipped with an automatic loading system and a wide range of munitions including rocket-assisted projectiles, although these pay the penalty of lower explosive content. The vehicle has an automatic loader, giving it a rate of fire of one round every 15 seconds. There are no variants as such, though its chassis has been fitted with twin 25mm guns in an anti-aircraft configuration

Country of origin:	Italy
Crew:	5
Weight:	46,632kg (102,590lb)
Dimensions:	length 11.474m (37ft 7.75in); width 2.35m (7ft 8.5in); height 2.874m (9ft 5.25in)
Range:	400km (250 miles)
Armour:	classified
Armament:	one 155mm (6.1in) howitzer; one 7.62mm (0.3in) machine gun
Powerplant:	one eight-cylinder diesel engine developing 750hp (559kW)
Performance:	maximum road speed 60km/h (37mph); fording 1.2m (3ft 11in); vertical obstacle 1m (3ft 3in); trench 3m (9ft 10in)

G6 Rhino

The G6 is a high-mobility, heavily armoured and technologically advanced 155mm (6.1in) self-propelled gun system from South Africa. Its gun can be used in both direct- and indirect-fire roles. Its direct-fire range is 3km (1.9 miles) and its indirect-fire range is 30km (19 miles). Mobility is provided by a purpose-built 6x6 vehicle with run-flat tyres and a central tyre-pressure control system. Turret and hull are both heavily armoured to resist small-arms fire, landmine explosions, and even 20mm (0.78in) cannon fire across the vehicle's 60 degree frontal arc. Full NBC protection is optional. Despite sophisticated features such as night-vision equipment and a muzzle-velocity analyser, export sales have not been good.

Country of origin:	South Africa
Crew:	6
Weight:	47,000kg (103,600lb)
Dimensions:	Length (chassis): 10.2m (33.4ft); width: 3.4m (11.2ft); height: 3.5m (11.5ft)
Range:	700km (430 miles)
Armour:	Not available
Armament:	1 x 155mm (6.1in) gun
Powerplant:	1 x diesel, developing 525hp (391kW)
Performance:	Maximum road speed: 90km/h (56mph); fording: 1m (3.3ft)

PRAM-S

The Slovakian PRAM-S, also known as the Vzor 85, is a 120mm (4.7in) self-propelled mortar. It is heavily influenced by Russian weapons carriers, and its chassis is that of the Soviet BMP-2 armoured personnel carrier lengthened to incorporate seven road wheels. The 120mm (4.7in) Model 1982 mortar is a potent weapon designed for sustained fire support. It can fire out to a range of 8000m (26,250ft) with a rate of fire of 18 to 20 rounds per minute via an automatic feeder. In addition, a 12.7mm (0.5in) NSV machine gun is mounted on the hull rear, while internally, the PRAM-S carries RPG-75 anti-tank rocket launchers and a 9K113 Konkurz ATGW.

Country of origin:	Slovakia
Crew:	4
Weight:	16,970kg (37,419lb)
Dimensions:	Length: 7.47m (24.5ft); width: 2.94m (9.65ft); height: 2.25m (7.38ft)
Range:	550km (340 miles)
Armour:	(Steel) 23mm (0.9in)
Armament:	1 x 120mm (4.7in) Model 1982 mortar; 1 x 12.7mm (0.5in) NSV MG; RPG-75 anti-tank rocket launchers; 9K113 Konkurz ATGW
Powerplant:	1 x UTD-40 6-cylinder diesel, 300hp (224kW)
Performance:	Maximum road speed: 63km/h (39mph); fording: amphibious; gradient: 60 percent; vertical obstacle: 0.9m (2.9ft); trench: 2.7m (8.9ft)

Rascal

The Rascal is one of a new generation of lightweight fighting vehicles. Produced by Soltam Ltd of Israel, it is a 20-ton 155mm (6.1in) self-propelled howitzer, light enough to be airlifted by modern transport aircraft, including the C-130 Hercules. Its low weight is combined with a powerful engine to provide fast speeds both on- and off-road. When firing, two hydraulically powered spades drop down to the rear of the hull, and the gun is elevated on a turntable, also hydraulically powered. The howitzer has a range of 24km (15 miles). Rascal is armoured throughout, and has sophisticated features such as night-vision devices, armoured shutters for the windows and high-performance brakes.

Country of origin:	Israel
Crew:	4
Weight:	19,500kg (43,000lb)
Dimensions:	Length (with gun): 7.5m (24.6ft); width: 2.46m (8.07ft); height: 2.3m (7.55ft)
Range:	350km (220 miles)
Armour:	Not available
Armament:	1 x 155mm (6.1in) howitzer
Powerplant:	1 x diesel, developing 350hp (261kW)
Performance:	Maximum road speed: 50km/h (31mph); fording: 1.2m (3.9ft); gradient: 22 percent; vertical obstacle: 1m (3.3ft)

Panzerhaubitse 2000

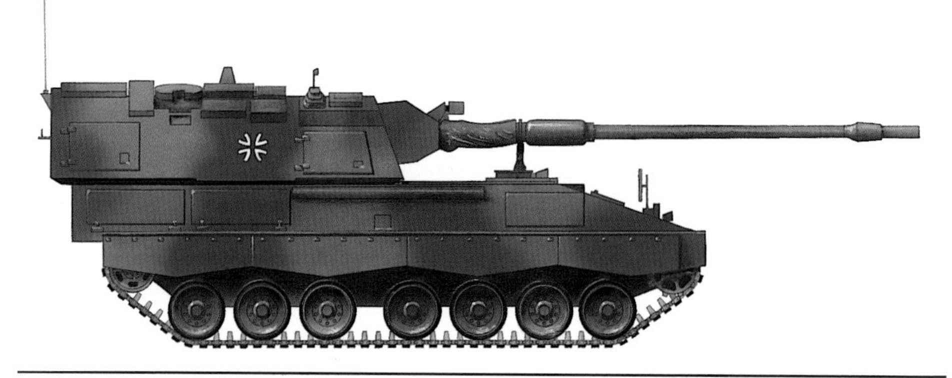

As a result of the collapse of the tri-national SP70 project, Germany had to find a new SP howitzer. Designs were solicited from two companies, and after examination, the one offered by Wegmann/MaK was accepted and contracts were issued. Development is still continuing and production will commence in 2000, about 250 equipments being envisaged. The hull and running gear are based on those of the Leopard II tank, but with the engine and transmission at the front of the hull. The rear is surmounted by a large turret containing the 52-calibre length gun which has a sliding block breech and a large multi-baffle muzzle-brake. The gun and turret are entirely power-operated and there is an automatic mechanical loading system which permits the firing of three rounds in ten seconds.

Country of origin:	Germany
Crew:	5
Weight:	55,000kg (54.13 tons)
Dimensions:	length 7.87m (25ft 10in); width 3.37m (11ft); height 3.40m (11ft 2in)
Range:	420km (260 miles)
Armour:	not disclosed
Armament:	one 155mm (6.1in) howitzer
Powerplant:	one MTU 881 V-12 diesel developing 1000hp (745.7kW)
Performance:	maximum road speed 60km/h (27mph); fording 2.25m (7ft 5in); vertical obstacle 1m (3ft 3in); trench 3m (9ft 10in)

M109A6 Paladin

The 155mm (6.1in) M109A6 Paladin has the same hull and suspension as the previous M109s, but everything else has been changed. The turret is larger with improved armour, Kevlar ballistic lining and a full-width bustle, the new 39-calibre M284 howitzer has a new chamber contour and several detail improvements to the breech ring and mechanism, a reinforced muzzle and muzzle brake has been added, as well as a new firing mechanism. In addition, there is an entirely new fire control system which is allied to a position-finding system, thus permitting the automatic pointing of the gun when supplied with target data. The modifications have created a weapons system that can react quicker to target opportunities, hit targets that are further away and is far better protected than the original M109.

Country of origin:	United States
Crew:	4
Weight:	28,738kg (28.28 tons)
Dimensions:	length 6.19m (20ft 4in); width 3.149m (10ft 4in); height 3.236m (10ft 7in)
Range:	405km (252 miles)
Armour:	not disclosed
Armament:	one 155mm (6.1in) howitzer M284
Powerplant:	one Detroit Diesel 8V-71T, V-8 turbocharged two-stroke diesel, 405hp (302kW) at 2300 rpm
Performance:	maximum road speed 56km/h (35mph); fording 1.95m (6ft 5in); vertical obstacle 0.53m (21in); trench 1.83m (6ft)

AS-90

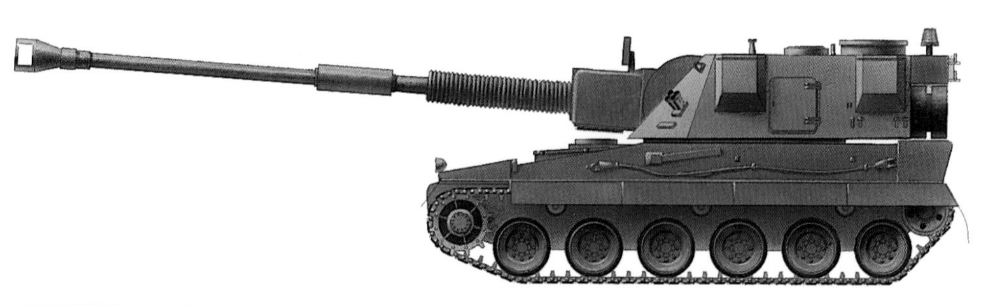

Vickers Armstrong, while carrying out sub-contract work on the failed SP70 project, could see the defects in the design and thus set about preparing an improved version of their own. At first it was developed as a turret and gun unit which could be dropped into a suitable tank hull in order to produce an SP gun, but as SP70 became more impractical, a complete vehicle was developed. When SP70 was aborted, the British had the choice between the latest version of the US M109, or the AS-90. The former was, by this time, stretching its design to the limits, whereas the latter was new and had a long upgrade life ahead of it. It was selected and went into service in 1993. It mounts a 39-calibre howitzer, but a number are being upgraded to 52-calibre weapons, called the AS90 Braveheart by the manufacturer.

Country of origin:	United Kingdom
Crew:	5
Weight:	45,000kg (44.29 tons)
Dimensions:	length 7.20m (23ft 8in); width 3.40m (11ft 2in) height: 3m (9ft 10in)
Range:	240km (150 miles)
Armour:	17mm (0.66in) maximum
Armament:	one 155mm (6.1in) howitzer
Powerplant:	one Cummins V-8 diesel developing 660hp (492kW) at 2800 rpm
Performance:	maximum road speed 55km/h (34 mph); fording 1.50m (5ft); vertical obstacle 0.88m (35in); trench 2.8m (9ft 2in)

155/45 Norinco SP Gun

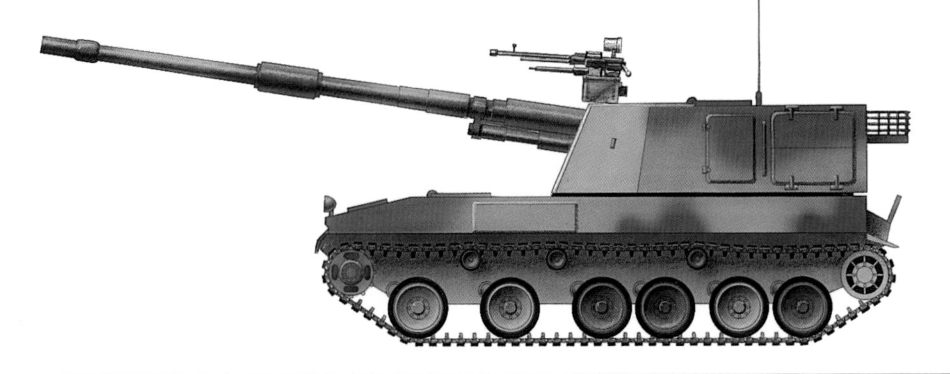

The Chinese 155/45 Norinco SP Gun is of conventional form – a tracked chassis with the driver and engine forward, leaving space at the rear of the hull for a fighting compartment surmounted by a large turret carrying a 45-calibre 155mm (6.1in) gun. The gun has a muzzle brake and fume extractor, and is provided with mechanical assistance for loading and ramming at any angle of elevation. Since 155mm is not a Chinese service calibre and the system is capable of firing NATO standard ammunition, it is assumed that this weapon was produced for export, but there is no information available about possible purchasers. There are rumours that some were sold to a country in the Middle East in 1996.

Country of origin:	China
Crew:	5
Weight:	32,000kg (31.50 tons)
Dimensions:	length 6.10m (20ft); width 3.20m (10ft 6in); height 2.59m (8ft 6in)
Range:	450km (20 miles)
Armour:	not disclosed
Armament:	one 155mm (6.1in) gun WAC-21
Powerplant:	one diesel developing 525hp (391.4kW)
Performance:	maximum road speed 56 km/h (35mph); fording 1.20m (4ft); vertical obstacle 0.70m (28in); trench 2.70m (8ft 10in)

Light Dragon Mk II

The Light Dragon Mk II was built from the chassis of the Vickers Mk II medium tank, of which about 200 were manufactured in the mid-1920s. The Light Dragon Mk I originally used the chassis of the Whippet, the British Army's first lightweight tank. The switch to the Vickers chassis made the Light Dragon Mk II more durable and gave the crew more armoured protection. An eight-cylinder Armstrong Siddeley petrol engine also produced the power to pull heavy field artillery. The Mk II was specifically an artillery tractor, with space for 10 artillery crewmen to sit in the troop compartment behind the driver and a capacity to carry/tow 118 shells. The Light Dragon was unarmed.

Country of origin:	United Kingdom
Crew:	1 + 10
Weight:	8000kg (17,600lb)
Dimensions:	Length: 5.33m (17.49ft); width: 2.78m (9.12ft); height: 2.17m (7.12ft)
Range:	300km (190 miles)
Armour:	Not available
Armament:	None
Powerplant:	1 x Armstrong Siddeley 8-cylinder petrol, developing 90hp (67kW)
Performance:	Maximum road speed: 35km/h (22mph)

Raupen Schlepper Ost

The Eastern Front presented the German Army with severe environmental challenges: deep snow in the winter and deep mud during the autumn rains and spring thaw. In 1942, the Raupen Schlepper Ost (RSO) was developed to cope with these conditions. It was little more than a four-ton transport truck powered by a V8 petrol engine, but fully tracked to handle demanding off-road terrain. Production began in 1943 under several manufacturers, and 27,000 units were produced by the end of the war. Its duties were varied, and included gun tractor, snow plough, trailer tractor and even ambulance. Two main versions were produced, the RSO/01 with a solid and enclosed cab, and the RSO/03, which had a soft-top cab.

Country of origin:	Germany
Crew:	2
Weight:	5200kg (11,500lb)
Dimensions:	Length: 4.42m (14.5ft); width: 1.99m (6.53ft); height: 2.53m (8.3ft)
Range:	250km (150 miles)
Armour:	None
Armament:	None
Powerplant:	1 x Steyr 1500A 8-cylinder petrol, developing 68hp (51kW)
Performance:	Maximum road speed: 17km/h (11mph)

Karl Ammunition Carrier

The Karl Ammunition Carrier was designed to supply the massive Karl Siege Howitzers, the sheer weight of the projectiles (over two tonnes [1.96 tons] each) necessitating a new vehicle. The basic tank hull of the PzKpfw IV Ausf D was used, with a platform for the ammunition and a crane added to lift the heavy rounds. The carriers were usually moved by train and assembled near to the point of use, before being driven into position. In 1941, 13 PzKpfw IV Ausf F chassis were converted to ammunition carriers. The Karl Howitzers and Carriers were designed to smash fortifications. They were used rarely in World War II, but did see service during the siege of Sevastopol and during the Battle of Warsaw in 1944, where they were put to devastating use against the defenders.

Country of origin:	Germany
Crew:	4
Weight:	25,000kg (55,000lb)
Dimensions:	length 5.41m (17ft 9in); width 2.883m (9ft 5.5in); height not recorded
Range:	209km (130 miles)
Armour:	60mm (2.4in)
Armament:	none
Powerplant:	one Maybach HL120 TRM petrol engine developing 300hp (223.7kW)
Performance:	maximum road speed 39.9km/h (24.8mph); fording 1.0m (3ft 3in); vertical obstacle 0.6m (2ft); trench 2.20m (7ft 3in)

M5 High-Speed Tractor

Development of what was to become the M5 began in 1941 when the T20 and T21 were developed using the tracks and suspension of the M3 tank. In October 1942, the T21 was standardised as the M5, designed to tow 105mm and 155mm howitzers as well as their crew and equipment. Five different models were produced in all, differing mainly in their track and suspension. The vehicle entered production in 1942 and was built by International Harvester. A winch was fitted as standard and a roller under the winch allowed it to be used to pull vehicles to the front or to the rear. The vehicle did not outlast World War II by very long in the US Army, but it continued to serve with the armies of Austria, Japan, Yugoslavia and Pakistan for many years after 1945.

Country of origin:	United States
Crew:	1 + 10
Weight:	13,791kg (30,340lb)
Dimensions:	length 5.03m (16ft 6in); width 2.54m (8ft 4in); height 2.69m (8ft 10in)
Range:	241km (150 miles)
Armour:	none
Armament:	one 12.7mm Browning anti-aircraft machine gun
Powerplant:	one Continental R6572 six-cylinder petrol engine developing 207hp (154kW)
Performance:	maximum road speed 48km/h (30mph); fording 1.3m (4ft 4in); vertical obstacle 0.7m (2ft 3in); trench 1.7m (5ft 6in)

M4 High-Speed Tractor

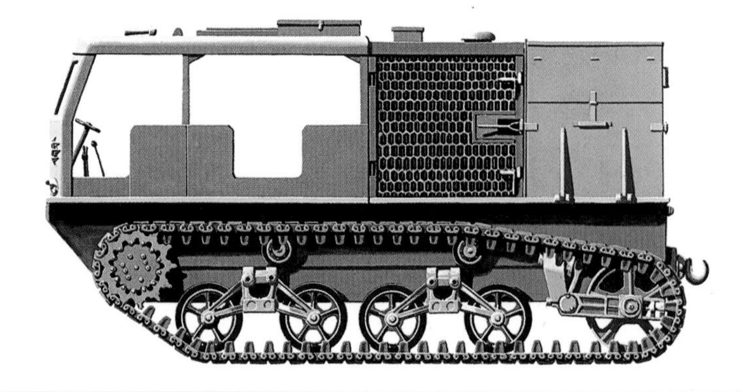

The M4 was developed following a 1941 requirement for a new medium tractor for the US Army field artillery to be based on the same automotive components used in the M2A1 tank. The vehicle was standardised as the M4 in August 1943. Two versions were built, one to tow anti-aircraft guns, the other to tow howitzers, as well as carrying the gun detachment and all equipment. The latter vehicles were fitted with a crane to help with loading the heavy projectiles. After World War II, the M4 was supplied in some quantity to various countries including Japan, Brazil, Yugoslavia and Pakistan under the Mutual Defence Assistance Program. The M4 was the first in a long line of tractors in service with the US Army, and which can fulfil a wide variety of roles, from ammunition carriers to heavy load towing.

Country of origin:	United States
Crew:	1 + 11
Weight:	14,288kg (31,433lb)
Dimensions:	length 5.232m (17ft 2in); width 2.464m (8ft 1in); height 2.515m (8ft 3in)
Range:	290km (180 miles)
Armour:	none
Armament:	one 12.7mm anti-aircraft machine gun
Powerplant:	one Waukesha 145GZ six-cylinder inline petrol engine developing 210hp (156kW)
Performance:	maximum road speed 53km/h (33mph); fording 1.04m (3ft 5in); vertical obstacle 0.7m (2ft 3in); trench 1.5m (5ft 0in)

M8 High-Speed Tractor

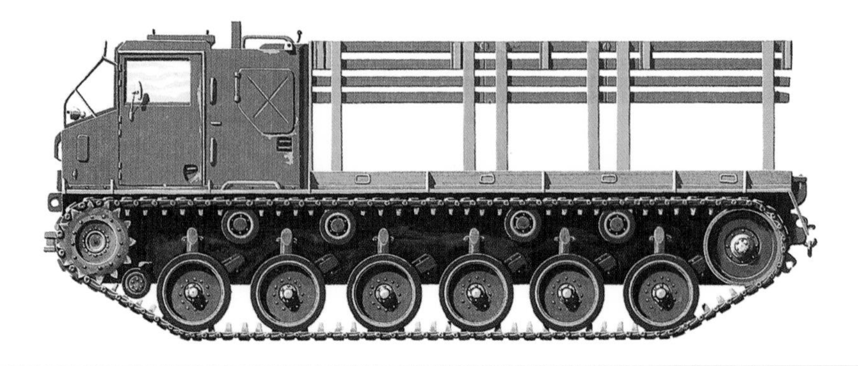

The M8 was developed during World War II following the failure of the T33 cargo-carrier, which was based on the chassis of the M24 Chaffee light tank. The new vehicle was standardised as the M8 after the war had ended and was based on the chassis of the M41 Walker Bulldog light tank, production lasting from 1950 until 1955. As well as towing cargo trailers, the M8 towed a variety of weapons such as the 75mm anti-aircraft gun and the M59 'Long Tom' gun. The cargo area of the basic version could be quickly adapted for carrying projectiles and charges. Unlike many other such tractors, the M8's engine was at the front of the vehicle. Some M8s were equipped with a hydraulic dozer blade for clearing battlefield obstacles, and in the process having a useful engineering capability.

Country of origin:	United States
Crew:	1 + 1
Weight:	24,948kg (54,885lb)
Dimensions:	length 6.731m (22ft 1in); width 3.327m (10ft 11in); height 3.048m (10ft 0in)
Range:	290km (180 miles)
Armour:	none
Armament:	one 12.7mm anti-aircraft machine gun
Powerplant:	one Continental AOS-895-3 six-cylinder air-cooled petrol engine developing 863hp (644kW)
Performance:	maximum road speed 64.4km/h (40mph); fording 1.06m (3ft 6in); vertical obstacle 0.46m (1ft 6in); trench 2.13m (7ft)

AT-P

The AT-P series of armoured artillery tractors entered service with Soviet forces in the early 1950s. It was developed mainly for towing anti-tank and anti-aircraft guns, but it was also capable of pulling larger-calibre weapons such as 155mm (6.1in) field howitzers and heavy-calibre mortars. The suspension was that of the SU-76/T-70, and the superstructure featured an open troop compartment holding six men – the three-man crew were inside an armoured compartment at the front. The AT-P was fast and durable, with solid torsion bar suspension. Several variants were produced, including the ASU-57 air-droppable vehicle armed with a 76mm (3in) airborne assault gun and a command-and-control version of the same, without the gun.

Country of origin:	USSR
Crew:	3 + 6
Weight:	7200kg (15,900lb)
Dimensions:	Length: 4.5m (14.76ft); width: 2.5m (8.2ft); height: 1.83m (6ft)
Range:	500km (310 miles)
Armour:	Not available
Armament:	None
Powerplant:	1 x ZiL-123F 6-cylinder petrol, developing 110hp (82kW)
Performance:	Maximum road speed: 50km/h (31mph)

AT-S Tractor

The AT-S was developed in the 1940s and entered service with the Soviet Army in the early 1950s. The fully enclosed cab had room for six passengers and carried the gun crew when towing artillery. The open-topped cargo body was sometimes swapped for an enclosed hull when carrying specialised equipment such as communications and radar. The AT-S was used as the basis for the BM-24T rocket launcher and the AT-S also formed the basis for the Sbkh, which was used for transport in snow-covered terrain. The OTS was an AT-S fitted with a dozer blade for removing obstacles. The AT-S was widely exported, being used by nearly all Warsaw Pact countries as well as Syria, Egypt, Yugoslavia, Finland and China. A Polish version of this vehicle also exists.

Country of origin:	USSR
Crew:	1 + 6
Weight:	15,000kg (33,000lb)
Dimensions:	length 5.87m (19ft 3.1in); width 2.57m (8ft 5.2in); height 2.535m (8ft 3.8in)
Range:	350km (217 miles)
Armour:	none
Armament:	none
Powerplant:	one V-54-T V-12 water-cooled diesel engine developing 250hp (186kW)
Performance:	maximum road speed 35km/h (22mph); fording 1.0m (3ft 3in); vertical obstacle 0.6m (2ft 0in); trench 1.45m (4ft 9in)

M992 FAASV

The M992 Field Artillery Ammunition Support Vehicle (FAASV) goes beyond the tradition of ammunition supply trucks by being as fast and manoeuvrable as the self-propelled artillery piece it supports (usually an M109A2). It can move off-road at 56km/h (35mph) and can travel on all terrains, whether mud, snow, rock or sand. It can also ford water obstacles up to 1.06m (3.48ft) deep. The M992's ammunition supplies are stored in racked containers behind the driving position, with separate compartments for shells and fuses. An extendable conveyor belt moves the shells from the racks to the artillery crew. The M992 has a crew of two men, but six other personnel can also be carried.

Country of origin:	United States
Crew:	2 + 6
Weight:	25,900kg (57,100lb) fully loaded
Dimensions:	Length: 6.27m (20.57ft); width: 3.15m (10.33ft); height: 3.24m (10.63ft)
Range:	Not available
Armour:	Not available
Armament:	None
Powerplant:	1 x Detroit Diesel 8V-71T 8-cylinder diesel, developing 398hp (297kW)
Performance:	Maximum road speed: 56km/h (35mph)

Kraftfahrzeug (Kfz) 11

The Auto-Union/Horch Typ 830 was a commercial vehicle fitted with a military body as an initial method of motorising the armed forces prior to the introduction of the standard vehicles (contrary to popular opinion, the German Army was not fully mechanised when war broke out in 1939). Given larger tyres and V8 engine to improve cross-country capability, the vehicle was developed in the late 1920s and early 1930s. Mostly open-topped, it was used in the main for carrying infantry, towing light guns or as a communications vehicle. The Kfz 11 was a closed body version, designed for signal troops, the body being initially made of wood and later sheet metal. Production ended in 1937 with the arrival of standard personnel carriers, but the vehicle saw action in most theatres of World War II.

Country of origin:	Germany
Crew:	1
Weight:	990kg (2178lb)
Dimensions:	length 4.80m (15ft 9in); width 1.80m (5ft 11in); height 1.85m (6ft 1in)
Range:	136km (225 miles)
Armour:	none
Armament:	none
Powerplant:	one Horch V-8 2.98-litre petrol engine developing 70hp (52.2kW)
Performance:	maximum road speed 75km/h (46.85mph); fording 0.4m (1ft 4in)

Type 95 Scout Car

The Type 95 Scout Car, known as the 'Black Medal', was developed after Japanese experiences in Manchuria had revealed the need for such a vehicle. Some 4800 were built by Kurogane and this was the only native vehicle of its type used by the Japanese Army before and during World War II, most others being of American origin or pattern. Built in closed cab, truck and convertible versions, this proved an ideal vehicle for operations in northern China and Manchuria as it coped well with low temperatures and its air-cooled engine was not reliant on the limited supplies of unpolluted water found in the region. Special tyres with heavy rubber treads were added to cope with difficult terrain.The Type 95's transmission was a selective sliding type giving three forward and one reverse gears

Country of origin:	Japan
Crew:	1
Weight:	1100kg (2420lb)
Dimensions:	length 3.38m (11ft 1in); width 1.52m (5ft 0in); height 1.68m (5ft 6in)
Range:	450km (281 miles)
Armour:	none
Armament:	none
Powerplant:	one two-cylinder four-stroke V-1-A-F petrol engine developing 33hp (24.6kW)
Performance:	maximum road speed 75km/h (46.8mph); fording 0.5m (1ft 7in)

Stöwer 40

In 1934, the Germans began to create standardised vehicles for the Wehrmacht in preparation for the inevitable war in Europe. Up until then, cross-country vehicles had been based on commercial designs, with all their disadvantages with relation to military uses. The new method would involve taking into account not only technical but operational considerations when designing a vehicle. The Kfz 2 entered production in 1936, based on a number of different manufacturers' components, including Stöwer, BMW and Hanomag. A 4 x 4 design, it was often used as the basis for radio cars. The chassis was normal, except for additional bracing on the engine, suspension and transmission for strength. The Stöwer 40 had five forward and one reverse gears, and was a solid and reliaible vehicle.

Country of origin:	Germany
Crew:	1
Weight:	1815kg (3993lb)
Dimensions:	length 3.58m (11ft 9in); width 1.57m (5ft 2in); height 1.78m (5ft 10in)
Range:	500km (311 miles)
Armour:	none
Armament:	none
Powerplant:	one Stower AW2 or R180W four-cylinder OHV petrol engine developing 50hp (37.3kW)
Performance:	maximum road speed 100km/h (62.5mph); fording 0.6m (1ft 11in)

Kraftfahrzeug (Kfz) 15

The main role of the Kfz 15 was as a communications vehicle. Powered by a V8 engine, the vehicle was based on a number of commercial chassis, including that of the Mercedes-Benz 340 chassis between 1938 and 1940. When the German Army was being rebuilt in the early 1930s, the theory was that that it should have specially built vehicles to carry out Blitzkrieg attacks. However, at first commercial car and light lorry chassis were used – with special bodies simply placed on top. The result was a whole series of poor military vehicles with low ground clearance. Thus the long wheelbase of this chassis tended to impair cross-country performance in spite of four-wheel drive. However, even after the introduction of the standard personnel carrier, many were used as staff cars and radio cars.

Country of origin:	Germany
Crew:	1
Weight:	2405kg (5291lb)
Dimensions:	length 4.44m (14ft 7in); width 1.68m (5ft 6in); height 1.73m (5ft 8in)
Range:	400km (250 miles)
Armour:	none
Armament:	none
Powerplant:	one Mercedes-Benz six-cylinder petrol engine developing 90hp (67.1kW)
Performance:	maximum road speed 88km/h (55mph); fording 0.6m (1ft 11in)

Daimler-Benz G5

The G series was developed to fill a Wehrmacht requirement for a personnel carrier with full cross-country capability. The first efforts by Daimler-Benz resulted in powerful vehicles with four-wheel drive and four-wheel steering, but their cross-country performance was poor. They were also too large and too expensive. Not chosen for production of the standard Einheit range of personnel carriers, Daimler-Benz continued to develop the G series. Between 1937 and 1941, 378 G5 vehicles were built, but few saw service with the Wehrmacht, although some were used as communications vehicles by high officials of the Nazi Party and the General Staff (an additional problem with many German light vehicles was that they were too complicated for reliability in rugged conditions, especially Russia).

Country of origin:	Germany
Crew:	1
Weight:	1630kg (3586lb)
Dimensions:	length 4.52m (14ft 10in); width 1.70m (5ft 7in); height 1.80m (5ft 11in)
Range:	480km (300 miles)
Armour:	none
Armament:	none
Powerplant:	one Mercedes-Benz six-cylinder petrol engine developing 90hp (67kW)
Performance:	maximum road speed 75km/h (46.8mph); fording 0.7m (2ft 4in)

Austin 10

The Austin 10 Light Utility Truck was developed directly from a civilian vehicle, the Austin 10 Saloon. Made in the late 1930s, the truck was specifically for military use. It was made at the Austin Motor Co. in Birmingham. A small canvas-covered cargo area was added to the rear of the vehicle, suitable for carrying a payload of up to 250kg (550lb). Nicknamed the 'Tilly' after its official military designation 'Car, Light Utility, 4 x2', the Austin 10 was ideal for staff duties, airfield duties and light ammunition carriage. Over 30,000 were produced during the war, recognizable by their angled front grille and cab-mounted spare wheel (though similar designs were produced by Standard, Hillman and Morris).

Country of origin:	United Kingdom
Crew:	2
Weight:	1003kg (2212lb)
Dimensions:	Length: 5.33m (17.49ft); width: 2.78m (9.12ft); height: 2.17m (7.12ft)
Range:	190km (119 miles)
Armour:	None
Armament:	None
Powerplant:	1 x Armstrong Siddeley 8-cylinder petrol, developing 90hp (67kW)
Performance:	Maximum road speed: 35km/h (21mph)

Humber Snipe

The Humber Snipe was one of several 0.4-ton utility vehicles which entered World War II service with the British Army (others included the Morris Commercial PU and the Ford WOC1). It was based on Humber's civilian vehicle, the Snipe sedan, directly utilizing the chassis, hood and radiator grille. To 'militarize' the vehicle, the bumpers were strengthened, storage boxes were added and a simple tarpaulin cover shielded the driver and passenger. Over 250,000 served British forces in World War II and many variants were produced. The 'General Service' version had seats in the rear area for troop transport or stretchers for medical evacuation. A communications vehicle designated FFW ('Fitted for Wireless') provided mobile radio facilities.

Country of origin:	United Kingdom
Crew:	4 or 5
Weight:	2170kg (4785lb)
Dimensions:	Length: 4.29m (14.07ft); width: 1.88m (6.17ft); height: 1.89m (6.2ft)
Range:	500km (310 miles)
Armour:	None
Armament:	None
Powerplant:	1 x Humber 6-cylinder petrol, developing 86hp (64kW)
Performance:	Maximum road speed: 75km/h (46mph)

Bedford MWD

The prototype of the Bedford MWD appeared in 1937. It was based on a commercial 2-tonnes (2-tons) truck with a modified chassis to increase ground clearance. The British War Office ordered 2000 trucks in August 1939, the early deliveries being constructed specifically to carry the 2-pounder anti-tank gun. The vehicle had a flat, full-width bonnet, designed to incorporate an extra-large air filter as per War Office requirements. Originally the vehicle was fitted with a canvas hood and collapsible windscreen, but this was replaced in 1943 by an enclosed cab. Bedford produced over 200,000 of these vehicles by the end of the war, and the type remained in service with the British Army until the late 1950s. Transmission consisted of four forward and one reverse gears.

Country of origin:	United Kingdom
Crew:	1
Weight:	2132kg (4690lb)
Dimensions:	length 4.38m (14ft 4.5in); width 1.99m (6ft 6.5in); height 2.29m (7ft 6in) with GS tilt and 1.93m (6ft 4in) without GS tilt
Range:	430km (268 miles)
Armour:	none
Armament:	none
Powerplant:	one Bedford six-cylinder OHV 3.5-litre petrol engine developing 72hp (53.7kW)
Performance:	maximum road speed 95km/h (59.4mph); fording 0.7m (2ft 4in)

Fiat 508

The major manufacturer of light vehicles for the Italian Army, Fiat had designed several military-type vehicles prior to World War II. The 508 CM was one such vehicle. The type was referred to as a colonial vehicle, specially designed for the rough terrain found in Italian-controlled territories in North Africa and adapted to avoid sinking in soft terrain. Produced in response to a requirement for a lightweight, inexpensive vehicle with good road speed and fair cross-country performance, the vehicle was based on the similar 'balilla' civilian model. The 508 CM was the most prolific military vehicle employed by the Italians, large numbers being built between 1939 and 1945. It was a capable vehicle, though uninspiring. Transmission was four forward and one reverse gears.

Country of origin:	Italy
Crew:	1
Weight:	1065kg (2343lb)
Dimensions:	length 3.35m (11ft 0in); width 1.37m (4ft 6in);
	height 1.57m (5ft 2in)
Range:	400km (250 miles)
Armour:	none
Armament:	none
Powerplant:	one Fiat 108C four-cylinder petrol engine developing 32hp (23.9kW)
Performance:	maximum road speed 80km/h (50mph); fording 0.45m (1ft 6in)

Chevrolet WA

When the British found themselves unable to supply their own needs for vehicles in World War II, they turned to Canada for help. The Canadians had been working since 1937 on a standard truck based around a Ford V8 chassis. This 'Canadian Military Pattern Chassis' was to form the basis of many light and medium trucks supplied to Allied forces. Produced by both Ford and Chevrolet, the 4 x 4 was the mainstay of Canadian production through the war years. The Chevrolets were produced with either wood or steel bodies and used in an enormous number of roles, from ambulances to mobile gun carriages. Many were adapted for use by special forces such as the Long Range Desert Group in North Africa. Over 900,000 of all types of the basic chassis were produced before 1945.

Country of origin:	Canada
Crew:	1
Weight:	3048kg (6705lb)
Dimensions:	6.579m (21ft 7in); width 2.49m (8ft 2in); height 3m (9ft 9in)
Range:	274km (170 miles)
Armour:	none
Armament:	two machine guns, various calibres
Powerplant:	one Ford V-8 petrol engine developing 95hp (71kW)
Performance:	maximum road speed 80km/h (50mph); fording 0.5m (1ft 7in)

Morris C8

The Morris C8 artillery tractor was one of the most successful of the range of vehicles produced by Morris for the British Army. Popularly known as the Quad, the vehicle was introduced in 1939. It was used to tow the 18- or 25-pounder gun and was equipped with a winch, which lift loads of up to 4000kg (8800lb). Inside there was room for the gun crew. The Morris C8 was a sturdy vehicle with good cross-country mobility and adequate stowage space for ammunition. Early models had a distinctive beetle shape, but from 1944 onwards the vehicle was fitted with an open top. A large number of C8s were lost during the British Expeditionary Force's withdrawal from Dunkirk in 1940, but the vehicle did go on to see service in North Africa. Transmission consisted of five forward and one reverse gears.

Country of origin:	United Kingdom
Crew:	1
Weight:	3402kg (7484lb)
Dimensions:	length 4.49m (14ft 8.75in); width 2.21m (7ft 3in); height 2.26m (7ft 5in)
Range:	480km (300 miles)
Armour:	none
Armament:	none
Powerplant:	one Morris four-cylinder 3.5-litre petrol engine developing 70hp (52.2kW)
Performance:	maximum road speed 80km/h (50mph); fording 0.4m (1ft 4in)

VW Kübel

The Kübel was one of the most famous military cars of World War II, and became something of a trademark with German forces in the conflict. Development began in 1936, and following design changes to accommodate more requirements, when it was announced that it would be the standard personnel carrier of the army, production began in 1940. The two main design considerations were lightness and ease of manufacture. It was also very cheap to make. Reliable, mobile and simple to maintain, the vehicle met all the demands made on it. By the time production ceased in 1944, some 55,000 had been made. Variants included the Type 92 with an enclosed body. In the desert the vehicle performed poorly, but a way round this was found in the Tropenfest version, which was equipped with sand tyres.

Country of origin:	Germany
Crew:	1
Weight:	635kg (1397lb)
Dimensions:	length 3.73m (12ft 3in); width 1.60m (5ft 3in); height 1.35m (4ft 5in)
Range:	600km (375 miles)
Armour:	none
Armament:	none
Powerplant:	one Volkswagen 14-cylinder HIAR 998cc petrol engine developing 24hp (17.9kW), or from March 1943 one Volkswagen four-cylinder 1131cc petrol engine developing 25hp (18.6kW)
Performance:	maximum road speed 100km/h (62.5mph); fording 0.4m (1ft 4in)

Humber

The Humber Heavy Utility Car was the standard staff and command car of the British Army during World War II (the army was the only fully motorised force when war broke out in September 1939). It was also the only 4 x 4 British-built four-wheel drive utility car employed. Production of the 'Box' began in May 1941 and continued until 1945. Widely used, the vehicle remained in service until the late 1950s – testimony to the quality of its design. Its fixed steel bodywork carried six seats and a folding map table. In the desert, the fixed cab was sometimes replaced by a canvas cover. The Humber was unspectacular in design, but more importantly it did the job required of it, and in different theatres. Transmission consisted of four forward and one reverse gears.

Country of origin:	United Kingdom
Crew:	1
Weight:	2413kg (5308lb)
Dimensions:	length 4.29m (14ft 1in); width 1.88m (6ft 2in); height 1.96m (6ft 5in)
Range:	500km (311 miles)
Armour:	none
Armament:	none
Powerplant:	one Humber six-cylinder 1-L-W-F 4.08-litre petrol engine developing 85hp (63.4kW)
Performance:	maximum road speed 75km/h (46.8mph); fording 0.6m (1ft 11in)

4 x 4 Jeep

In June 1940, the US Army issued a requirement for a 'go-anywhere' vehicle. After initial design changes, Ford and Willys both began production of the Jeep and between them manufactured nearly 650,000 vehicles. Intended for reconnaissance and liaison duties, the Jeep was so successful that it was soon adapted for other duties, including airborne landings and for use as rocket-launchers. They were adapted by the British SAS for long-range desert raids, mainly by being stripped of luxuries and heavily armed. Jeeps were used as ambulances and for laying telephone lines. If fitted with special flanged wheels, the Jeep could even travel along railway lines. Adapted for different climactic conditions, the Jeep served with distinction in all Allied theatres.

Country of origin:	United States
Crew:	1
Weight:	1247kg (2743lb)
Dimensions:	length 3.33m (11ft 0.25in); width 1.57m (5ft 2in); height 1.14m (3ft 9in)
Range:	363km (225 miles)
Armour:	none
Armament:	none (basic model)
Powerplant:	one Willys 441 or 442 'Go Devil' 4-cylinder petrol engine developing 60hp (44.7kW)
Performance:	maximum road speed 88.5km/h (55mph); fording 0.5m (1ft 7in)

Dodge WC53

The Dodge T214 WC53 Command and Reconnaissance Vehicle was used in a very similar way to the ubiquitous Jeep. The most common variant of the Dodge T214 series, it was used for reconnaissance as its name suggests and for liaising between different units. It also served as a staff vehicle for high-ranking officers. The vehicle was fitted with map boards and had a detachable canvas top and side-screens. A good all-round utility vehicle, reliable and mobile, it served in all theatres of the war. One of its greatest attributes was its Dodge six-cylinder petrol engine, which could withstand poor maintenance, hard treatment and a variety of adverse weather conditions. In addition, the chassis was able to take on most types of terrain, from the humid jungles of the Pacific to the snow of the northern Europe.

Country of origin:	United States
Crew:	1
Weight:	2449kg (5387lb)
Dimensions:	length 4.24m (13ft 11in); width 1.99m (6ft 6.5in); height 2.07m (6ft 9.5in)
Range:	450km (281 miles)
Armour:	none
Armament:	none
Powerplant:	one Dodge T214 six-cylinder petrol engine developing 92hp (68.6kW)
Performance:	maximum road speed 110km/h (68.75mph); fording 0.5m (1ft 7in)

Dodge T214

Introduced in 1942, the Dodge T214 0.75-tonnes (0.75-ton) truck was the successor to the T215 and was slightly wider and lower with larger wheels and stronger suspensions. Referred to as 'Beeps' (a contraction of 'Big Jeeps'), the T214 had a range of body types for different roles: weapons carrier, winch-equipped, ambulance, radio vehicle, command reconnaissance vehicle and repair vehicle. The differences were mainly in the number of seats, map boards and type of canvas cover. The fact that many vehicles are still in use around the world today is a tribute to the sturdy design of these vehicles, which were characterised by an ability to take a lot of punishment and ease of maintenance. Transmission consisted of four forward and one reverse gears.

Country of origin:	United States
Crew:	1
Weight:	2449kg (5388lb)
Dimensions:	length 4.24m (13ft 11n); width 1.99m (6ft 6.5in); height 2.07m (6ft 9.5in)
Range:	450km (281 miles)
Armour:	none
Armament:	none
Powerplant:	one Dodge T214 six-cylinder petrol engine developing 92hp (68.6kW)
Performance:	maximum road speed 110km/h (68.75mph); fording 0.5m (1ft 7in)

Car, Heavy Utility, 4 x 2, Ford C 11 ADF

The Ford C 11 ADF was based on the commercial 1942 Ford Fordor Station Wagon. Produced mainly for the British (and fitted with right-hand drive for this purpose), but also used by the Canadian Army, the vehicle saw extensive service as a staff vehicle in the Western Desert and in Italy. The all-steel body had space for five passengers. The vehicle was fitted with strengthened bumpers, internal rifle racks, entrenching tools and radio-interference suppression equipment, as well as a full medical kit and map containers. In short it was adequately equipped to allow staff officers to operate it as a mobile command centre. It was also rugged enough to stand up to the adverse terrain of North Africa. Transmission consisted of three forward and one reverse gears.

Country of origin:	Canada
Crew:	1
Weight:	1814kg (3990lb)
Dimensions:	length 4.93m (16ft 2in); width 2.01m (6ft 7in); height 1.83m (6ft 0in)
Range:	500km (311 miles)
Armour:	none
Armament:	none
Powerplant:	one Ford mercury V-8 3.91-litre petrol engine developing 95hp (70.8kW)
Performance:	maximum road speed 90km/h (56mph); fording 0.4m (1ft 4in)

GAZ-67B

The GAZ-67B was designed as a cross-country vehicle for transporting both personnel and light equipment. First produced in 1943, its design was greatly influenced by the US Bantam Jeep, many of which had been supplied to the Soviet Union under the Lend-Lease programme (one of the early Russian attempts at reverse engineering). Its performance was not quite as good, though, particularly in terms of acceleration which was poor. However, its simple and very basic design did not detract from the essential strength of the vehicle, which had very good cross-country mobility. The vehicle went on to see extensive service in Korea and Indochina, and formed the backbone of Soviet airborne divisions. Production ceased in 1953. Transmission consisted of four forward and one reverse gears.

Country of origin:	USSR
Crew:	1
Weight:	1220kg (2684lb)
Dimensions:	length 3.34m (10ft 11.33in); width 1.68m (5ft 6in); height 1.70m (5ft 7in)
Range:	750km (468 miles)
Armour:	none
Armament:	none
Powerplant:	one GAZ-A four-cylinder 3.28-litre petrol engine developing 54hp (40.3kW)
Performance:	maximum road speed 75km/h (46.8mph); fording 0.45m (1ft 6in)

M201 VLTT

With the end of World War II, France found itself with an urgent need to restock its store of military vehicles. Through a mixture of war surplus, the Lend-Lease agreement with the US and battle-recovered vehicles, the French government was able to gather some 22,000 Willys MB or Ford GPW Jeeps. These were either repaired, restored, reconditioned or used for spare parts at the ERGM vehicle plant at La Maltournée near Paris. The vehicles which emerged from the plant were known as VLTT (Voiture Légère Tous Terrains). Like the originals, these 4x4 jeeps had a 100km/h (62mph) top speed, good off-road handling and came fitted with a collapsible soft top.

Country of origin:	France
Crew:	1 + 3
Weight:	1520kg (3352lb)
Dimensions:	Length: 3.36m (11.02ft); width: 1.58m (5.18ft); height: 1.77m (5.81ft)
Range:	348km (216 miles)
Armour:	Not applicable
Armament:	None
Powerplant:	1 x 4-cylinder diesel, developing 61hp (46kW)
Performance:	Maximum road speed: 100km/h (62mph)

Land Rover 4 x 4

Since production started in 1948, the Land Rover has become one of the most famous light vehicles in service. Over one million had been produced by 1976. Designed by Rover to appeal to both domestic and export markets, the vehicle was initially targeted at agricultural and industrial customers. Constant design improvements demonstrated the potential of the vehicle, and in 1956 the British Army selected it to be the standard military vehicle in its class. Endlessly adaptable, from ambulance to artillery tractor to reconnaissance vehicle, the Land Rover has seen action all over the world with the British Army (which used specially armoured variants for patrols in Northern Ireland) and with numerous other armies. Transmission is manual with four forward and one reverse gears.

Country of origin:	United Kingdom
Crew:	1
Weight:	2120kg (4664lb)
Dimensions:	length 3.65m; width 1.68m; height 1.97m
Range:	560km (350 miles)
Armour:	none
Armament:	none
Powerplant:	one four-cylinder OHV diesel engine developing 51hp (30kW)
Performance:	maximum road speed 105km/h (65.6mph); fording 0.5m (1ft 7in)

M37

The M37 was the replacement vehicle for the World War II Dodge T214 'Beep'. Dodge built over 125,000 M37s between 1950 and 1970, both for the US Army and for export. The basic M37 was designed to carry cargo either by road or cross-country, and was similar in layout to a standard commercial pick-up truck. A winch was often mounted to assist with recovery operations, and the vehicle could be fitted with a deep-fording capability. Variants included an ambulance with fully enclosed body and a command vehicle, as well as more specialised vehicles, such as a telephone repair vehicle. A Japanese variant of the M37, built by Toyota, saw service with US forces during the Vietnam War. Rugged and reliable, the M37 served American forces well in the period immediately after World War II.

Country of origin:	United States
Crew:	1 + 2 (plus 6 or 8 in rear)
Weight:	3493kg (7684lb)
Dimensions:	length 4.81m (15ft 9in); width 1.784m (5ft 10in); height 2.279m (7ft 6in)
Range:	362km (225 miles)
Armour:	none
Armament:	none
Powerplant:	one Dodge T245 six-cylinder petrol engine developing 78hp (58kW)
Performance:	maximum road speed 88.5km/h (55mph); fording 1.066m (3ft 6in)

Fiat Campagnola 1107 AD

The Fiat Campagnola entered service with the Italian Army in 1951, and was based closely on the US Willys jeep. It featured four-wheel drive, an open structure, and a 1901cc petrol engine. This basic vehicle became the foundation of subsequent improved versions. The Campagnola A (1955), Campagnola B (1960) and Campagnola C (1968) had modified engines in either diesel or petrol formats. In 1974, the Campagnola 1107 AD was introduced. It was fitted with an 80hp (60kW) 1995cc engine and all wheels had independent suspension systems. With good handling and a top speed of 120km/h (75mph) the Campagnola became a popular vehicle not only with the Italian military, but also in civilian sports endurance driving.

Country of origin:	Italy
Crew:	1 + 5
Weight:	2420kg (5336lb)
Dimensions:	Length: 3.77m (12.37ft); width: 1.58m (5.64ft); height: 1.9m (6.23ft)
Range:	400km (250 miles)
Armour:	Not applicable
Armament:	None
Powerplant:	1 x Fiat 4-cylinder petrol, developing 80hp (60kW)
Performance:	Maximum road speed: 120km/h (75mph)

DAF YA 126

The YA 126 was one of a complete range of vehicles produced by what is now the DAF Trucks company for the Dutch Army in the immediate period after World War II. Production began in 1952 and lasted until 1960. Capable of carrying up to eight troops in addition to other duties, many YA 126 vehicles were fitted with a winch for recovering other stuck vehicles or for self-recovery. One unusual feature was that spare wheels were mounted on each side of the vehicle, which could spin freely and thus aid the vehicle in overcoming obstacles. Variants included a mobile workshop, a fully enclosed ambulance and command/radio vehicle. This vehicle was the precursor of whole range of DAF trucks which were built to serve the Dutch Army, and which continue to serve in the Netherlands.

Country of origin:	Netherlands
Crew:	1 + 1 (plus 8 in rear)
Weight:	3230kg (7106lb)
Dimensions:	length 4.55m (14ft 11in); width 2.10m (6ft 11in); height 2.20m (7ft 3in)
Range:	330km (205 miles)
Armour:	none
Armament:	none
Powerplant:	one Hercules JXC six-cylinder petrol engine developing 102hp (76kW)
Performance:	maximum road speed 84km/h (52mph); fording 0.76m (2ft 6in)

GAZ-69

The GAZ-69 was the Soviet equivalent of the ubiquitous American Jeep. The vehicle entered production in 1952 and continued to be built well into the 1960s. As well as being used for reconnaissance and general liaison duties, the vehicle's chassis was used for a number of different applications. One of these was the GAZ-69 anti-tank vehicle, which acted as the launch platform for an AT-1 'Snapper' missile launcher, which saw action during the numerous Arab–Israeli wars. An amphibious vehicle was built, designed to reconnoitre river crossing points, and a mine-detecting version also appeared, with the sensory equipment carried on the roof and then swung over in front of the vehicle when required. The vehicle stopped automatically when the alarm sounded.

Country of origin:	USSR
Crew:	1 + 1 (plus 4 in rear)
Weight:	1525kg (3355lb)
Dimensions:	length 3.85m (12ft 8in); width 1.85m (5ft 2in); height 2.03m (6ft 8in)
Range:	530km (330 miles)
Armour:	none
Armament:	none
Powerplant:	one M-20 four-cylinder petrol engine developing 52hp (39kW)
Performance:	maximum road speed 90km/h (56mph); fording 0.55m (1ft 10in)

Borgward B2000

The Borgward B2000 was one of the first military vehicles to enter service with the West German Federal Armed Forces created in 1955. Borgward already had a name for itself as the producer of cars and trucks for private use, and in that year it rose to the challenge of producing a 0.75-ton light military vehicle capable of transporting a squad of eight soldiers and all relevant equipment. The first prototype had four-wheel drive and an open driving cab with a hinged windscreen. This became designated the B2000. Unlike many other personnel carriers, the B2000 had a windowed superstructure. Between 1955 and 1961, 5672 vehicles were produced.

Country of origin:	West Germany
Crew:	1 + 8
Weight:	3050kg (6725lb)
Dimensions:	Length: 7.5m (24.6ft); width: 5.28m (17.32ft); height: 2.15m (7.05ft)
Range:	470km (290 miles)
Armour:	Not applicable
Armament:	None
Powerplant:	1 x Borgward 6-cylinder diesel, developing 80hp (60kW)
Performance:	Maximum road speed: 94km/h (58mph)

VW 181

The Volkswagen 181 was an updated version of the World War II-era Type 82 Kübelwagen, built to fill a gap in the Bundeswehr's vehicle range while they waited for production of the French, West German and Italian Europa Jeep. Volkswagen relied heavily on commercial technology for the Type 181. It was rear-wheel drive and could carry loads of up to 400kg (880lb). When the Europa Jeep project was cancelled in 1976, the Type 181 received an upgrade. It became a 4x4 vehicle with a 500kg (1100lb) cargo capacity and was renamed the Type 183 'Iltis'. Production of the Type 181 ran into the 1980s and thousands are still in service around the world today.

Country of origin:	West Germany
Crew:	2 + 3
Weight:	1350kg (2980lb)
Dimensions:	Length: 3.78m (12.4ft); width: 1.64m (5.38ft); height: 1.62m (5.31ft)
Range:	320km (200 miles)
Armour:	Not applicable
Armament:	None
Powerplant:	1 x VW 4-cylinder petrol, developing 44hp (32.5kW)
Performance:	Maximum road speed: 110km/h (68mph)

M151

The M151 was designed to a 1950 requirement for a 0.25-tonnes (0.25-tons) vehicle to replace the M38. Production began in 1960, and from then on the M151 became one of the most widely used vehicles in the world, seeing service in around 100 armies worldwide, as well as being extensively used by US forces in Vietnam as the standard light vehicle of the US Army. From the mid-1980s, all M151s were built solely for export, as the M151 was replaced in US service by the Hummer. The vehicle was used for reconnaissance and light transport duties. Among the many variants were an ambulance, a communications vehicle and several armed versions, carrying a 7.62mm machine gun, 12.7mm machine gun, recoilless rifle or the Hughes TOW anti-tank guided weapons system.

Country of origin:	United States
Crew:	1 + 1 (plus 2 in rear)
Weight:	1575kg (3465lb)
Dimensions:	length 3.352m (11ft); width 1.584m (5ft 2in); height 1.803m (5ft 11in)
Range:	483km (300 miles)
Armour:	none
Armament:	none (basic version); other versions a variety of weapons
Powerplant:	one four-cylinder petrol engine developing 72hp (53.69kW)
Performance:	maximum road speed 106km/h (66mph); fording 0.533m (1ft 9in)

Steyr-Puch 700 AP Haflinger

The Steyr-Puch 700 AP Haflinger was a light utility vehicle with extremely good off-road performance. It was originally designed for military mountain operations and came in a number of variants to aid small-unit manoeuvres. Its basic configuration was 4x4 with small 165mm x 12in tyres. There were two seats in the front of the vehicle and a flatbed cargo area to the rear. The entire vehicle could be covered with a canvas hood. In logistical roles, the Haflinger carried just under 500kg (1100lbs) of cargo. A winch with a 1500kg (3300lb) pull and a snow plough were optional fittings. After 1967, the Haflinger received a more powerful engine and models with a longer wheelbase were manufactured.

Country of origin:	Austria
Crew:	1 + 3
Weight:	645kg (1422lb)
Dimensions:	Length: 2.85m (9.35ft); width: 1.4m (4.6ft); height: 1.36m (4.46ft)
Range:	400km (250 miles)
Armour:	None
Armament:	1 x 12.7mm (0.5in) MG fitted on AA variant
Powerplant:	1 x Model 700 AP 2-cylinder petrol, developing 24hp (18kW)
Performance:	Maximum road speed: 75km/h (47mph); fording: 0.4m (1.3ft); gradient: 65 percent

Faun Kraka 640

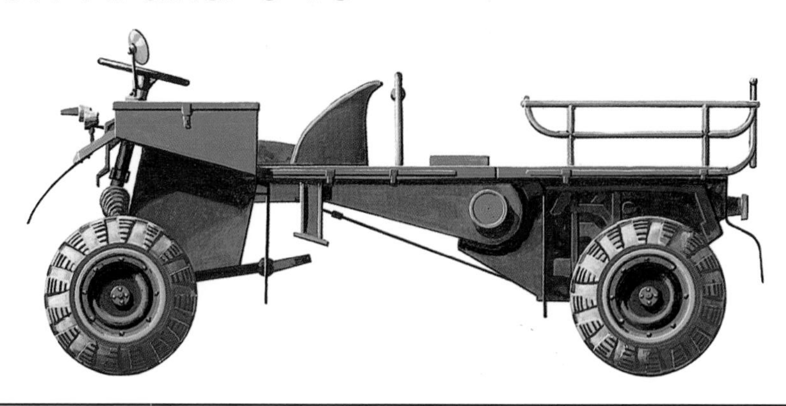

The Faun Kraka 640 began its development life in the early 1960s. It was designed by Union AG (a Faun-Werke subsidiary) as a multi-purpose general utility vehicle capable of operating in standard European off-road conditions. The very small dimensions of the vehicle, plus the fact it could be folded down for air transit, meant that most orders (around 860 vehicles) went to the Bundeswehr paratroop forces. It is an extremely simple vehicle, powered by a two-cylinder BMW engine which chain-drives the wheels. With a cargo capacity of 0.75 tons, the Kraka has hosted several large weapons platforms, including 20mm (0.78in) AA cannon and MILAN ATGW systems.

Country of origin:	West Germany
Crew:	2 + 6
Weight:	1610kg (3550lb)
Dimensions:	Length: 2.78m (9.12ft); width: 1.51m (4.95ft); height: 1.28m (4.19ft)
Range:	Not available
Armour:	None
Armament:	None as standard (see text)
Powerplant:	1 x BMW 427 2-cylinder petrol, developing 25hp (19kW)
Performance:	Maximum road speed: 55km/h (34mph); gradient: 50 percent

Steyr-Puch Pinzgauer 716 M

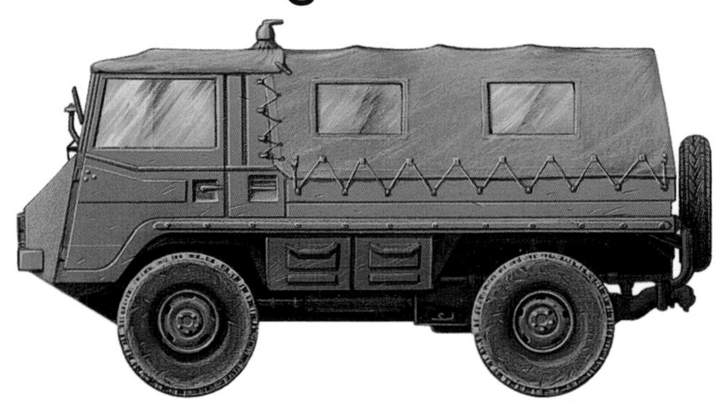

The Pinzgauer series of light utility vehicles were first introduced in 1965 as simple 4x4 trucks, and over 20,000 vehicles have been sold to date. Today, Pinzgauers come in two basic versions: the 716 series (4x4) and the 718 series (6x6). An 8x8 version did not make it past the prototype stage. The Pinzgauer 716 M can take a load of up to 1400kg (3100lb) and carry it at 122km/h (76mph). Off-road mobility is excellent – a major client for the Pinzgauer is the Austrian alpine forces. An automatic level control system alters the cargo suspension according to the load. Apart from utility vehicles, Pinzgauers have also been configured for 20mm (0.78in) AA cannon, as command-and-control centres and as ambulances.

Country of origin:	Austria
Crew:	1 + 9
Weight:	2200kg (4850lb)
Dimensions:	Length: 4.48m (14.69ft); width: 1.8m (5.91ft); height: 2.04m (6.69ft)
Range:	1200km (750 miles)
Armour:	None
Armament:	None
Powerplant:	1 x 6-cylinder turbo diesel, developing 105hp (78kW) at 4350rpm
Performance:	Maximum road speed: 122km/h (76mph); fording: 0.7m (2.3ft)

UAZ-469B

The UAZ-469B is a light 4x4 utility vehicle developed in the late 1960s at the Ul'yanovsk Motor Vehicle Plant. In many ways it is a basic civilian-type off-road vehicle. A payload of 600kg (1300lb) can be carried (though only if a maximum of two men are on board) and a similar weight can be towed. The standard vehicle has a soft top and a folding windscreen. A hard-top version is available for more heavyweight logistical duties. There is also an ambulance version, the UAZ-469G, with space for four stretcher-carried patients. Today the UAZ-469B is the primary light vehicle in the Russian Federation with export destinations including Afghanistan, Cuba, Egypt, Iran, Poland and Syria.

Country of origin:	USSR
Crew:	1 + 8
Weight:	2290kg (5050lb)
Dimensions:	Length: 4.03m (13.22ft); width: 1.79m (5.87ft); height: 2.02m (6.63ft)
Range:	620km (385 miles)
Armour:	Not applicable
Armament:	None
Powerplant:	1 x ZMZ-451 4-cylinder petrol, developing 75hp (56kW)
Performance:	Maximum road speed: 100km/h (62mph); fording: 0.8m (2.6ft); gradient: 62 percent

Land Rover One-Tonne

The Land Rover One-Tonne was developed in the mid-1960s, when it was realised that the original Land Rover would not be capable of towing the heavier weapon systems of the future, as well as those earmarked to enter service in the immediate future. The first production models appeared in 1975. This version of the Land Rover was designed specifically for military use (rather than as a multi-purpose vehicle suitable for agricultural and industrial use) and thus far fewer were built than of its more famous ancestor. Typical roles for the vehicle included towing the 105mm (4.1in) Light Gun and Rapier surface-to-air missile (SAM) system. Variants included an ambulance, communications vehicle and electronic warfare vehicle. Like all Land Rover vehicles, this truck was rugged and reliable.

Country of origin:	United Kingdom
Crew:	1 + 1 (plus 8 in rear)
Weight:	3120kg (6864lb)
Dimensions:	length 4.127m (13ft 6in); width 1.842m (6ft 1in); height 2.138m (7ft)
Range:	560km (348 miles)
Armour:	none
Armament:	none
Powerplant:	one Rover V-8 petrol engine developing 128hp (95.5kW)
Performance:	maximum road speed 120km/h (74mph); fording 1.1m (3ft 7in)

Auverland A3

The Auverland A3 is a 4x4 light vehicle in extensive use with the French Army, gendarmerie and air force. It was developed from the SAMO 4x4 vehicle after Auverland took over the SAMO concern in the mid-1980s. Little known outside Europe, it remains one of the most competent off-road military vehicles available today. It has a top road speed of 115km/h (71mph) and it has excellent traction in rough or muddy terrain. Two basic versions are available: the A3 standard vehicle and the A3L with a lengthened wheelbase. Both versions come with soft- or hard-top options. A3 vehicles are unarmed on delivery, but a weapons post is provided behind the front seats to mount a machine gun, usually an AAT-52 or an FN MAG.

Country of origin:	France
Crew:	1 + 3
Weight:	1710kg (3771lb)
Dimensions:	Length: 3.85m (12.63ft); width: 1.54m (5.05ft); height: 1.7m (5.58ft)
Range:	800km (500 miles)
Armour:	Not available
Armament:	None
Powerplant:	1 x Peugeot XUD-9A 4-cylinder turbo diesel, developing 93hp (69kW)
Performance:	Maximum road speed: 115km/h (71mph)

Mercedes-Benz U 1300

The Mercedes-Benz Unimog was designed for industrial and agricultural purposes in the years following World War II. Having undergone many modifications, the U 1300L vehicle was chosen to fill a West German Army requirement for 17,000 military trucks to be delivered between 1978 and 1989. A versatile vehicle, the 1300 L has been used as an ambulance, a dump truck and a pole erector. Many are fitted with winches and the chassis has been used as the basis for an armoured personnel carrier (the UR 416). The vehicle has seen service with the Australian and New Zealand Armies and is used by the RAF for towing Harrier jump jets in the field. For normal road use the vehicle is driven with only the rear wheels engaged, the front wheels being engaged for cross-country driving.

Country of origin:	West Germany
Crew:	1 + 2
Weight:	7500kg (16,500lb)
Dimensions:	length 5.54m (18ft 2.1in); width 2.30m (7ft 6.6in); height (including tarpaulin) 2.83m (9ft 3.4in)
Range:	900km (559 miles)
Armour:	none
Armament:	none
Powerplant:	one Mercedes-Benz OM-352 six-cylinder diesel engine developing 96hp (71.6kW)
Performance:	maximum road speed 80km/h (50mph); fording 1.2m (3ft 11.2in)

BR-100 Bombi

The BR-100 Bombi entered production with Bombardier Limited of Quebec in 1978. Bombardier is one of Canada's premier manufacturers of oversnow vehicles. Usually these are destined for civilian markets, but military customers have been a growth area. The BR-100 is a small oversnow transport vehicle in service with the Canadian Armed Forces. It is capable of pulling a 450kg (1000lb) load over very soft snow conditions. With very wide tracks and a vehicle weight of just 1500kg (3300lb), the Bombi imparts a ground pressure of only 100g/sq cm (1.42lb/sq in) using summer tracks and 80g/sq cm (1.13lb/sq in) using winter tracks. The Bombi also has Middle Eastern customers, as it is ideal for travel over soft sand.

Country of origin:	Canada
Crew:	1 + 2
Weight:	1500kg (3300lb)
Dimensions:	Length: 3.15m (10.33ft); width: 2.2m (7.21ft); height: 2.01m (6.59ft)
Range:	Not available
Armour:	None
Armament:	None
Powerplant:	1 x Ford 4-cylinder petrol, developing 84hp (63kW)
Performance:	Maximum road speed: 22km/h (14mph)

Lohr Fardier FL 500

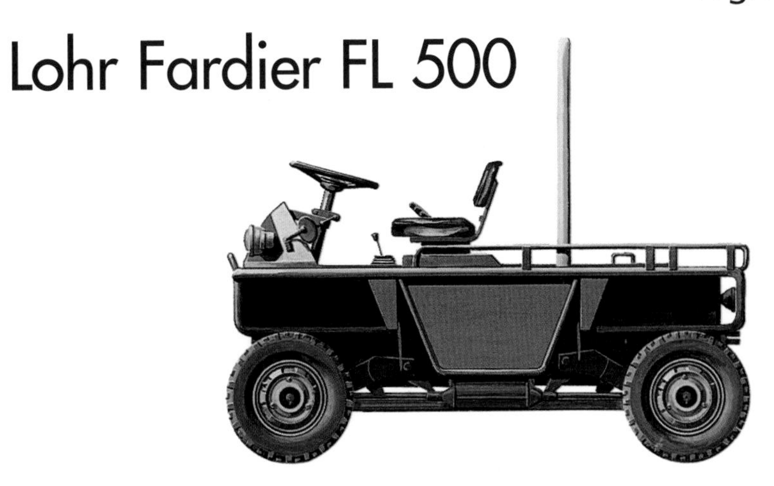

The Lohr Fardier FL 500 is a diminutive 4x4 vehicle developed to provide airborne forces with a basic form of transport and logistics at the battlefront. It is easily air transportable – the basic vehicle weighs only 680kg (1500lb) and is only 2.41m (7.91ft) long and less than 2m (6.6ft) high. During operations, its primary role is the transport of ammunition or other supplies, and it can tow guns or trailers up to its own weight. The FL 500 is both unarmoured and unarmed, though some have been fitted with MILAN anti-tank guided weapons as a more aggressive option. Currently the FL 500 serves with the French Foreign Legion and French and Argentine airborne units.

Country of origin:	France
Crew:	1
Weight:	680kg (1500lb)
Dimensions:	Length: 2.41m (7.91ft); width: 1.5m (4.92ft); height: 1.18m (3.87ft)
Range:	200km (125 miles)
Armour:	None
Armament:	See text
Powerplant:	1 x Citroën 2-cylinder petrol, developing 28hp (21kW)
Performance:	Maximum road speed: 80km/h (50mph)

M561 Gama-Goat

The M561 Gama-Goat is so called because its mobility was meant to be goatlike, and its creator was called Roger Gamaunt. It is a six-wheel-drive utility vehicle capable of tackling the roughest terrain and consists of two sections – a front section containing the engine and crew cab and a rear section for the cargo. The two sections are connected by a flexible coupling which allows the carrier body to pitch plus or minus 40 degrees and roll plus or minus 30 degrees in relation to the front vehicle. Fully amphibious capability is available without preparation, and the M561 can achieve 3km/h (2mph) on the water. Propulsion is provided by the wheels only. The M561 can pull 1.25 tons of cargo.

Country of origin:	United States
Crew:	2
Weight:	4630kg (10,200lb)
Dimensions:	Length: 5.76m (18.89ft); width: 2.13m (6.99ft); height: 2.31m (7.58ft)
Range:	840km (520 miles)
Armour:	None
Armament:	None
Powerplant:	1 x GM 3-53 3-cylinder diesel, developing 103hp (77kW)
Performance:	Maximum road speed: 88km/h (55mph); fording: amphibious

Supacat ATMP

The Supacat All-Terrain Mobile Platform (ATMP) has been in service with the British Army since 1984, and has proved to be a versatile workhorse. Its purpose is to provide logistical mobility to infantry units. With a 6x6 configuration and a weight of only 2520kg (5600lb), it can move over the roughest terrain. It is also amphibious. The latest versions feature the Ackerman steering system; steering is performed by the front wheels when on the road, but the driver can switch to skid steering when going cross-country, locking the wheels on one side of the vehicle when turning corners. The Supacat is air-portable by Chinook helicopter and it can pull loads of 3.2 tons, 1.5 tons more than a Land Rover.

Country of origin:	United Kingdom
Crew:	1 + 5
Weight:	2520kg (5560lb)
Dimensions:	Length: 3.15m (10.33ft); width: 2m (6.6ft); height: 1.89m (6.2ft)
Range:	600km (370 miles)
Armour:	(Aluminium) 5mm (0.19in)
Armament:	1 x 7.62mm (0.3in) MG optional
Powerplant:	1 x VW-Audi ADE 1900 4-cylinder turbo diesel, developing 54hp (40kW)
Performance:	Maximum road speed: 48km/h (30mph); fording: amphibious; gradient: 45 percent

M998

The High Mobility Multi-Purpose Wheeled Vehicle (HMMWV) – 'Hummer' – prototype appeared in August 1980, and in March 1983 AM General was awarded a contract to build 54,973 vehicles, of which 39,000 were for the US Army. The vehicle has a four-man crew, who sit on either side of the drive chain, which allows for a low centre of gravity. The frame is strong enough to serve as a roll bar and support for various equipment kits. The Hummer can also mount of variety of weapons: such as the TOW anti-tank system, 7.62mm and 12.7mm machine guns, Mk 19 40mm grenade launchers and even batteries of Stinger surface-to-air missiles (SAMs). The vehicle has a fully synchronised transmission with 16 forward and eight reverse gears. The M998 has been exported to the Middle East and Asia.

Country of origin:	United States
Crew:	1 + 3
Weight:	3870kg (8375lb)
Dimensions:	length 4.457m (14ft 7in); width 2.15m (7ft); height 1.75m (5ft 8in)
Range:	563km (352 miles)
Armour:	none
Armament:	various, including machine guns, grenade launchers and surface-to-air missile (SAM) launchers
Powerplant:	one V-8 6.21 air-cooled diesel engine developing 135hp (101kW)
Performance:	maximum road range 105km/h (65.6mph); fording 0.76m (2ft 6in); vertical obstacle 0.56m (1ft 9in)

SAS Land Rover

The British Special Air Service (SAS) has made good use of a long-wheelbase version of the Land Rover, specially adapted for the conditions faced in the types of low-intensity warfare in which the SAS has become expert. Painted pink for camouflage during desert operations (where its colour blends in with the desert haze), and known as Pink Panthers, the vehicles used a similar chassis to that of ordinary British Army Land Rovers. Widely used in the Persian Gulf, they were equipped with metal sand-crossing channels, smoke dischargers and machine guns. In addition, they carried specialist navigational equipment and external stowage racks, to give them the capability to carry out long-range desert reconnaissance missions behind enemy lines.

Country of origin:	United Kingdom
Crew:	1
Weight:	3050kg (6710lb)
Dimensions:	length 4.67m (15ft 4in); width 1.79m (5ft 11in); height 2.03m (6ft 8in)
Range:	748km (4655 miles)
Armour:	none
Armament:	two 7.62mm machine guns
Powerplant:	one V-8 water-cooled petrol engine developing 134hp (100kW)
Performance:	maximum road speed 105km/h (65.6mph); fording 0.5m (1ft 7in)

IVECO 40-10 WM

In basic form, the IVECO 40-10 WM is a 4x4 truck based on the Fiat Daily commercial vehicle, though it has been strengthened for military use. The rear section of the vehicle defines its role. Apart from a basic open cargo area format, the vehicle can take various box bodies, including a command-and-control centre, a field ambulance, an engineering unit, a vehicle refuelling system and a police secure unit. Alternatively, a 106mm (4.17in) recoilless rifle, various heavy machine-gun configurations, and ATGW launchers can be mounted on the flat bed. The 40-10 WM is in service in Italy, Canada, Pakistan and Belgium. A key advantage of the vehicle is that it is air-transportable within a C-130 Hercules aircraft.

Country of origin:	Italy
Crew:	1 + 2
Weight:	4400kg (9700lb)
Dimensions:	Length: 4.9m (16.08ft); width: 2m (6.56ft); height: 2.38m (7.8ft)
Range:	500km (310 miles)
Armour:	Not available
Armament:	Various (see text)
Powerplant:	1 x Type 8142 4-cylinder diesel, developing 103hp (77kW)
Performance:	Maximum road speed: 100km/h (62mph)

ATF 2 Dingo

The ATF 2 Dingo is one of the more recent additions to German military vehicle ranks. Its carrying capacity is only four soldiers, apart from the one-man crew, but the occupants are well protected by the mine deflector system in the hull. This diverts the force of both anti-personnel and anti-tank mine explosions away from the troop and operator compartments. Air conditioning, onboard intercom, a rear driving camera, and NBC protection make the Dingo a particularly user-friendly vehicle to operate in hostile areas. Its chassis is that of the Unimog U1550L, which provides the Dingo with excellent off-road mobility. The Dingo is now in service with the German Army.

Country of origin:	Germany
Crew:	1 + 4
Weight:	8800kg (19,400lb)
Dimensions:	Length: 5.23m (17.16ft); width: 2.31m (7.58ft); height: 2.38m (7.8ft)
Range:	700km (430 miles)
Armour:	Not available
Armament:	1 x 7.62mm (0.3in) MG
Powerplant:	1 x Mercedes-Benz OM 366LA 6-cylinder turbo diesel, developing 237hp (177kW)
Performance:	Maximum road speed: 106km/h (66mph)

URO VAMTAC

The URO VAMTAC (Vehículo de Alta Movilidad Táctico – Vehicle of High Tactical Mobility) is one of the new generation of modular vehicles. Different modular compartments can be fitted to the rear of the vehicle to change its role. Current modules include ATGW carrier, SAM system, ambulance (pictured here), command-and-control centre and infantry shelter. It is powered by a Steyr M16-TCA diesel which generates 119hp (89kW) and a maximum road speed of 130km/h (81mph). Its fording depth is 0.75m (2.46ft) without preparation, but with a snorkel fitted this increases to 1.5m (4.9ft). The VAMTAC is intended to become the Spanish Army's standard light vehicle, though an expensive price tag may reduce sales.

Country of origin:	Spain
Crew:	1
Weight:	5000kg (11,000lb)
Dimensions:	Length: 4.85m (15.91ft); width: 2.19m (7.18ft); height: 1.89m (6.2ft)
Range:	600km (370 miles)
Armour:	Not available
Armament:	Depends on module (see text)
Powerplant:	1 x Steyr M16-TCA 6-cylinder turbo diesel, developing 119hp (89kW)
Performance:	Maximum road speed: 130km/h (81mph); fording: 1.5m (4.9ft) with snorkel

ZiS-5

The ZiS-5 had its origins in the reformed Automobil Moscow Obshchestvo (AMO) company in 1931. AMO built a range of trucks between 1931 and 1933, at which point the company was renamed Zavod imeni Stalina (ZiS). The AMO trucks were relabelled and on 1 October 1933 production of the ZiS-5 officially began. It became one of the Russian Army's most prolific vehicles. Nearly one million were produced between 1933 and the mid-1950s. Its wartime service was crucial to Red Army logistics. Wartime vehicles can be spotted by austerity features, such as wooden doors and seats, the absence of bumpers and a fitting of only the left headlight. Production of the ZiS-5 ceased in 1958.

Country of origin:	USSR
Crew:	2
Weight:	3100kg (6800lb)
Dimensions:	Length: 6.06m (19.88ft); width: 2.24m (7.35ft); height: 2.16m (7.09ft)
Range:	Not available
Armour:	None
Armament:	None
Powerplant:	1 x ZiS-5 6-cylinder petrol, developing 72hp (54kW)
Performance:	Maximum road speed: 65km/h (40mph); fording: 0.6m (2ft)

GAZ-AAA

The GAZ-AAA was one of the earlier offerings from the GAZ company. Production of the vehicle ran between 1933 and 1942. Like many Russian wartime trucks, the 1942 version has radically simplified bodywork – there are no bumpers, the wings and cabin have simplified lines, and there is only one headlight. Though the GAZ-AAA never reached the production figures of the ZiS-5 (qv), 37,373 were made in total. It was a 6x4 with a 2500kg (5500lb) payload capacity out of a total loaded weight of 4975kg (10,970lb). The gearbox consisted of eight forward gears and two reverse gears, and it could achieve a maximum road speed of 65km/h (40mph). The chassis of the GAZ-AAA was used to produce the BA-10 armoured car.

Country of origin:	USSR
Crew:	2
Weight:	2475kg (5457lb)
Dimensions:	Length: 5.34m (17.52ft); width: 2.04m (6.69ft); height: 1.97m (6.46ft)
Range:	Not available
Armour:	None
Armament:	None
Powerplant:	1 x GAZ-M1 4-cylinder petrol, developing 50hp (37kW)
Performance:	Maximum road speed: 65km/h (40mph)

Laffly W15T

Laffly was founded in France in 1858, and specialized mainly in civilian haulage vehicles or utility vehicles for the fire service. In the first decades of the 20th century, it began to produce all-wheel-drive vehicles for military markets, particularly in collaboration with the Hotchkiss company in the 1930s. The W15T was one such vehicle. It was designed as an artillery tractor in 6x6 configuration and was manned by three crew, but three other soldiers could also be transported. Two small auxiliary wheels were placed at the front of the truck to facilitate climbing ditches. The W15T was a solid vehicle, and after German occupation in 1940, many were converted to Wehrmacht use, particularly as command vehicles.

Country of origin:	France
Crew:	3 + 3
Weight:	5000kg (11,000lb)
Dimensions:	Length: 5.4m (17.7ft); width: 1.9m (6.2ft); height: 1.8m (5.9ft)
Range:	280km (170 miles)
Armour:	Not applicable
Armament:	1 x 7.5mm (0.29in) MG
Powerplant:	1 x Hotchkiss 486 4-cylinder petrol, developing 51hp (38kW)
Performance:	Not available

Fiat/Spa

The Italian Army in World War II was heavily reliant on trucks of somewhat dated design. Prior to World War II, though, some measure of standardisation had been achieved, with Fiat supplying the bulk of the vehicles. *Dovunque* means literally 'go anywhere', and the truck had adequate cross-country capability, being one of a range of Fiat and other Italian vehicles which saw extensive service, particularly in North Africa. The fact that most needed to be hand-crank started belied their effective performance. The Germans appropriated large numbers of Italian trucks for service in all theatres, and British troops valued captured Italian trucks highly because the vehicles did not rely on a carburettor, which tended to clog up in the dusty desert conditions.

Country of origin:	Italy
Crew:	1
Weight:	1615kg (3553lb)
Dimentions:	length 3.80m (12ft 5.6in); width 1.30m (4ft 3.2in); height 2.15m (7ft 0.6in)
Range:	250km (156 miles)
Armour:	none
Armament:	none
Powerplant:	one OM Autocarretta 32 four-cylinder petrol engine developing 21hp (15.7kW)
Performance:	maximum road speed 63km/h (40mph); fording 0.5m (1ft 7in)

Krupp Kfz 81

The Kfz 81 was one of the most commonly-used German light trucks during the early stages of World War II. The role in which it was most frequently seen was that of artillery tractor (it was the prime mover for the 20mm (0.78in) anti-aircraft gun), replacing the Kfz 69 purpose-built artillery tractor. The Kfz 81, or Krupp Boxer as it was known, had all-round independent suspension which allowed reasonable cross-country mobility. It was similar in many ways to contemporary six-wheeler British light trucks. In addition the indigenous light trucks, the Germans made extensive use of captured material such as the Czechoslovakian Tatra T92. Early German vehicles stub axles amidships to carry the spare wheels, though there were never enough to go round even the élite field divisions.

Country of origin:	Germany
Crew:	1
Weight:	2600kg (5720lb)
Dimensions:	length 4.95m (16ft 2.9in); width 1.95m (6ft 4.8in); height 2.30m (7ft 6.6in)
Range:	300km (187 miles)
Armour:	none
Armament:	none
Powerplant:	one Krupp M304 4-cylinder engine developing 52hp (38.8kW)
Performance:	maximum road speed 70km/h (43.75mph); fording 0.4m (1ft 4in)

Büssing-Nag

Germany relied heavily on modified civilian models for its heavy trucks as the war broke out when her rearmamment programme was nowhere near completion. One of the types adapted was the Büssing-Nag 454 4x4 truck, designed to be used as a transporter unit for tanks. Only a small number were ever constructed as the 6x4 Faun was preferred for the role in most cases. Even this vehicle saw limited service as a tank-transport, as the German logistics system relied mainly on the railways for the movement of general supplies during World War II, with medium trucks taking on the task of distributing the equipment to the point of use. Heavy trucks were used most often for specialist roles such as carrying mobile radio stations for controlling armoured forces.

Country of origin:	Germany
Crew:	1
Weight:	9200kg (20,240lb)
Dimensions:	length 10.40m (34ft 1.4in); width 2.50m (8ft 2.4in); height 2.60m (8ft 6.4in)
Range:	270km (169 miles)
Armour:	none
Armament:	none
Powerplant:	one Deutz F6M517 six-cylinder diesel engine developing 150hp (111.8kW)
Performance:	maximum road speed 65km/h (40.62mph); fording 0.4m (1ft 4in)

Opel Blitz

The Opel Blitz was one of the most successful products of an attempt by the Germans to standardise their vehicle fleet (100 different vehicles were in service by the late 1930s, leading to massive logistical difficulties). The Blitz had a steel cab and wooden body and was used in many roles, from field ambulance to mobile workshop to command vehicle. To improve cross-country performance, the vehicle was given four-wheel drive, these vehicles being designated 'Allrad'. They were used in all theatres of the war, with later models being constructed of pressed card to conserve steel. Production lasted until 1944, when Allied bombing and ground advances overtook the factories. The Blitz was well built, but suffered from being too complicated for reliability in rugged conditions.

Country of origin:	Germany
Crew:	1
Weight:	3290kg (7238lb)
Dimensions:	length 6.02m (19ft 9in); width 2.265m (7ft 5.2in); height 2.175m (7ft 1.6in)
Range:	410km (255 miles)
Armour:	none
Armament:	none
Powerplant:	one Opel six-cylinder petrol engine developing 73.5hp (54.8kW)
Performance:	maximum road speed 80km/h (50mph); fording 0.5m (1ft 7in)

Chevrolet C60L

The Chevrolet C60L was one of the most numerous trucks built by the Canadians during World War II for supply to the British and other Commonwealth forces. This 3-tonnes (3-tons) 4 x 4 was a tremendously reliable vehicle, of sturdy yet simple design which allowed for rapid production. An enormous number of different models were produced including fuel tankers, ambulances and recovery vehicles. As well as different chassis, there was great differentiation in cab design as production progressed. For example, the number 13 cab was a complete redesign to allow more interior space and better positioning of the foot pedals. Other designs replaced the all-steel cab with a soft-top. The versatility of the range was remarkable and was reflected in the numbers in use.

Country of origin:	Canada
Crew:	1
Weight:	2100kg (4620lb)
Dimensions:	length 6.20m (20ft 4in); width 2.29m (7ft 6in); height 3.05m (10ft)
Range:	270km (168 miles)
Armour:	none
Armament:	none
Powerplant:	one Ford V-8 petrol engine developing 95hp (71kW)
Performance:	maximum road speed 80km/h (50mph); fording 0.5m (1ft 7in)

GMC 6 x 6

The GMC 6 x 6 was built for the US Army as part of a standardisation programme, begun in 1939, which allowed for only two of each type of vehicle to be considered, and emphasised commonality of parts and accessories wherever possible. Known as 'Jimmies', the vehicles were supplied to Britain under the Lend-Lease scheme before America's entry into World War II, and the trucks served with distinction in all theatres, including in the Soviet Union, which also received significant numbers. The 'Jimmy' made an enormous contribution to the Allied victory after the D-Day landings by ensuring a reliable method of transport for supplies to units at the front, all of which had to be trucked across France until ports nearer Germany had been captured.

Country of origin:	United States
Crew:	1
Weight:	11,939kg (26,265lb)
Dimensions:	length 6.82m (22ft 4.5in); width 2.44m (8ft 0in); height 3.01m (9ft 10.5in)
Range:	255km (165 miles)
Armour:	none
Armament:	none
Powerplant:	one Hercules RXC six-cylinder petrol engine developing 106hp (79kW)
Performance:	maximum road speed 64km/h (40mph); fording 0.75m (2ft 5in)

Dodge T215

Dodge was the sole provider of 0.5-tonnes (0.5-ton) trucks for the US Army. The order for 14,000 was made in mid-1940. Dodge altered the basic commercial chassis slightly for military use, giving it four-wheel drive. There was the option of an open cab (as with the command, reconnaissance, radio and weapons carrier versions) or fixed bodywork as with the ambulance). The Dodge was a sturdy vehicle manufactured in large numbers, many of which were shipped to the United Kingdom and USSR under the Lend-Lease scheme of World War II. Interestingly, the Russians were less than impressed with the tanks supplied by the British and Americans under the scheme, but they were very grateful when it came to the jeeps and lorries supplied, using them for many years after the end of the war.

Country of origin:	United States
Crew:	1
Weight:	2046kg (4501lb)
Dimensions:	length 4.67m (15ft 4in); width 1.93m (6ft 4in); height 2.13m (7ft 0in)
Range:	500km (311 miles)
Armour:	none
Armament:	none
Powerplant:	one Dodge T215 six-cylinder petrol engine developing 92hp (68.6kW)
Performance:	maximum road speed 70km/h (43.75mph); fording 0.6m (1ft 11in)

Bedford QLD

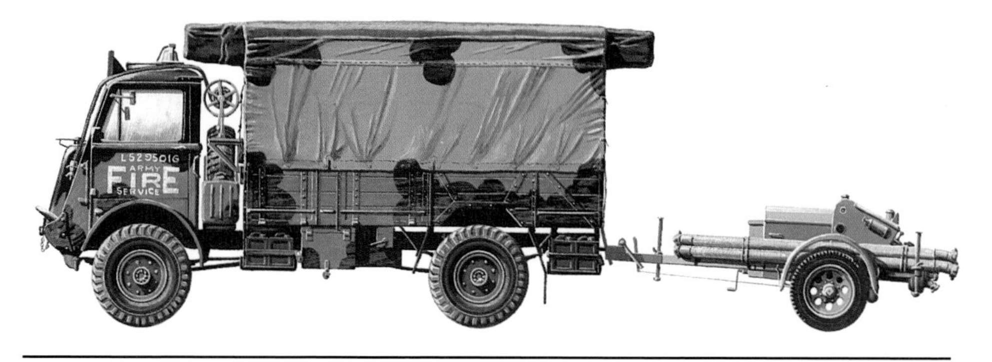

At the outbreak of World War II, Bedford was contracted by the British War Office to produce a 3-tonnes (3-tons) 4 x 4 general service truck. The Bedford QLD was rapidly developed and the first production vehicles began to arrive in early 1941. Commendably, despite the speed of development, there were hardly any early problems with the vehicle. There were a number of variants on the basic design: the QLT troop carrier with room for 29 troops and kit, popularly known as the 'Drooper'; the QLR wireless truck; a vehicle adapted specifically to carry and fire the 6-pounder anti-tank gun from the body; and a fire tender. The Royal Air Force used them extensively as fuel tankers. An amphibious version, the Giraffe, was developed but never passed the prototype stage.

Country of origin:	United Kingdom
Crew:	1
Weight:	12,727kg (26,998lb)
Dimensions:	length 5.99m (19ft 8in); width 2.26m (7ft 5in); height 3.0m (9ft 10in)
Range:	370km (230 miles)
Armour:	none
Armament:	none
Powerplant:	one Bedford six-cylinder petrol engine developing 72hp (53.7kW)
Performance:	maximum road speed 61km/h (38mph); fording 0.4m (1ft 4in)

Bedford Three-ton

The Bedford Three-ton truck was the British equivalent of the American 2.5-ton trucks, in other words the largest cargo vehicle which could be produced in large quantities. After the huge losses of equipment suffered by the British Army at Dunkirk in 1940, the British had been unable to concentrate on development of new vehicles and relied instead on current models and American imports. Once the crisis has eased, ie the threat of German invasion had subsided, new truck development could begin. The Bedford Three-ton was one of the most significant of the new vehicles produced. In addition to general cargo-carrying duties, the vehicle was capable of being converted to a fuel (as shown here) and water tanker with the help of a detachable superstructure.

Country of origin:	United Kingdom
Crew:	1
Weight:	7490kg (16,478lb)
Dimensions:	length: 6.7m (22ft); width: 2.3m (7ft 7in); height: 3m (9ft 9in)
Range:	300km (187 miles)
Armour:	none
Armament:	none
Powerplant:	one Austin six-cylinder petrol engine developing 72hp (54kW)
Performance:	maximum road speed 80km/h (50mph); fording 0.6m (1ft 11in)

Mack 6 x 6

Mack was a well-established name in the truck manufacturing industry prior to World War II, and was thus well-placed to fulfil the transport needs of the US Army. The most prominent model produced, perhaps because of its size and power, was the 7.6-tonnes (7.5 tons) NO 6 x 6. This was mainly used by both British and American forces to tow heavy artillery pieces, such as the 155mm 'Long Tom' howitzers. The Canadians also used the truck widely for a variety of purposes. The truck was first seen in action in Italy. Despite their size, the Macks negotiated the difficult mountainous terrain to be at the forefront of the advance. The layout of the 6 x 6 was conventional, with the engine at the front, two-door cab in the centre with a fold-forward windscreen, and a cargo area at the rear.

Country of origin:	United States
Crew:	1
Weight:	19,813kg (43,588lb)
Dimensions:	length 7.54m (24ft 9in); width 2.62m (8ft 7in); height 3.15m (10ft 4in)
Range:	340km (212 miles)
Armour:	none
Armament:	none
Powerplant:	one Mack EY six-cylinder petrol engine developing 159hp (118.6kW)
Performance:	maximum road speed 84km/h (52.5mph); fording 0.76m (2ft 6in)

Leyland Hippo Mk II GS

The Leyland Hippo was introduced into the British Army during the last two years of World War II. It was developed to increase the logistical capacity of Allied forces operating in northern Europe. Far larger than most other British trucks, the Hippo was a 6x4 vehicle with a 10-ton load-carrying capacity. The loading area at the rear was sunk low over the wheel arches to make a low loading height. In the Mk I Hippo, the cab was open, weather protection provided only by a canvas cover. The Mk II Hippo was an upgraded vehicle which featured an enclosed all-steel cab and a variety of van bodies, some including specialist facilities such as photo-processing and print machines.

Country of origin:	United Kingdom
Crew:	1 + 2
Weight:	8941kg (19,715lb)
Dimensions:	Length: 8.31m (27.26ft); width: 2.46m (8.07ft); height: 3.33m (10.92ft)
Range:	840km (520 miles)
Armour:	None
Armament:	None
Powerplant:	1 x Leyland Type L 6-cylinder diesel, developing 100hp (75kW)
Performance:	Maximum road speed: 60km/h (37mph)

M35

Developed after World War II, the M35, known as the 'Eager Beaver', became the standard US Army 6 x 6 truck and was the most widely used military truck in the West, with the US Army alone having 65,000 in use. BY early 1980, AM General had produced over 150,000 M35/44 series 6 x 6 trucks. Initially equipped with a petrol engine, later variants were converted to multi-fuel and diesel systems to make them more fuel-efficient. Other improvements included a redesigned suspension, brakes and steering, and forward-tilting bonnet. Optional extras were a winch, special heating for cold-weather operations, deep-fording kit and centre troop seats for carrying personnel. The many variants of the M35 included the M48 tractor truck, M50 water tanker, M59 Dumper, M60 wrecker and M185 repair van.

Country of origin:	United States
Crew:	1 + 2
Weight:	8168kg (17,969lb)
Dimensions:	length 6.71m (22ft 0in); width 2.39m (7ft 10in); height 2.90m (9ft 6in)
Range:	483km (300 miles)
Armour:	none
Armament:	none
Powerplant:	one LDT-465-IC six-cylinder diesel engine developing 140hp (104.4kW)
Performance:	maximum road speed 90km/h (56mph); fording 0.76m (2ft 6in)

M36

The M36 is the long wheelbase version of the M35 truck. The layout of the basic cargo version is conventional, with the engine at the front, two-door cab in the centre with a windscreen that can be folded forward onto the bonnet and a canvas top. The cargo area at the back has a drop tailgate, removable bows, tarpaulin cover and troop seats positioned down either side. Many trucks are fitted with a 4536kg- (9979lb-) capacity winch which can be used to the front or rear of the vehicle. It has a steel cable with two speeds forward and one speed in reverse. The truck itself has a manual gearbox with five forward and one reverse gears. A large number of kits are available for this vehicle, including a ring mount for a machine gun over the cab, a hard top for the cab and central seats for troops in the rear.

Country of origin:	United States
Crew:	1
Weight:	11,500kg (25,300lb)
Dimensions:	length 8.4m (27ft 6in); width 2.4m (7ft 10in); height 3.2m (10ft 6in)
Range:	480km (300 miles)
Armour:	none
Armament:	none (basic version)
Powerplant:	one LDT-456-1C six-cylinder inline diesel engine developing 140hp (104kW)
Performance:	maximum road speed 90km/h (56.26mph); fording 0.76m (2ft 6in)

Praga V3S

The V3S was developed in the early 1950s by the Prague Automobile Factory (Praga), specifically for military use. Such was the success of the design that it remained in production until the 1980s. With a slow top speed of only 62km/h (38mph) and a high diesel consumption, the V3S nonetheless compensated with good off-road handling by virtue of its 6x6 all-wheel-drive configuration (it came first in its class in a Paris–Dakar rally in the 1990s). The V3S could carry over five tons of cargo, but it was also fitted with a mobile office shell which gave 3.9m (13ft) of standing room. Its engine came from the Tatra company. The V3S chassis was later used to produce the M53/59 anti-aircraft vehicle.

Country of origin:	Czechoslovakia
Crew:	1 + 1
Weight:	5350kg (11,800lb)
Dimensions:	Length: 6.91m (22.67ft); width: 2.31m (7.58ft); height: 2.92m (9.58ft)
Range:	500km (310 miles)
Armour:	None
Armament:	None
Powerplant:	1 x Tatra T-912 6-cylinder diesel, developing 98hp (73kW)
Performance:	Maximum road speed: 62km/h (38mph)

Ford G398 SAM

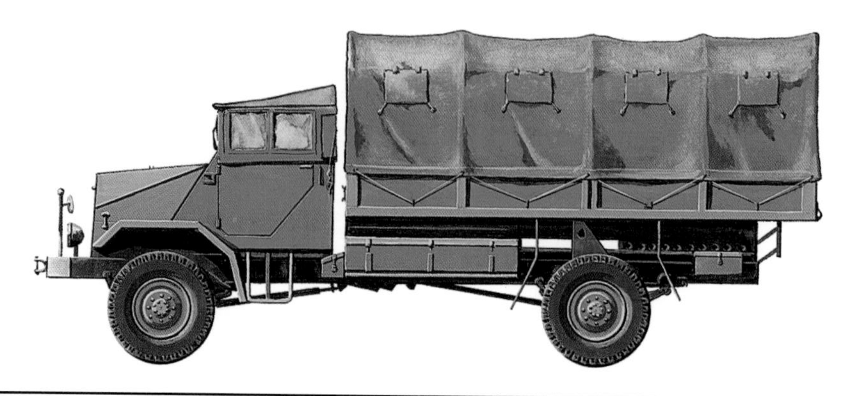

The Ford G398 SAM was part of the German Federal Armed Forces vehicle-procurement initiative after World War II. Like many designs for the cash-strapped force, the G398 was a modification of an existing design. However, of all the vehicles modified for service, the G398 was the one which gave least satisfaction. At its most basic, the G398 had an open cab for three crew, a hinged windshield, and a simple plank-bed cargo area. Some 5446 of these vehicles were produced between 1957 and 1961. A further 2582 were manufactured with enclosed cargo areas in various configurations. The G398 was high on fuel consumption and had poor, even dangerous, road handling and was quickly discontinued as a result.

Country of origin:	West Germany
Crew:	1 + 2
Weight:	7480kg (16,500lb)
Dimensions:	Length: 7.25m (23.79ft); width: 2.24m (7.35ft); height: 3.14m (10.3ft)
Range:	280km (175 miles)
Armour:	None
Armament:	None
Powerplant:	1 Ford G28T 8-cylinder petrol, developing 91hp (68kW)
Performance:	Maximum road speed: 85km/h (53mph)

M274 Mechanical Mule

The M274 Mechanical Mule was a dimunitive utility vehicle developed by Willys for US forces in the mid-1950s. Its was designed to transport ammunition, personnel, cargo and heavy infantry weapons. The Mule satisfied this requirement admirably, being able to carry a 450kg (1000lb) cargo on a small flatbed area behind the driver, who was seated on the left of the vehicle. While the A1 version had a four-cylinder petrol engine, later models had a two-cylinder powerplant. The materials used to make the Mule varied. Some were made from steel, others from aluminium or magnesium alloy. All models had four-wheel drive and most (the A5 being the exception) had four-wheel steer.

Country of origin:	United States
Crew:	1
Weight:	380kg (840lb)
Dimensions:	Length: 2.98m (9.78ft); width: 1.78m (5.84ft); height: 1.19m (3.9ft)
Range:	180km (110 miles)
Armour:	None
Armament:	None
Powerplant:	1 x Willys A053 4-cylinder petrol, developing 21hp (16kW)
Performance:	Maximum road speed: 40km/h (25mph)

MAN 630 L2

The MAN 630 L2 was one of the first logistical vehicles manufactured within Germany to equip the newly formed German Federal Armed Forces, the Bundeswehr. It is also one of the longest serving, with isolated examples still in use today (though the replacement for the 630 was officially completed during the 1990s). The basic vehicle in 1958 and 1959 had a cab-behind-engine configuration, was a 4x4 and featured a one-piece plank cargo bed 4.5m (14.8ft) long. Load-carrying capacity was around five tons. It was designed with a MAN D1243 MV3A/W multi-fuel engine which could burn diesel, petrol, kerosene and even waste-fuel mixtures (though impure fuels could adversely affect power output).

Country of origin:	West Germany
Crew:	1 + 2
Weight:	13,000kg (28,700lb)
Dimensions:	Length: 7.9m (25.9ft); width: 2.5m (8.2ft); height: 2.84m (9.32ft)
Range:	420km (260 miles)
Armour:	None
Armament:	None
Powerplant:	1 x MAN D1243 MV3A/W 4-cylinder multi-fuel, developing 130hp (97kW)
Performance:	Maximum road speed: 66km/h (41mph)

Daimler-Benz Unimog S 404 B

The Unimog S 404 B was a 1955 addition to a series of vehicles which entered development in 1946. 'Unimog' stands for Universal Motor Geräf, and the first of these general utility vehicles was put into production in the late 1940s. The basic Unimog vehicle was a 4x4 light truck carrying payloads of 1250–5000kg (2800–11,000lb). A 6x6 Unimog was also produced, which could carry a 8000kg (17,600lb) load. The S 404 B version was the standard 4x4 vehicle with a load-carrying capacity of 2300kg (5100lb). Some 65,000 vehicles have been produced, 35,000 of which went to the German armed forces. Modern Unimog variants are still in production today.

Country of origin:	West Germany
Crew:	2 + 8
Weight:	2910kg (6417lb)
Dimensions:	Length: 5m (16.4ft); width: 2.05m (6.73ft); height: 2.74m (8.99ft)
Range:	570km (350 miles)
Armour:	None
Armament:	None
Powerplant:	1 x Daimler-Benz m 180/II 6-cylinder petrol, developing 80hp (60kW)
Performance:	Maximum road speed: 95km/h (59mph)

Ural-375D

Production of the Ural-375 series truck began in 1961. The most numerous version of the truck was the 375D. The truck was equipped with an all-steel, fully enclosed cab (an improvement on the initial 375 design) and, like most Soviet vehicles, carried a pre-heater for the engine to deal with the cold climate found in Russia. A tyre-pressure regulation system ensured that the truck was capable of carrying considerable weights cross-country. Variants included a recovery truck, fuel truck and one adapted especially for service in the tropics. The TMS-65 was a version designed as a decontamination vehicle. The body was replaced by a modified jet engine and decontamination liquid tanks. Vehicles were decontaminated by being driven slowly past while the jet was in operation.

Country of origin:	USSR
Crew:	1 + 2
Weight:	12,400kg (27,280lb)
Dimensions:	length 7.35m (24ft 1.4in); width 2.69m (8ft 9.9in); height 2.68m (8ft 9.5in)
Range:	650km (404 miles)
Armour:	none
Armament:	none
Powerplant:	one ZIL-375 V-8 petrol engine developing 180hp (134.2kW)
Performance:	maximum road speed 75km/h (47mph); fording 1.0m (3ft 3.4in)

M520 GOER

The GOER was based on vehicles designed for the civil construction industry in the 1950s. The designs attracted army interest and were adapted to fulfil battlefield requirements. The first production GOERs were delivered in 1964. They were soon deployed to South Vietnam, where their excellent cross-country mobility, especially in the rainy season where normal 6 x 6 trucks fared badly, prompted the US Army to expand their use. Despite being the heaviest truck then in use with the US Army, the vehicle was fully amphibious. Unusually, it had no suspension, relying on its huge tyres to absorb the shock. The vehicle has a windscreen and a removable canvas top with removable side curtains. Variants included a fuel tanker and a recovery vehicle. Around 1300 of all types of GOER were delivered by 1976.

Country of origin:	United States
Crew:	1 + 1
Weight:	18,500kg (40,700lb)
Dimensions:	length 9.753m (32ft 0in); width 2.743m (9ft 0in); height 3.404m (11ft 2in)
Range:	660km (410 miles)
Armour:	none
Armament:	none
Powerplant:	one Caterpillar D333 six-cylinder turbocharged diesel engine developing 213hp (158.8kW)
Performance:	maximum road speed 48.3km/h (30mph); fording amphibious

Faun L912/45A

Fahrzeugfabriken Ansbach und Nürnberg (Faun) was born in Germany in 1918, though the company traces its history back to 1845, when the constituent companies began manufacturing horse-drawn or steam-powered fire-fighting vehicles. The L912/45A was born from Faun's post-World War II reconstruction. Remarkably for such a small company, Faun secured orders with the German Federal Armed Forces for logistics vehicles in the 10 to 12-ton class, of which the L912 series was one. The L912/45A was a three-axle 6x6 truck distinguished by a long cab and a short wheelbase. It was designed for heavy cargo transportation (up to 15 tons) or use as an artillery tractor pulling 155mm (6.1in) field howitzers.

Country of origin:	West Germany
Crew:	1 + 2
Weight:	15,000kg (33,100lb)
Dimensions:	Length: 7.65m (25.09ft); width: 2.5m (8.2ft); height: 2.77m (9.09ft)
Range:	660km (410 miles)
Armour:	None
Armament:	None
Powerplant:	1 x Deutz F12 L714a 12-cylinder multi-fuel, developing 264hp (197kW)
Performance:	Maximum road speed: 77km/h (48mph)

Stalwart

The Stalwart High Mobility Load Carrier comes from the same family as the Saracen armoured personnel carrier and the Saladin armoured car, and uses many of the same basic components as those vehicles. The Stalwart is fully amphibious and has excellent cross-country performance. In the water it is driven by two marine jets. It can carry up to half a tonne (0.4 tons) of cargo. Its main role is to supply the rest of the battle group with fuel and ammunition. Alternatively, the stalwart can be adapted to carry up to 30 fully equipped soldiers. The engine is under the cargo area, and the engine drive is taken through a twin dry plate clutch and five-speed gearbox to the transfer box with a no-spin differential. The driver is positioned in the centre of the cab with a single passenger sea either side.

Country of origin:	United Kingdom
Crew:	1
Weight:	14,480kg (31,856lb)
Dimensions:	length 6.36m (20ft 10in); width 2.6m (8ft 6in); height 2.64m (8ft 8in)
Range:	515km (322 miles)
Armour:	none
Armament:	none (basic version)
Powerplant:	one Rolls-Royce B-81 Mk 8B eight-cylinder water-cooled petrol engine developing 220hp (164kW)
Performance:	maximum road speed 63km/h (39.37mph); fording amphibious

Fiat 6605

The Fiat 6605 stemmed from Italian development of a medium artillery tractor in the 1960s. The 6 x 6 6605 was subsequently adapted by the Italian Army to tow such heavy artillery pieces as the 155m howitzer. Known as the TM69, the vehicle had a very long cab which extended back to the centre of the chassis, carrying both the crew and the gun detachment. Charges, projectiles and general stores were kept in separate compartments within the hull for safety reasons, and a winch was fitted as standard. Variants included a cargo-carrying version with a hydraulic crane fitted at the rear of the cab, and a recovery version with telescopic crane and stabilisers. In addition to seeing service with the Italian Army, the Fiat 6605 series was exported to Libya and Somalia.

Country of origin:	Italy
Crew:	1 + 11
Weight:	17,000kg (37,400lb)
Dimensions:	length 7.33m (24ft 0.6in); width 2.50m (8ft 2.4in); height (cab) 2.92m (9ft 7in)
Range:	700km (435 miles)
Armour:	none
Armament:	none
Powerplant:	one FIAT Model 8212.02.500 six-cylinder diesel engine developing 219hp (163.3kW)
Performance:	maximum road speed 78km/h (48mph); fording 1.5m (4ft 11in)

Tatra T813

Developed in the 1960s, the Tatra T 813 range of vehicles included cargo trucks and prime movers for artillery systems. The basic cargo truck had an unusual four-door fully enclosed cab which was fitted with a nuclear, biological and chemical (NBC) defence system. Four-wheel power-steering and tyre-pressure regulation system were standard, giving impressive cross-country mobility. All vehicles were fitted with a winch for recovery of other vehicles, or to haul themselves out of trouble and some were fitted with a hydraulic dozer blade on the front. As well as moving cargo and towing artillery systems, the vehicle was also used as the basis for the M1972 122mm multiple rocket launcher. The vehicle saw service with Libya and East Germany, in addition to the Czech Army.

Country of origin:	Czechoslovakia
Crew:	1 + 6
Weight:	22,000kg (48,400lb)
Dimensions:	length 8.75m (28ft 8.5in); width 2.50m (8ft 2.4in); height 2.69m (8ft 9.9in)
Range:	1000km (621 miles)
Armour:	none
Armament:	none
Powerplant:	one Tatra T-930-3 12-cylinder diesel engine developing 250hp (186.4kW)
Performance:	maximum road speed 80km/h (50mph); fording 1.4m (4ft 7in)

ACMAT VLRA

ACMAT has based their vehicle design on the premise that for full reliability, a military truck must be able to fulfil all requirements while remaining as simple as possible. The VLRA family of trucks all use the same tyres, axles and wheels to avoid the need for carrying different types of spares. All vehicles have long-range fuel tanks and sand channels for desert operations. The trucks can be fitted with a wide range of weapons including machine guns, mortars or Milan anti-tank guided weapons. The command and control version, the TPK 4.20 VCT, is fitted with extensive communications equipment and the many other variants include a fire-fighting truck and a type of armoured personnel carrier. Reliable and durable, the ACMAT VLRA is in service with more than 30 countries worldwide.

Country of origin:	France
Crew:	1 + 2
Weight:	6800kg (14,960lb)
Dimensions:	length 6.00m (19ft 8.2in); width 2.07m (6ft 9.5in); height 1.83m (6ft)
Range:	1600km (1000 miles)
Armour:	none
Armament:	basic version – none. Optional 7.62mm machine gun; Milan anti-tank weapon; 60mm mortar; twin 20mm anti-aircraft cannon
Powerplant:	one Perkins Model 6.354.4 diesel engine developing 120hp (89.5kW)
Performance:	maximum road speed 100km/h (62mph); fording 0.9m (2ft 11.4in)

ACMAT TPK 6.40

The ACMAT TPK 6.40 is part of a vast range of ACMAT utility vehicles developed on the basis of the ACMAT VLRA (Véhicule de Liaison, de Reconnaissance et d'Appui). VLRA vehicles come in either 4x4 or 6x6 versions. At the start of the range is the TPK 4.20, a two-ton vehicle which itself has radio command post, armoured personnel carrier and ambulance variants to name but a few. The TPK 6.40 is a much larger variant of the VRLA, with an unladen weight of 5700kg (12,600lb) and the capacity to carry over 4300kg (9500lb) of cargo, or 21 fully equipped soldiers. It has six variants including a tar spreader and a 4000-litre (880-gal) water carrier for fire-fighting support. ACMAT trucks have sold to over 30 countries worldwide.

Country of origin:	France
Crew:	3 + 21
Weight:	5700kg (12,600lb)
Dimensions:	Length: 6.94m (22.77ft); width: 2.25m (7.38ft); height: 2.64m (8.66ft)
Range:	1600km (1000 miles)
Armour:	None
Armament:	None as standard, though MGs optional
Powerplant:	1 x Perkins 6.354.4 diesel, developing 138hp (103kW)
Performance:	Maximum road speed: 85km/h (53mph)

Steyr 680 M3

The original Steyr 680 M vehicle was a fairly conventional 4x4 truck. It had a cab-over-engine configuration with an observation hatch in the cab roof (this accepted a machine gun on a pintle mount if desired). It could carry a 4.5-ton load or 20 soldiers sat on bench seats. Though the 680 M was a perfectly acceptable vehicle – many are still in use today – it had inadequate off-road performance. The Steyr 680 M3 resolved this. It was a larger 6x6 truck with independent suspension fitted to all wheels. Load-carrying capacity remained unchanged, but cross-country mobility was greatly improved. A 4.5-ton capacity winch was also fitted in the front of the vehicle.

Country of origin:	Austria
Crew:	1 + 17
Weight:	6500kg (14,300lb)
Dimensions:	Length: 6.73m (22.1ft); width: 2.4m (7.87ft); height: 2.63m (8.63ft)
Range:	500km (310 miles)
Armour:	None
Armament:	None (see text)
Powerplant:	1 x Steyr WD 610.74 6-cylinder diesel, developing 164hp (122kW)
Performance:	Maximum road speed: 80km/h (50mph)

GAZ-66

The GAZ-66 has been yet another successful Soviet truck, running in production from 1964 until the present day. It is a 4x4 vehicle with a two-ton cargo capacity and a reputation for rugged reliability. Its engine is the same as that used in the GAZ-53, the ZMZ-66 8-cylinder overhead-valve diesel, providing 113hp (85kW). The basic GAZ-66 acts as the framework for many different specialist and utility vehicles, including engineer vehicles, troop transporters, and even a mobile NBC decontamination centre when fitted with the DDA-53C or DDA-66 decontamination unit. Modern versions like the GAZ-66-40 have special engines which allow them to operate at heights of 4500m (14,800ft) above sea level.

Country of origin:	USSR
Crew:	2
Weight:	3470kg (7650lb)
Dimensions:	Length: 5.8m (19.02ft); width: 2.32m (7.61ft); height: 2.44m (8ft)
Range:	800km (500 miles)
Armour:	None
Armament:	None
Powerplant:	1 x ZMZ-66 8-cylinder diesel, developing 113hp (85kW)
Performance:	Maximum road speed: 90km/h (56mph)

ZIL-131

The ZIL-131 entered production in 1966 as the replacement for the ZIL-157. Capable of carrying up to 0.4 tonnes (0.4 tons) cross-country and towing about the same amount, the vehicle was fitted with a tyre-pressure regulation system as standard. Also standard was a 4.5-tonnes (4.4-tons) winch. The cab was fully enclosed with a heated engine, while the cargo area at the rear had drop sides and a drop tail-gate. In addition to cargo carrying, the truck was widely used to tow 122m guns, and the chassis was used for mounting multiple rocket launchers such as the 122mm BM-21. Variants included a dump truck, fuel tanker (including the MA-41 tanker which carried diesel, water, oil and petrol in specially heated tanks to refuel vehicles even in the coldest weather) and decontamination vehicle.

Country of origin:	USSR
Crew:	1 + 2
Weight:	10,425kg (22,935lb)
Dimensions:	length 7.04m (23ft 1.2in); width 2.50m (8ft 2.4in); height (cab) 2.48m (8ft 1.6in)
Range:	525km (326 miles)
Armour:	none
Armament:	none
Powerplant:	one ZIL-131 V-8 petrol engine developing 150hp (111.9kW)
Performance:	maximum road speed 80km/h (50mph); fording 1.4m (4ft 7.1in)

Berliet GBU 15

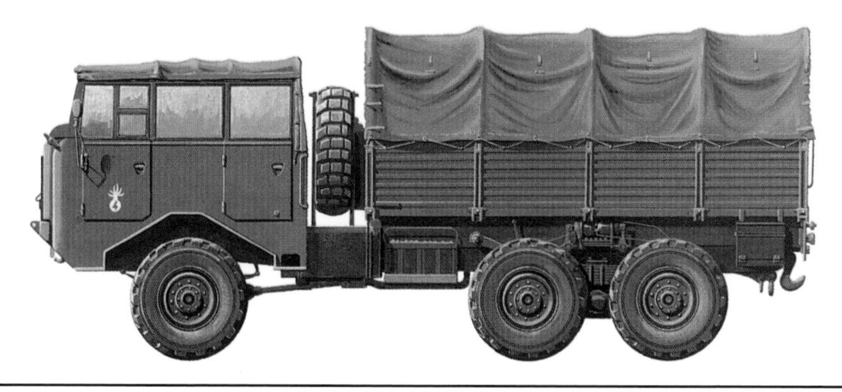

For nearly a quarter of a century up to the mid-1980s, the Berliet GBU 15 was the standard 6 x 6 heavy truck of the French Army. It was capable of carrying a cross-country load of up to six tonnes (5.9 tons), and was capable of towing a load of up to 15 tonnes (14.8 tons). The engine was housed under the unusual four-door cab, which has a removable top and windscreen. The vehicle was able to run a variety of fuels including petrol, paraffin, JP4, gas oil, light fuel and mineral or vegetable oils in the lower power ranges. A winch was fitted as standard, which has a lifting capacity of 8000kg (17,600lb). As well as normal cargo-carrying duties, the GBU 15 was used to tow the 155mm Model 1950 howitzer. Variants included an artillery tractor, fuel tanker and recovery vehicle.

Country of origin:	France
Crew:	1 + 3
Weight:	20,500kg (45,100lb)
Dimensions:	length 7.974m (26ft 1.9in); width 2.50m (8ft 2.4in); height (cab) 3.00m (9ft 10.1in)
Range:	800km (497 miles)
Armour:	none
Armament:	none
Powerplant:	one Berliet six-cylinder multi-fuel engine developing 214hp (159.6kW)
Performance:	maximum road speed 75km/h (46.6mph); fording 1m (3ft 3in)

Bedford MK

Following a competition in the 1960s to find a successor to the Bedford RL (which continued in service up until the 1980s), Vauxhall was selected to build the Bedford MK based on the civilian 4 x 2 TK truck. Military modifications included a new engine, all-wheel drive and bigger wheels. The vehicle has an all-steel fully enclosed cab with a mounting for an anti-aircraft machine gun. The chassis is of the ladder type with six cross-members, two of the 'alligator jaw' design. Optional extras included a winch and rear dual wheels, while seats can be inserted in the centre of the cargo area for carrying passengers. The vehicles were used for carrying specialist repair systems, as recovery vehicles, for carrying portable trackways and general cargo-carrying duties.

Country of origin:	United Kingdom
Crew:	1 + 1
Weight:	9650kg (21,230lb)
Dimensions:	length 6.579m (21ft 7in); width 2.489m (8ft 2in); height (cab) 3.404m (11ft 2in)
Range:	560km (348 miles)
Armour:	none
Armament:	none
Powerplant:	one Bedford six-cylinder diesel engine developing 103hp (76.8kW)
Performance:	maximum road speed 77km/h (48mph); fording 0.76m (2ft 6in)

KrAZ-255B

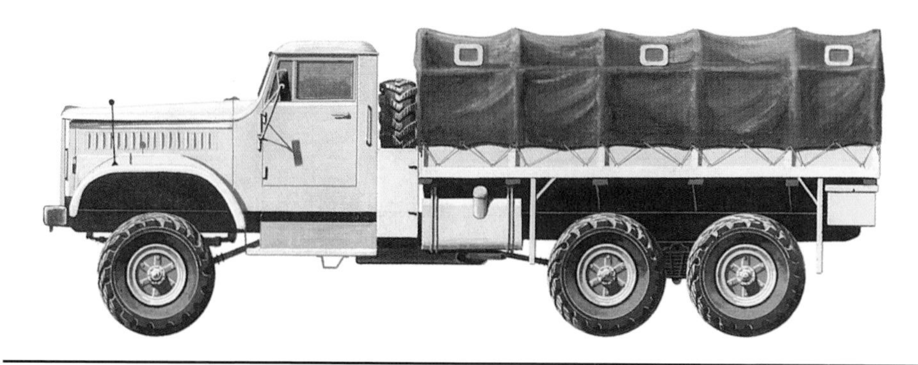

The KrAZ-255B replaced one of the standard trucks of the Soviet Army, the KrAZ-214, production of which ceased in 1967. The main improvements of the later vehicle were increased payload, a more powerful engine and the installation of a tyre-pressure regulation system to improve mobility. The 255B was used for a wide range of specialised roles, such as carrying engineers' cranes, laying the TMM treadway bridge and launching the PMP heavy floating pontoon bridge system. Other engineer versions included an excavator truck, fuel tanker, tractor truck and a USM pile driving set used for constructing bridges. The layout of the vehicle is conventional, with the engine at the front, two-door fully enclosed cab in the centre and the cargo area at the rear which could be covered with tarpaulin (as here).

Country of origin:	USSR
Crew:	1 + 2
Weight:	19,450kg (42,790lb)
Dimensions:	length 8.645m (28ft 4.4in); width 2.75m (9ft 0.3in); height (cab) 2.94m (9ft 7.75in)
Range:	650km (404 miles)
Armour:	none
Armament:	none
Powerplant:	one YaMZ-238 V-8 diesel engine developing 240hp (179kW)
Performance:	maximum road speed 71km/h (44mph); fording 0.85m (2ft 10in)

M813

The M813 was part of the M809 family, all-based on a standard chassis, which entered production in 1970. This in turn was a development of the M54 series, the first range of trucks to be produced for the US Army after World War II. Capable of carrying 4.5 tonnes (4.4 tons) of cargo cross-country, and towing considerably more, the vehicle proved a durable workhorse. It was the standard vehicle in its class in use with US forces until being replaced in the 1980s by the M939. It had foldable seats in the rear which allowed up to 26 troops to be carried. Optional equipment included a deep-fording kit, essential when used by the US Marine Corps in amphibious operations, a winch and special cold-weather equipment. As well as a cargo carrier, the vehicle was used to tow artillery and various missiles.

Country of origin:	United States
Crew:	1 + 2
Weight:	14,294kg (31,446lb)
Dimensions:	length 7.645m (25ft 1in); width 2.464m (8ft 1in); height 2.946m (9ft 8in)
Range:	563km (350 miles)
Armour:	none
Armament:	(optional) one 0.5in anti-aircraft machine gun
Powerplant:	one NHC-250 six-cylinder diesel engine developing 240hp (179.0kW)
Performance:	maximum road speed 85km/h (53mph); fording 0.76m (2ft 6in)

Tatra T 148

The Tatra T 148 is another workhorse vehicle to emerge from the Eastern Bloc during the 1970s. It is far larger than the Praga V3S, weighing in at 25,640kg (56,540lb) fully loaded of which 14,580kg (32,150lb) is payload. To handle such weights, the vehicle uses a Tatra 2-928-1 eight-cylinder diesel engine with direct fuel injection, producing a slightly better road speed than the Praga V3S (71km/h/44mph). The T 148 uses three different brake systems to stop: (1) a pressurized airbrake which acts on all the wheels of the vehicle, including trailer wheels; (2) a mechanically applied emergency and parking brake; and (3) an exhaust brake which closes off the exhaust to increase the braking effect.

Country of origin:	Czechoslovakia
Crew:	1 + 2
Weight:	25,640kg (56,536lb) fully loaded
Dimensions:	Length: 9m (29.53ft); width: 2.5m (8.2ft); height: 2.44m (8ft)
Range:	500km (310 miles)
Armour:	None
Armament:	None
Powerplant:	1 x Tatra 2-928-1 8-cylinder diesel, developing 211hp (158kW)
Performance:	Maximum road speed: 71km/h (44mph)

BAZ-135 TZM

The DR-3 unmanned aerial reconnaissance vehicle (UAV) was developed by the Tupolev aircraft company in the early 1970s. It is launched from the back of an 8x8 BAZ-135 TZM transloader vehicle. The UAV is contained in a cylindrical container mounted on the back of the lorry. This is raised to an angle of around 35 degrees for launching, a booster jet ejecting the UAV from the container for 550m (1800ft) before the DR-3's main jet ignites. The DR-3 flies for 150km (90 miles) at which point the main engine cuts out and the aircraft descends to earth by parachute. Intelligence is gathered by a PA-1 wet-film camera or a Chibis-B television camera mounted in the nose at the aircraft.

Country of origin:	USSR
Crew:	3
Weight:	15,000kg (33,100lb)
Dimensions:	Length: 11.5m (37.73ft); width: 3m (9.84ft); height: 3.35m (11ft)
Range:	500km (310 miles)
Armour:	Not applicable
Armament:	Not applicable
Powerplant:	2 x ZIL-375 8-cylinder petrol, each developing 177hp (132kW)
Performance:	Maximum road speed: 70km/h (43mph)

Oshkosh M911

Realising that using the combination of the M746 vehicle towing the M747 semi-trailer for transporting tanks was unnecessarily complicated and expensive, the US Army issued a requirement for a simpler, cheaper vehicle in 1976. The Oshkosh F2365 civilian truck was selected and designated the M911. A total of 747 were eventually delivered to the US Army, with a small number being exported to Thailand. Tanks are loaded with the help of two winches mounted to the rear of the cab, unusually, the M911 is an 8 x 6 vehicle, with the second axle being lowered to the ground when heavy loads are carried. Standard equipment for the cab includes an adjustable seat for the driver, heater and defroster. The brakes have a dual air supply system, one for the front and one for the rear axles.

Country of origin:	United States
Crew:	1 + 2
Weight:	39,917kg (87,818lb)
Dimensions:	length 9.38m (30ft 9in); width 2.89m (9ft 6in); height 3.658m (12ft)
Range:	990km (619 miles)
Armour:	none
Armament:	none
Powerplant:	one Detroit-Diesel model 8V-92TA-90 V-8 diesel engine developing 450hp (335kW)
Performance:	maximum road speed 71km/h (44.37mph); fording 1.0711m (3ft 6in)

KAMAZ-4310

The KAMAZ-4310 derived from the civilian three-axle 6x6 KAMAZ-5320. In the late 1970s, this vehicle was modified for military use and renamed the KAMAZ-4310. The KAMAZ-4310 has proved itself an excellent logistics vehicle with a 6000kg (13,200lb) cargo capacity and a rugged off-road ability. It retains the 5320's 6x6 configuration, with all axles power-driven, and the central tyre-pressure regulation system ensures smooth travelling over the roughest of surfaces. Other features include a self-recovery winch. The 4310 comes in many variants, including the tanker version shown here. A more recent model – the 43114 – has seen the power plant upgraded from 206hp (154kW) to 260hp (194kW).

Country of origin:	USSR
Crew:	3
Weight:	15,000kg (33,100lb)
Dimensions:	Length: 7.9m (25.92ft); width: 2.5m (8.2ft); height: 3.09m (10.14ft)
Range:	Not available
Armour:	None
Armament:	None
Powerplant:	1 x YaMZ-740 8-cylinder diesel, developing 206hp (154kW)
Performance:	Maximum road speed: 85km/h (53mph)

Ural-4320B

The Uralsky Avtozavod OAO company has manufactured 1.2 million trucks since it was founded in November 1941. The first of the 6x6 Ural-4320 series came much later in 1977, and had a seven-ton carrying capacity or a towing strength of 18.5 tons. Durable and dependable, the 4320 quickly established itself as the market leader and the company began to add a string of variants and upgrades. The Ural-4320B entered production in 1983. It is a modern 6x6 vehicle designed for carrying cargo, people or towing trailers. Its maximum load is 5000kg (11,000lb) or 27 soldiers, who can be seated in the cargo compartment. Its body is fully armoured against small-arms fire up to 12.7mm (0.5in).

Country of origin:	USSR
Crew:	2 + 27
Weight:	15,000kg (33,100lb) fully loaded
Dimensions:	Length: 7.6m (24.93ft); width: 2.7m (8.86ft); height: 2.8m (9.19ft)
Range:	1000km (620 miles)
Armour:	Details classified
Armament:	None
Powerplant:	1 x YamAZ-238M2 8-cylinder diesel, developing 236hp (176kW)
Performance:	Maximum road speed: 82km/h (51mph)

DAF YA 4440

DAF produced around 4000 YA 4440 trucks for the Dutch Army between 1977 and 1980 for the initial order, and have continued to supply the Dutch since with several thousand more. Essentially a civilian truck, the YA 4440 has been modified for military use. The all-steel cab has a reinforced roof so that a machine gun can be mounted for anti-aircraft defence. The suspension comprises double-acting hydraulic shock absorbers to help with cross-country driving. The engine is mounted at the front of the chassis and power is transmitted to the two-speed transfer box via the five-speed synchromesh transmission. Optional equipment includes a manual crane and hydraulic crane (stabilisers are fitted to the sides and must be lowered when the crane is in use).

Country of origin:	Netherlands
Crew:	1 + 1
Weight:	10,900kg (23,980lb)
Dimensions:	length 7.19m (23ft 7.1in); width 2.44m (8ft); height (tarpaulin cover) 3.42m (11ft 2.6in)
Range:	500km (331 miles)
Armour:	none
Armament:	(optional) one 7.62mm machine gun
Powerplant:	one DAF DT615 six-cylinder turbocharged diesel engine developing 153hp (114.1kW)
Performance:	maximum road speed 80km/h (50mph); fording 0.9m (2ft 11.4in)

Foden 8 x 4

The Foden is a low-mobility truck, adapted from a civilian design and minimally modified to suit military requirements (the emphasis being on ease of maintenance). They were used mainly for carrying heavy cargo over long distances, the cargo being deployed to more mobile vehicles close to the point of use. For example, they were often used to transport cargo from the Channel ports to bases in West Germany before the unification of Germany. Typically the truck carried up to 6 tonnes (5.9 tons). Variants included two types of fuel tanker and a tipper truck for the Royal Engineers. In addition, some basic models were fitted with the French Ampliroll system, which allowed a vehicle to be quickly adapted for a number of roles such as tanker or armoured car transport.

Country of origin:	United Kingdom
Crew:	1 + 2
Weight:	27,000kg (59,400lb)
Dimensions:	length 10.287m (33ft 9in); width 2.489m (8ft 2in); height 3.327m (10ft 11in)
Range:	499km (310 miles)
Armour:	nonen
Armament:	none
Powerplant:	one Rolls-Royce 220 Mk 111 six-cylinder diesel engine developing 220hp (164.1kW)
Performance:	maximum road speed 76km/h (47mph); fording 0.914m (3ft 0in)

Sisu A-45

Sisu-Auto AB was a natural choice to fulfil the Finnish Army's requirement for a rugged truck capable of carrying considerable loads cross-country, as the company was well used to building trucks for the exacting local climate and terrain. The vehicle is unusual in having a steel lower cab but fibre glass upper. This is useful for airborne operations as it can be dismantled and reassembled quickly. The cargo body is attached to the chassis by special rubber mountings which give greater flexibility and thus reduce wear and tear. The vehicle can be fitted with a winch for vehicle recovery, or to drag itself out of trouble, and the engine has a special heater to cope with the extreme cold in Finland. The cargo area can be fitted with bows and a tarpaulin cover if required.

Country of origin:	Finland
Crew:	1 + 2
Weight:	9000kg (19,800lb)
Dimensions:	length 6.00m (19ft 8.2in); width 2.30m (7ft 6.6in); height (cab) 2.60m (8ft 6.4in)
Range:	700km (435 miles)
Armour:	none
Armament:	none
Powerplant:	one six-cylinder diesel engine developing 130hp (96.9kW) or turbocharged diesel, developing 160hp (119.3kW)
Performance:	maximum road speed 100km/h (62mph); fording 1.0m (3ft 3.4in)

KAMAZ-5320

KAMAZ-5320 trucks are general-purpose logistics vehicles from the Kama Motor Vehicle Plant at Naberezhynye Chelmy. They are simple 6x6 vehicles with a cab-over-engine configuration and an all-steel cargo unit (usually covered with a tarpaulin). Maximum road-load capacity is 8000kg (17,600lb), dropping to 6000kg (13,200lb) when travelling cross-country. The cargo unit folds down at the rear and the sides. Kama has also produced the 5320 in 8x8 and 6x4 configurations. KAMAZ-5320 vehicles are still in production and are as prevalent in civilian use as in military use (including applications as civilian passenger buses). Naturally there are numerous variants including a 6x4 fuel tanker, grain trucks and even milk tankers.

Country of origin:	USSR
Crew:	3
Weight:	7080kg (15,611lb)
Dimensions:	Length: 7.44m (24.41ft); width: 2.51m (8.23ft); height: 2.83m (8.28ft)
Range:	485km (300 miles)
Armour:	None
Armament:	None
Powerplant:	1 x YaMZ-740 8-cylinder diesel, developing 209hp (156kW)
Performance:	Maximum road speed: 85km/h (53mph)

Faun SLT 50-2 Elefant

The Faun SLT 50-2 Elefant is, as its name suggests, a massive vehicle capable of hauling a Leopard 2 main battle tank, which weighs 54,981kg (120,960lb). Such a load takes the vehicle's maximum weight up to 107,400kg (236,800lb). Faun GmbH is one of the world's largest producers of military cranes and haulage vehicles and the Elefant, as well as the SaZgM FS 42 Fransziska (also by Faun), are the German Army's main tank transporters. An 8x8 configuration is used in conjunction with an eight-axled semi-trailer to support the load. The Elefant relies on an MTU MB8837 Ea500 engine to draw its enormous load, with a power output of 729hp (544kW). Faun has recently introduced a new tank transporter, the MLC 100.

Country of origin:	West Germany
Crew:	1 + 3
Weight:	107,400kg (236,800lb) maximum loaded weight
Dimensions:	Length with trailer: 18.97m (62.24ft); width: 3.05m (10.01ft); height: 3.24m (10.63ft)
Range:	600km (370 miles)
Armour:	None
Armament:	1 x 7.62mm (0.3in) MG
Powerplant:	1 x MTU MB8837 Ea500 8-cylinder diesel, developing 729hp (544kW)
Performance:	Maximum road speed: 65km/h (40mph)

Bedford TM

The TM 4-4 was developed following a British Army request for a medium-mobility 4 x 4 truck to be based on a proven commercial chassis. Bedford delivered the first of over 2000 vehicles in 1981, with Marshall providing the rear cargo body. There were four basic models: the basic cargo vehicle; basic cargo with winch; cargo with Atlas hydraulic crane; and a tipper truck, this having a shorter wheelbase than the other versions. Military modifications included an observation hatch in the roof and a mounting for a machine gun for anti-aircraft defence. As well as seeing service with the British Army, the vehicle was exported to a number of countries including Oman, Abu Dhabi and Bahrain. Like all Bedford vehicles, this truck is rugged and able to operate in varied climatic and terrain conditions.

Country of origin:	United Kingdom
Crew:	1 + 1
Weight:	16,300kg (35,860lb)
Dimensions:	length 6.629m (21ft 9in); width 2.489m (8ft 2in); height (cab) 2.997m (9ft 10in)
Range:	499km (310 miles)
Armour:	none
Armament:	(optional) one 7.62mm machine gun
Powerplant:	one Bedford turbocharged diesel engine developing 206hp (153.6kW)
Performance:	maximum road speed 93km/h (58mph); fording 0.762m (2ft 6in)

Pegaso 3055

In 1982, the Spanish Army selected the Pegaso 3055 to be the successor to the 3050 as the standard military truck in its class. The vehicle is fitted with a removable canvas hood and fold-down windscreen which facilitates air transport (there is an optional metal top to the cab). The Pegaso 3055 is able to carry six tonnes (5.9 tons) of cargo cross-country and almost double that on roads. The many variants include a tractor truck, recovery and crane trucks, a fuel tanker, dump truck and fire-fighting vehicle. The vehicle is also used to tow field artillery. When used as a personnel carrier, there is capacity for up to 30 fully equipped infantrymen. The current version of the Pegaso 3055 is the longer-wheelbase Model 7323, which is powered by a Pegaso naturally aspiring diesel engine.

Country of origin:	Spain
Crew:	1 + 1
Weight:	15,000kg (33,000lb)
Dimensions:	length 6.956m (22ft 9.8in); width 2.406m (7ft 10.7in); height 2.765m (9ft 0.9in)
Range:	550km (342 miles)
Armour:	none
Armament:	none
Powerplant:	one Pegaso Model 10 six-cylinder naturally aspirated diesel engine developing 220hp (164kW)
Performance:	maximum road speed 80km/h (50mph); fording 1.0m (3ft 3in)

Oshkosh HEMTT

Following a US Army requirement for a Heavy Expanded Mobility Tactical Truck (HEMTT), Oshkosh was selected to produce around 5000 vehicles to be delivered over a five-year period. The first production vehicles arrived in 1982, but problems occurred due to a lack of proper testing. The problems were soon overcome, though, and the truck saw service with US forces in West Germany and South Korea as well as within the United States itself. To keep down development costs, the truck used many standard commercial automotive parts. The basic model came fitted with a winch and cargo crane. Variants included a fuel tanker, and a tractor truck as well as a recovery truck which has a cargo platform between the second and third axle for carrying spare parts. Some 4536 vehicles have been funded.

Country of origin:	United States
Crew:	1 + 1
Weight:	28,123kg (61,870lb)
Dimensions:	length 10.16m (33ft 4in); width 2.39m (7ft 10in); height (cab) 2.565m (8ft 5in)
Range:	483km (300 miles)
Armour:	none
Armament:	none
Powerplant:	one Detroit-Diesel Model 8V-92TA V-8 diesel engine developing 445hp (331.8kW)
Performance:	maximum road speed 88km/h (55mph); fording 1.524m (5ft 0in)

Oshkosh PLS

The Oshkosk Palletized Load System (PLS) is a heavy load-carrying system fitted to the Oshkosh High Expanded Mobility Tactical Truck (HEMTT). Since the US Army placed a large order in 1981, HEMTT has become a principal US military transport vehicle with over 11,000 units in use. The basic HEMTT vehicle is an 8x8 M977 with a maximum cargo capacity of 11,840kg (26,100lb). PLS vehicles differ by having an extra axle, making a 10x10 configuration. The vehicle works with a variety of trailers and flat-track load-carrying systems. Using an M1076 three-axle trailer, for example, the PLS can add an additional 16.5 tons to its load, with a combined truck and trailer payload of 33 tons.

Country of origin:	United States
Crew:	2
Weight:	17,600kg (38,800lb)
Dimensions:	Length: 10.67m (35ft); width: 2.43m (7.97ft); height: 3.28m (10.76ft)
Range:	540km (340 miles)
Armour:	None
Armament:	None
Powerplant:	1 x Detroit Diesel 8V-92TA 8-cylinder diesel, developing 500hp (373kW)
Performance:	Maximum road speed: 91km/h (57mph)

MAN N 4510 5t mil gl

The MAN N 4510 5t mil gl is a 4x4 vehicle which emerged from a long development process by MAN during the 1970s. The German Federal Armed Forces had issued a requirement for a logistics vehicle to follow the Leopard main battle tank during operations. MAN produced several prototypes, but most were too expensive owing to features such as amphibious floats with propeller propulsion and sealed cabs. Once these features were dropped, however, a successful prototype emerged and MAN received orders for over 8000 vehicles in the five-, seven- and 10-ton classes. The MAN N 4510 represents the five-ton category, the 4520 the seven-ton, and the 4540 the 10-ton. All the variants have a cab-before-engine configuration.

Country of origin:	West Germany
Crew:	3 + 2
Weight:	14,460kg (31,880lb)
Dimensions:	Length: 8.01m (26.28ft); width: 2.5m (8.2ft); height: 2.85m (9.35ft)
Range:	750km (470 miles)
Armour:	None
Armament:	None
Powerplant:	1 x Deutz F8 L 413F 8-cylinder diesel, developing 252hp (188kW)
Performance:	Maximum road speed: 90km/h (56mph)

MAN 15 t mil gl A1

In the 1980s, the MAN 15 t mil gl A1 met the German Federal Armed Forces' requirements for a new series of high-mobility tactical trucks. The trucks had to be capable of multi-tasking logistical roles, have an armoured cab and offer a lifespan of 20 to 30 years. After extensive testing of various vehicles, the German military procurement agencies ordered 358 MAN 15 t mil gl A1 vehicles. Each vehicle can carry a payload of 18,200kg (40,100lb) and its Atlas Weyhausen trailer can be hydraulically raised to a 45-degree angle for the rapid unloading. The vehicle also has exceptional 8x8 manoeuvrability, and can cross ditches 1.9m (6.2ft) wide and tackle 60 percent gradients fully loaded.

Country of origin:	West Germany
Crew:	1 + 2
Weight:	32,000kg (70,600lb) fully loaded
Dimensions:	Length: 10.27m (33.7ft); width: 2.9m (9.51ft); height: 2.93m (9.61ft)
Range:	750km (470 miles)
Armour:	Not applicable
Armament:	None
Powerplant:	1 x MAN D2566MF 6-cylinder turbo diesel, developing 394hp (294kW)
Performance:	Maximum road speed: 90km/h (56mph); gradient: 60 percent; trench: 1.9m (6.2ft)

Iveco 6605 TM

The Iveco 6605 TM is essentially a 6x6 artillery tractor, but its cab's capacity to hold 12 men almost makes it a troop transporter. An entire artillery unit can be carried by the vehicle, and in relative comfort – the cab has a canvas cover but is fitted with a ventilator and heater. Maximum load for the vehicle is five tons, though it can tow 15 tons if required. Usually, the artillery piece is towed and the crew and auxiliary equipment carried in the vehicle. An Iveco 6605 FH – an identical vehicle apart from weight and carrying capacity – often accompanies the TM, transporting the ammunition. The TM's cargo area can be separated into three areas by removable partitions, and can be used to carry 21 additional men.

Country of origin:	Italy
Crew:	1 + 11
Weight:	11,800kg (26,000b)
Dimensions:	Length: 7.33m (24ft); width: 2.5m (8.2ft); height: 2.92m (9.58ft)
Range:	700km (430 miles)
Armour:	None
Armament:	None
Powerplant:	1 x Fiat 8212.02.500 6-cylinder diesel, developing 219hp (163kW)
Performance:	Maximum road speed: 80km/h (50mph)

MAN 40.633

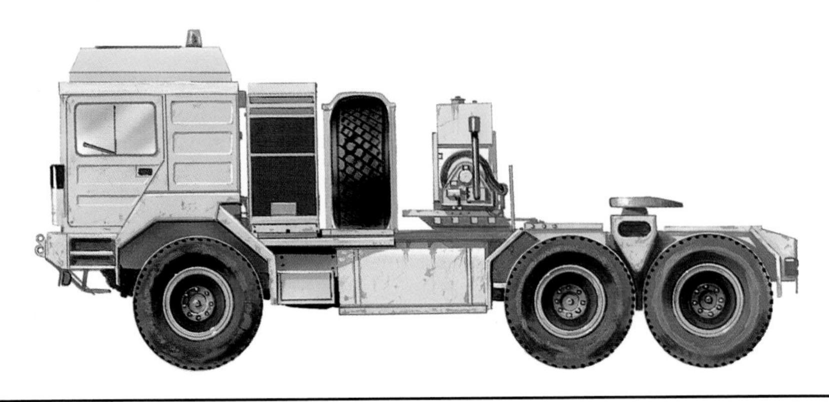

The MAN 40.633 DFAETX was the winner of the competition to supply the United Arab Emirates with transporters for main battle tanks and heavy equipment. The 40.633 weighs 40,000kg (88,200lb); moving such weight across rocky desert terrain is especially hard on tyres, so the vehicle has a tyre-pressure adjustment system which works from a compressor mounted in the towing vehicle. The single-tyre format, rather than the European-variant double-tyre configuration, stops the vehicle sinking into soft sand, a problem which many double-tyre vehicles experienced during the initial competition. There are many rivers in the Middle East, so the 40.633 was constructed with a fording capability of 0.85m (2.78ft).

Country of origin:	Germany
Crew:	3 + 5
Weight:	40,000kg (88,200lb)
Dimensions:	Length: 8.22m (26.97ft); width: 2.9m (9.51ft); height: 3.17m (10.4ft)
Range:	1000km (620 miles)
Armour:	None
Armament:	None
Powerplant:	1 x MAN D 2840 10-cylinder turbo diesel, developing 621hp (463kW)
Performance:	Maximum road speed: 88km/h (55mph); fording: 0.85m (2.78ft)

Index

Index

Index

Index

Index

Index

Index

Index